CHEMISTRY RESEARCH AND APPLICATIONS

REACTIVE OXYGEN SPECIES, LIPID PEROXIDATION AND PROTEIN OXIDATION

CHEMISTRY RESEARCH AND APPLICATIONS

Additional books in this series can be found on Nova's website
under the Series tab.

Additional e-books in this series can be found on Nova's website
under the e-book tab.

CHEMISTRY RESEARCH AND APPLICATIONS

REACTIVE OXYGEN SPECIES, LIPID PEROXIDATION AND PROTEIN OXIDATION

ANGEL CATALÁ
EDITOR

publishers

New York

Copyright © 2015 by Nova Science Publishers, Inc.

NOTICE TO THE READER

The Publisher has taken reasonable care in the preparation of this book, but makes no expressed or implied warranty of any kind and assumes no responsibility for any errors or omissions. No liability is assumed for incidental or consequential damages in connection with or arising out of information contained in this book. The Publisher shall not be liable for any special, consequential, or exemplary damages resulting, in whole or in part, from the readers' use of, or reliance upon, this material. Any parts of this book based on government reports are so indicated and copyright is claimed for those parts to the extent applicable to compilations of such works.

Independent verification should be sought for any data, advice or recommendations contained in this book. In addition, no responsibility is assumed by the publisher for any injury and/or damage to persons or property arising from any methods, products, instructions, ideas or otherwise contained in this publication.

This publication is designed to provide accurate and authoritative information with regard to the subject matter covered herein. It is sold with the clear understanding that the Publisher is not engaged in rendering legal or any other professional services. If legal or any other expert assistance is required, the services of a competent person should be sought. FROM A DECLARATION OF PARTICIPANTS JOINTLY ADOPTED BY A COMMITTEE OF THE AMERICAN BAR ASSOCIATION AND A COMMITTEE OF PUBLISHERS.

Additional color graphics may be available in the e-book version of this book.

Library of Congress Cataloging-in-Publication Data

Reactive oxygen species, lipid peroxidation, and protein oxidation / editor, Angel Catala (Instituto de Investigaciones Fisicoqummicas Tesricas y Aplicadas, (INIFTA-CCT La Plata-CONICET), Facultad de Ciencias Exactas, Universidad Nacional de La Plata, Argentina).
    pages cm. -- (Chemistry research and applications)
  Includes index.
  ISBN 978-1-63321-886-4 (hardcover)
  1. Oxidative stress. 2. Stress (Physiology) 3. Lipids--Metabolism--Disorders. 4. Lipids--Peroxidation. I. Catala, Angel, editor.
  RB170.R3345 2014
  615.7'9--dc23
                        2014037735

Published by Nova Science Publishers, Inc. † New York

CONTENTS

PREFACE

Many studies have shown that free radical damage and lipid peroxidation increase as a function of the degree of unsaturation of the fatty acids present in the phospholipids of biological membranes. Membrane phospholipids are particularly susceptible to oxidation not only because of their highly polyunsaturated fatty acid content but also because of their association in the cell membrane with non-enzymatic and enzymatic systems capable of generating prooxidative-free radical species. There are two broad outcomes to lipid peroxidation: structural damage to membranes and generation of secondary products. Membrane damage derives from the generation of fragmented fatty acyl chains, lipid–lipid cross-links, lipid–protein cross-links and endocyclization to produce isoprostanes and neuroprostanes. These processes combine to produce changes in the biophysical properties of membranes that can have profound effects on the activity of membrane-bound proteins. The consequence of peroxidation of unsaturated fatty acids is severe: damage of membranes function, enzymatic inactivation, toxic effects on the cellular division, etc. This new book presents and discusses current research on oxidative stress, and lipid oxidation – non-inhibited and inhibited; assessment of oxidative balance in the lipo- and hydro-philic cellular environment in biological systems; mass spectrometry detection of protein modification by cross-reaction with lipid peroxidation products; diagonal gel electrophoretic analysis of protein disulfides: principles and applications. Other chapters describe: heavy metals exposure and cells oxidative damage; biodegradation of metallic biomaterials: its relation with the generation of reactive oxygen species; Oxidative modifications of proteins in the aging heart; role of reactive oxygen species as signalling molecules involved in the regulation of physiological processes of the nervous system; oxidative stress in diabetes and hypertension treated with alternative therapy of medicinal plants; impairment of redox homeostasis of tissue damage in inborn errors of metabolism with intoxication: insights from human and animal studies and finally lipid peroxidation of phospholipids in the vertebrate retina or in liposomes made of retinal lipids: similarities and differences are described.

Chapter 1 - Oxidative stress is associated with increased production of so called reactive oxygen species (ROS), i.e., different active radicals and peroxides $OH^{\bullet}$, $O_2^{-\bullet}$, $LO_2^{-\bullet}$, HOOH, LOOH, or with a significant decrease in the effectiveness of antioxidant defenses, such as antioxidant enzymes, glutathione, antioxidant vitamins A, C, E. The penetration of oxygen and free radicals in the hydrophobic interior of biological membranes initiates radical disintegration of the hydrocarbon "tails" of the lipids. This process is known as "lipid peroxidation" and accumulation of oxidation products as peroxides and derived from them aldehydes and acids as well as the ratio of reduced glutathione to oxidized glutathione within cells are often used as a measure of oxidative stress. Kinetics and mechanism of unsaturated lipid oxidation including isomerization and decomposition of lipid peroxyl radicals and influence of various factors (structural, physical) are discussed. Kinetics of inhibited oxidation in close connection with chemical mechanism of inhibitor transformation under oxidative stress is considered. Computer simulation is used to clarify the role of inhibitor's derived species in pro- and antioxidant effects. A special attention has been paid to chemical reactions resulting in initiation of free radicals – a key stage of oxidative stress. New possibilities for optimal stabilization of lipids and lipid-containing products are established, based on modeling the kinetics of uninhibited and inhibited lipid oxidation. Correlations between experimental and /or theoretical data are summarized and discussed. Some future trends are discussed as well. The significance of these studies is closely related to the improvement of the quality and increase in the oxidative stability of lipids and products containing them as well as with the social impacts associated with improved nutrition and human health.

Chapter 2 - Over the last decade, Electron Paramagnetic Resonance (EPR) technology has been successfully applied to detect free radicals in order to establish oxidative stress conditions. Since a variety of stable products are formed during the oxidation of lipids, several assays have been developed over the years in order to evaluate lipid peroxidation. EPR spectroscopy has shown the capacity to detect, in the presence of exogenous traps, the presence of lipid radicals (LR•) formed during peroxidation, by yielding unique and stable compounds. On the other hand, the one-electron oxidation of AH⁻ produces ascorbyl radical (A•) which is easily detectable by EPR, even at room-temperature in aqueous solution. The A• free radical has a relatively long lifetime compared to other species, such as hydroxyl radical, peroxyl, alkoxyl, and LR• and has been proposed as a marker of oxidative stress, either *in vitro* or *in vivo*, in numerous systems, such as plasma. All biological systems contain many antioxidants, including both water-soluble compounds (such as AH⁻ and glutathione), and lipid-soluble antioxidants, such as α-tocopherol (α-T). In this chapter, the most widely used indexes of oxidative balance in biological systems will be briefly summarized. Moreover, special mention will be made about the application of the A•/AH⁻ and LR•/α-T ratios to situations of oxidative stress. The goal of this work is to discuss the possibility of detecting the actual state of lipid- and water-soluble fractions of a biological system, providing an early and simple diagnosis of stressing conditions.

Chapter 3 - Lipid oxidation, which occurs during oxidative stress, leads to the formation of a wide array of lipid peroxidation products (LPPs). Among them are several highly reactive products with terminal electrophilic carbonyl groups (oxoLPPs), which can covalently react with different nucleophilic molecules, including proteins. Lysine, histidine, arginine and cysteine residues within the protein backbone are most susceptible to modifications by oxoLPPs via formation of Michael and Schiff base adducts. These reactions are considered to be one of the major pathways of protein carbonyl formation. The protein-oxoLPPs adducts, commonly referred as advanced lipoxidation end products (ALEs), can have negative health effects, being responsible for the loss of protein function. Several studies indicated a role of ALEs in different pathologies, however, an exact mechanism of their action is yet to be fully understood. Identification and characterization of ALEs is an essential step in understanding the biological effects of these protein modifications. However, this task requires an extensive chemical characterization of a myriad of aldehyde/keto compounds adducted to peptides and proteins, as well as type of the linkage and adduction sites. High dynamic range of oxoLPP molecular weights, ranging from small aldehydes to truncated phospholipids (PLs) with shortened fatty acyl chains, further complicate this task. Nowadays, mass spectrometry (MS) utilizing soft ionization techniques, such as electrospray ionization (ESI) and matrix-assisted laser desorption/ionization (MALDI), coupled to liquid chromatography (LC), is one of the commonly used techniques for characterization of protein-oxoLPP adducts. Such MS-based approaches have proven successful in identification of modified peptides and proteins both *in vitro* and *in vivo*. The detailed structural assignment of protein-oxoLPP adducts is usually based on a tandem MS experiments. Presence of specific product ions in MS/MS spectra depends on the chemical structure of oxoLPP as well as on the type of protein-oxoLPP linkage. To improve the sensitivity of MS analysis, specific derivatization and/or enrichment strategies can be used in combination with different MS approaches. This chapter aims to cover the main MS based methodologies currently used to identify lipid-peptide/protein adducts.

Chapter 4 - Protein cysteine residues are constantly undergoing redox modifications, and many of them are involved in disulfide formation. In this chapter, the authors first give an overview of the diagonal gel analysis method for the identification of protein disulfides followed by the application of the method for the identification of mitochondrial proteins that have endogenous disulfide bonds or form disulfide bonds upon oxidative stress. Data that show that the albumin precursor protein could be identified by this method, and that many proteins form disulfide bonds after treatment with diamide are presented. The data presented in this chapter indicate that this diagonal gel analytical method, when used in conjunction with mass spectrometric peptide sequencing, can provide a powerful tool for studying protein disulfide proteomics.

Chapter 5 - Upon the industrial revolution in the XVIII century, the mobilization of metals from their natural reservoirs as well as their use increased exponentially. As a result, many heavy metals were mobilized towards the Earth's surface, contaminated the soils, water and air, and became available for living organisms. Among others, Co, Ni, Cd and Hg are highly toxic metals for humans, and their mechanisms of toxicity are still under elucidation. However, they share with other metals a common mechanism of toxicity that involves the alteration of the intracellular redox status. This may be caused by increased generation of oxidant species, the impairment of the antioxidant defense system, or both. Among the oxidant species, the generation of reactive oxygen species (ROS) seems to be a common feature in the toxicity of most heavy metals, regardless of their redox-active or redox-inactive condition. The excessive production of ROS, together with the inhibition of certain components of the antioxidant defense system leads to the oxidative damage of key intracellular components, such as lipids, proteins and DNA. Moreover, by promoting oxidative stress these metals induce cell death via apoptosis or necrosis. In the present work, the current knowledge regarding the mechanisms involved in Co, Ni, Cd, and Hg-mediated oxidative stress will be discussed.

Chapter 6 - Some specific clinical problems, particularly those related to orthopedic trauma and some cardiovascular diseases need only temporary support for healing. This support can be provided by biodegradable metallic materials such as, Fe-, Mg- based alloys that avoid some of the side effects of traditional biomaterials. They are expected to support the healing process of a diseased tissue or organ with slowly degrading after fulfilling their function. However, the excess of metal ions may catalyze the formation of reactive oxygen and nitrogen species (ROS and RNS). An increase in the intracellular levels of free metal ions affects the normal balance ROS-antioxidant. ROS could cause lipid peroxidation with changes in the composition and fluidity of cell membrane and alterations in other macromolecules as proteins and DNA. Considering that the concentration of metal ions can reach high values in the biomaterial-tissue interface inducing ROS generation it is important to evaluate the possible adverse effects of the degradation products of biodegradable biomaterials.

Chapter 7 - Aging is a major risk factor for cardiovascular diseases. The aging heart is characterized by a variety of structural and functional changes, including contractile dysfunction, ultimately leading to increased morbidity and mortality in the elderly. Although the molecular mechanisms underlying cardiac decay are not fully elucidated, the increase in formation of reactive oxygen species (ROS) and a result, increased oxidative stress, has been proposed to be an important factor in the aging process. Besides DNA mutations and changes in gene expression, the post-translational modifications of proteins by ROS appear to be a principal mechanism of age-related oxidative injury. The mitochondrial electron transport chain (ETC) is the major intracellular site of ROS and non-uniform decline in activities of ETC complexes may cause increased ROS leakage during aging. As a primary source of ROS the mitochondria are also the main target of their damaging effects. Mitochondrial proteins undergo complex modifications during aging; however, growing evidence suggests that structural alterations do not correlate with protein functions. Aging also affects the function of sarcoplasmic reticulum (SR), the major intracellular store of Ca^{2+} ions, regulating cardiac contraction-relaxation. The results suggest that both irreversible and reversible oxidation/nitration of SR Ca^{2+}-ATPase (SERCA2a) and other Ca^{2+} handling proteins may contribute to the loss of their transporting activities and impaired ventricular relaxation during aging. Cross-talk between mitochondria and SR is an important factor in cell redox signaling and dysregulation in Ca^{2+}-ROS interplay is likely involved in heart aging. Aging is also associated with loss in total antioxidant capacity and altered levels/activities of redox balance regulating proteins. Overall, the present results suggest that ROS-related alterations in mitochondrial bioenergetics, intracellular Ca^{2+} handling and redox regulatory components may contribute to age-associated decline in the heart function.

Chapter 8 - In the nervous system, reactive oxygen species (ROS) have been implicated in several physiological and pathological events. It has been suggested that the members of the family of the NADPH-oxidases (NOX) could be a source of ROS involved in many of these processes. In hippocampus, ROS produced by NOX are required for the NMDA receptor-dependent long-term potentiation (LTP), thereby regulating hippocampal synaptic plasticity and memory formation. In developing neurons, ROS regulate the dynamics of the axonal growth cone during the establishment of neuronal networks and, in neurons from *Aplysia*, ROS produced by NOX promote axonal growth. In addition, ROS produced by NOX critically influence the neuronal proliferation and neurogenesis and they have been implicated in the progression of the programmed cell death of neurons during cerebellar development.

Most of the physiological and pathological actions of ROS are mediated by modification of the redox state of several proteins. The oxidation of these proteins occurs in specific amino acid residues such as cysteine, tyrosine and tryptophan. In particular, the oxidation of cysteine residues is a major mechanism for the control of several proteins. These molecules include channels, enzymes and proteins from the cytoskeleton. For example, in the striatum, the hydrogen peroxide modulates dopamine release by the oxidation of the ATP-sensitive K^+

channels and, in dorsal root ganglion neurons, ROS induce the growth cone collapse by the oxidation of CRMP2.

It has been proposed that ROS also alter the redox state of the proteins of the signaling pathways. For example, ROS produced in response to growth factors control the proliferation and neurogenesis of neural precursor cells through the redox regulation of PI3K/Akt pathway. On the other hand, the oxidation of thioredoxins (Trx) and glutaredoxins (Grx1) leads to their dissociation from ASK1 that dephosphorylates and promotes its activation and the consequent stimulation of JNK and p38, which are involved in several physiological processes such as apoptosis. Other proteins such as thioredoxin-interacting protein (TXNIP) negatively regulates Trx1 and controls the cellular redox state. Finally, Akt has also been reported to be inactivated by direct oxidation, but it can also be activated by the oxidation of PTEN.

In this chapter, the authors review the experimental evidences supporting a role for ROS in cell signaling in the nervous system and they discuss the interactions of ROS with several proteins as part of the mechanisms that regulates neuronal physiology.

Chapter 9 - Diabetes mellitus (DM) and hypertension are the most common diseases with high risk affecting most of the worldwide adult population in both genders. DM is the first cause of death in women and ischemic heart disease becomes the leading cause of mortality in men. High blood pressure, also called hypertension, is one of the major risk factors for coronary artery disease, stroke, and is currently among the ten leading causes of death worldwide. DM is a metabolic disorder of multiple etiologies, characterized by chronic hyperglycemia caused by defects in the secretion of insulin or the action of insulin, or both. In the early stages of the disease the symptoms of DM are not severe or may be absent. Consequently, hyperglycemia may be present and cause pathological and functional changes before the diagnosis is made. Hypertension represents a major risk factor for developing other diseases such as endothelial dysfunction, metabolic syndrome, DM, congestive heart failure, coronary artery disease, stroke and renal dysfunction. In both diseases, there is a characteristic in common, the generation of oxidative stress that is an exacerbated complication when each disease increases. Generally, multiple drugs with different chemical structures and different mechanisms of action are used for the therapeutic management of both diseases, with the aim to normalize blood glucose and blood pressure levels. These are managed for a long time, which often represents a high economic cost. On the other hand, some patients have no adherence to treatment. This is ineffective, and the adverse effects are situations that require change or immediate discontinuance of medication. It is important to develop new antidiabetic or antihypertensive agents, and medicinal plants are an option. Scientific interest aimed at the search of phytotherapeutic drugs for the treatment of these diseases has led the conduct of research that validates the use of medicinal plants, or they have found new agents with antidiabetic and antihypertensive properties. Some examples of medicinal plants have described their potential effects as antidiabetic or antihypertensive on animal models. This chapter is discussed along with traditional medicine that involves the use of plant extracts to treat DM and/or hypertension.

Chapter 10 - Aminoacidopathies and organic acidemias are inherited metabolic disorders caused by defects in proteins, generally enzymes, resulting in tissue accumulation and elevated urinary excretion of potentially toxic compounds. Affected individuals present predominantly neurological symptoms and brain abnormalities that may be accompanied by liver, heart and skeletal muscle alterations. The pathogenesis of the tissue damage observed in these disorders is not yet fully established, but oxidative stress has been suggested to be involved in this injury. This chapter focuses on the role of oxidative stress in the pathophysiology of four prevalent IEM, namely phenylketonuria, maple syrup urine disease, methylmalonic acidemia and homocystinuria. The discussion will be concentrated more particularly on the brain pathomechanisms because of its vulnerability to reactive species due to its high oxygen demand, low antioxidant content and abundance of highly oxidizable polyunsaturated fatty acids. In the last few decades, several findings in animal models and patients affected by these disorders indicate that the accumulating metabolites (amino acids and organic acids) may cause mitochondrial dysfunction and/or increase free radical formation leading to oxidative damage to biomolecules (lipids, proteins and DNA) and to a decrease of antioxidant defenses. It is also important to emphasize that a dietary restriction of nutrients with antioxidant properties generally employed for the treatment of these diseases may contribute to the altered antioxidant status. These findings offer new perspectives for potential therapeutic strategies, which may include the early use of appropriate antioxidants with the ability to easily cross the blood-brain barrier, besides the usual therapies based on preventing metabolite accumulation and accelerating their removal through special diets and pharmacological agents.

Chapter 11 - The *retina* is the *neurosensorial tissue* of the *eye*. It is very rich in membranes and, therefore, in polyunsaturated fatty acids. Oxygen radicals participate in a variety of eye pathological processes because reactive oxygen species production induces the lipid peroxyl radical formation. This specie initiates chain reaction of lipid peroxidation what can injure the retina, especially the membranes that play important roles in visual function. Furthermore, bio-molecules such as proteins or amino lipids can be covalently modified by lipid decomposition products. In retinal membranes, peroxidation of lipids is also usually accompanied by oxidation of membrane proteins. In consequence, lipid peroxidation may alter the arrangement of proteins in bilayers and by that interfere with their physiological role on the membrane function. In this chapter, I review a series of studies on the lipid peroxidation of phospholipids in retinal membranes and in liposomes made of retinal lipids. Particular emphasis is placed on the molecular changes of very long chain polyunsaturated fatty acids associated with protein modifications during peroxidation of photoreceptor membranes. Furthermore the authors suggest the use of liposomes as a tool to analyze peroxidation of retinal lipids. Conjugated dienes formed from the double-bond rearrangement of oxidized PUFAs, and TBARS products derived from the breakdown of these fatty acids located in phospholipids can be analyzed during progress of lipid peroxidation of sonicated and non-sonicated liposomes made of retinal lipids in different aqueous media using Fe^{2+} and Fe^{3+} as initiators.

In: Reactive Oxygen Species, Lipid Peroxidation ...
Editor: Angel Catalá

ISBN: 978-1-63321-886-4
© 2015 Nova Science Publishers, Inc.

Chapter 1

OXIDATIVE STRESS AND LIPID OXIDATION: NON-INHIBITED AND INHIBITED

Vessela D. Kancheva[*]

Lipid Chemistry Department,
Institute of Organic Chemistry with Centre of Phytochemistry,
Bulgarian Academy of Sciences, Sofia, Bulgaria

ABSTRACT

Oxidative stress is associated with increased production of so called reactive oxygen species (ROS), i.e., different active radicals and peroxides $OH^{\cdot}$, $O_2^{-\cdot}$, $LO_2^{-\cdot}$, HOOH, LOOH, or with a significant decrease in the effectiveness of antioxidant defenses, such as antioxidant enzymes, glutathione, antioxidant vitamins A, C, E. The penetration of oxygen and free radicals in the hydrophobic interior of biological membranes initiates radical disintegration of the hydrocarbon "tails" of the lipids. This process is known as "lipid peroxidation" and accumulation of oxidation products as peroxides and derived from them aldehydes and acids as well as the ratio of reduced glutathione to oxidized glutathione within cells are often used as a measure of oxidative stress. Kinetics and mechanism of unsaturated lipid oxidation including isomerization and decomposition of lipid peroxyl radicals and influence of various factors (structural, physical) are discussed. Kinetics of inhibited oxidation in close connection with chemical mechanism of inhibitor transformation under oxidative stress is considered. Computer simulation is used to clarify the role of inhibitor's derived species in pro- and antioxidant effects. A special attention has been paid to chemical reactions resulting in initiation of free radicals – a key stage of oxidative stress. New possibilities for optimal stabilization of lipids and lipid-containing products are established, based on modeling the kinetics of uninhibited and inhibited lipid oxidation. Correlations between experimental and /or theoretical data are summarized and discussed. Some future trends are discussed as well. The significance of these studies is closely related to the improvement of the quality and increase in the oxidative stability of lipids and products containing them as well as with the social impacts associated with improved nutrition and human health.

[*] Phone: + 359 2 9606 187; Fax: +359 2 8700 225. E-mail: vedeka@abv.bg.

1. OXIDATIVE STRESS

The human body is constantly subjected to a significant oxidative stress as a result of the misbalance between antioxidative protective systems and the formation of strong oxidizing substances, including free radicals. The stress can damage DNA, proteins, lipids and carbohydrates and could cause negative effect on intracellular signal transmission [1,2].

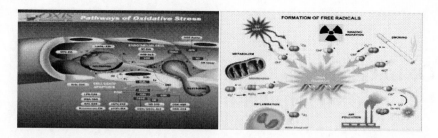

The free radicals formation in the hydrophobic parts of the biological membranes initiates radical disintegration of the hydrocarbon "tails" of the lipids. This process is known as lipid peroxidation".

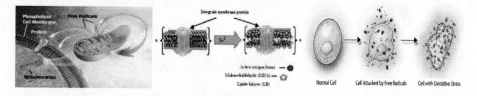

Lipid Peroxidation.

Free radicals are responsible for the pathogenesis of a wide range of diseases: the most serious and difficult to treat health problems such as cancer and cardiovascular diseases, they also cause asthma, arthritis, inflammations, neurodegenerative disorders, Parkinson's disease and dementia. Aging is a complex combination of deleterious free radical reactions, which affect cells and tissues [3-9].

We would like to focus your attention not on the various specific causes for the different diseases, but to the fact that in all cases of diseases a change of the rate of peroxide oxidation is observed. It has been found that in the first stage of the development of atherosclerosis the system works in its normal regime. The introduction of antioxidants in the affected body normalizes not only the peroxide oxidation, but also the lipid content. Antioxidants used in oncology are effective mainly as additives in the complex tumor therapy [10]. In this respect the medical treatment of most of diseases includes formulations based on a combination of traditional drugs with targeted functionality and different antioxidants [11,12]. Last years the attention of scientists was focused on searching and creation of a new approach to identify and prevent oxidative stress induced by drug therapy and radiation. Free radicals are formed in very socially important diseases such as malignant, thyroid disorders, diabetes, rheumatoid arthritis, etc. Studying parameters of oxidative stress in these conditions is important to define the role of free radicals in the therapeutic response of the treatment regimes. Nowadays the antioxidants play an important role in the prevention and treatment of certain diseases.

Antioxidant therapy is a contemporary method which is effective in preventing the abnormal production of ROS and limiting their overall harmful impact on the body. Application of suitable antioxidants leads to a significant decrease of the lipid peroxidation and increases activity of the antioxidant protective enzyme system, thus reducing the oxidative stress and negative consequences [12, 13]. Based on this, Gadjeva et al. [14-16] look for opportunities to reduce the toxic effects of drug therapy and damage induced by ionizing radiation by application of antioxidants (natural and synthetic). It has been proved recently [17-18] that oxidative stress was induced by antitumor drugs and of L-Dopa using for Parkinson disease. In Parkinson disease, oxidative stress induced by free radicals damages neuronal membrane lipids, proteins and other components of brain tissue. There are several potential sources of the increased free radical production in Parkinson disease, including mitochondrial dysfunction, increased free iron levels and increased dopamine metabolism [19-22]. Last decade much attention has been focused on searching the radio protection from plants to overcome the oxidative stress induced by irradiation [23,24]. New antioxidant compositions with natural and synthetic antioxidants applied lead to reducing significantly the oxidative stress induced by anticancer drugs and drugs towards Parkinsons' disease [25, 26].

2. LIPID OXIDATION

Oxygen is essential for all living organisms, but at the same time it is a source of constant aggression for them. In its ground triplet state ($^3O_2$) oxygen has weak reactivity, but it can produce strongly aggressive and reactive particles such as singlet state oxygen ($^1O_2$), hydroperoxides (H_2O_2), superoxide anion ($O_2^{\cdot-}$), hydroxyl radical ($OH^{\cdot}$) and various peroxide ($LO_2^{\cdot}$) and alkoxyl radicals ($LO^{\cdot}$). It is well known that the latter lead to an oxidative degradation of biological macromolecules, changing their properties and thus the cell structure and functionality [2].

Lipids are essential for cell membranes and are a major energy reserve in plants and animals. Unsaturated fatty acids present in cell membranes provide transport of substances through the membrane. The oxidation of lipids proceeds like that of many other organic compounds by free radical chain mechanism, which can be described in terms of initiation, propagation, and termination processes. There is a great interest in oxygen radicals because their attack on lipid biomembranes is related to many important pathological events in biological systems [11].

Lipid peroxidation is probably the most studied oxidative process in biological systems. Unsaturated lipids are particularly susceptible to oxidative modification and lipid peroxidation is a sensitive marker of oxidative stress. Lipid peroxidation is a result of attack by radicals on the double bond of unsaturated fatty acid, leading to generation of highly reactive lipid peroxyl radicals that initiate a chain reaction of further attacks on other unsaturated fatty acid. Lipid oxidation is undesirable process, resulting not only in decrease in the biological activity of lipids, but is a serious human health hazard. It is no doubt; various inhibitors are used for stabilization of lipid-containing products of bakery, cosmetics and pharmaceutical industry against oxidation. To create food products with high quality and to protect human health are problems all over the world. These problems could be solved both by searching new nontoxic antioxidants, and by expanding the knowledge about the reactions, resulting in regeneration of the antioxidant in the oxidation process [27-29]. As a result, the antioxidant efficiency and reactivity increase and lead to a higher lipid oxidation stability. The antioxidant capacity has at least two sides: the antioxidant potential, determined by its composition and the properties of its constituents, which is the subject of food chemistry, and the biological effects, depending, among other things, on bioavailability of antioxidants, and is a medico-biological problem [30, 31].

2.1. Kinetics of Lipid Oxidation and Rate Constants of the Individual Steps [32]

No	Reactions	k, $M^{-1}s^{-1}$	References
1	$rN{\equiv}Nr \rightarrow 2r{\cdot} + N_2$	$5\ 10^{-6}$	[33]
2	$r{\cdot} + O_2 \rightarrow rO_2{\cdot}$	$5\ 10^6$	[33]
3	$rO_2{\cdot} + LH \rightarrow L{\cdot} + rOOH$	$1\ 10^3$	[33]
4	$L{\cdot} + O_2 \rightarrow LO_2{\cdot}$	$5\ 10^6, 1\ 10^8$	[33,34]
5	$LO_2{\cdot} + LH \rightarrow L{\cdot} + LOOH$	$90, 100$	[33,34]
6	$LH + O_2 \rightarrow L{\cdot} + HO_2{\cdot}$	$5.8\ 10^{-11}$	[33]
7	$LOOH + LH \rightarrow L{\cdot} + LO{\cdot} + H_2O$	$2.3\ 10^{-7}$	[33]
8	$2LOOH \rightarrow LO{\cdot} + LO_2 + H_2O$	$2.4\ 10^{-6}$	[33]
9	$2\ LO_2{\cdot} \rightarrow Alc + Ket$	$4.4\ 10^6, 1\ 10^7$	[34,35]
10	$LO{\cdot} + LH \rightarrow Alc + Ket$	$1\ 10^5, 1\ 10^7$	[33,36]
11	$LO{\cdot} + LO_2{\cdot} \rightarrow Ket + LOOH$	$5\ 10^6$	[33]
12	$LO_2{\cdot} + IO_2{\cdot} \rightarrow Alc + Ket$	$5\ 10^6$	[33]

Note: The rate constants (k_0 correspond to the oxidation of MeLi at $60°C$) in reaction 1,2 and 4, k are presented in s^{-1}. Initial concentrations: [LH]=2.9M. $[LOOH]_0$=1 10^{-5}M, [AIBN] = 4 10^{-3} M, $[O_2]$=10^{-3}M=const; oxidation usually occurs at a constant oxygen pressure, therefore, $[O_2]$ is included in the corresponding rate constants: k_2=k_4=k_6=$k_i[O_2]$.

Scheme 1. Basic kinetic scheme of lipid oxidation.

The kinetic scheme of liquid-phase (homogeneous) oxidation of lipids (LH) includes reactions 1-12. In the presence of an initiator AIBN ($rN{\equiv}Nr$), i.e., initiated oxidation, the formation of radicals occurs with a constant initiation rate R_{IN}=$2k_1[rN{\equiv}Nr]$. Under autoxidation conditions $[rN{\equiv}Nr]$ = 0), the rates of radical formation in the reactions of LH with O_2 (6) and decomposition of lipid hydroperoxides (LOOH) (reactions 7 and 8) increase as LOOH is accumulated.

The chain termination occurs due to recombination or disproportionation of radicals (reactions 9, 11 and 12).

2.2. Kinetics of Non-Inhibited Lipid Autoxidation [27, 32, 39]

A characteristic feature of lipid autoxidation is the auto-accelerated kinetics of the chain-chemical process. In the absence of an initiator or an initiating agent (light, radiation), the initial rate of the chain initiation, in an oxidizing organic compound, LH, is very low. During oxidation lipid hydroperoxides (LOOH) is formed and accumulates. With the increasing concentration of LOOH, the rate of initiation increases due to the decomposition of LOOH into radicals. Therefore the rate of chain oxidation increases in time. We observe a positive feedback between the proceeding reaction and the reaction rate. The main steps of lipid autoxidation kinetics consist of chain generation, propagation, branching and termination [37-39].

Kinetic Modeling of Lipid Oxidation for Different Mechanism of LOOH Decomposition

A kinetic analysis of non-inhibited lipid (LH) autoxidation for different mechanisms of hydroperoxides (LOOH) decay is proposed [39]. It is based on using mathematical simulation methods of LH autoxidation kinetics. Kinetic schemes of LH autoxidation for some different ways of hydroperoxides decay - monomolecular, pseudo-monomolecular and/or bimolecular mechanism are presented. This analysis permits establishing the influence degree of different hydroperoxides decay mechanisms on the kinetic parameters, characterizing the substrate oxidizability. The proposed kinetic analysis has been applied to methyl linoleate, MeLi, autoxidation at 60°C [39].

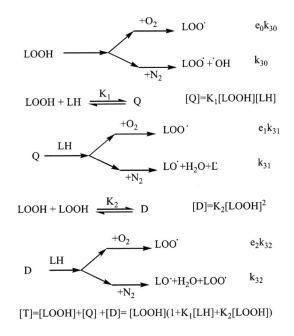

$$[T]=[LOOH]+[Q]+[D]=[LOOH](1+K_1[LH]+K_2[LOOH])$$

Scheme 2. Kinetic scheme of lipid hydroperoxide decomposition reactions.

The kinetic model that describes lipid hydroperoxides decomposition, taking into account the possibility of monomolecular (LOOH), pseudo-monomolecular (LOOH+LH) and bimolecular (2LOOH) mechanism in both cases: in presence of an oxygen (O_2) and in its absence, i.e., in an inert atmosphere (N_2), is illustrated in Scheme 2. In this equations: LH – lipid substrate under oxidation, L• и LO• - corresponding lipid alkyl and alkoxy radicals, LO_2• - lipid peroxide radicals, LOOH - lipid hydroperoxides, k_i – rate constants of individual reactions, K_1 and K_2 are the equilibrium constants for complexes Q and D, respectively; [T]: summary concentration of LOOH; k_{30}, k_{31} and k_{32}: are the corresponding rate constants; e_0, e_1, e_2: are the corresponding radicals yield.

$$\text{Chain Generation} \xrightarrow{\ +O_2,\ +LH\ } LOO^\bullet + HO_2^\bullet \qquad R_{IN}$$

$$LOO^\bullet + LH \xrightarrow{\ +O_2\ } LOO^\bullet + LOOH \qquad k_p$$

$$LOOH \xrightarrow{\ +O_2,\ +LH\ } LOO^\bullet + products \qquad e_0 k_{30}$$

$$LOOH + LH \rightleftharpoons Q \xrightarrow{\ +O_2,\ +LH\ } LOO^\bullet + products \qquad e_1 k_{31}$$

$$LOOH + LOOH \rightleftharpoons D \xrightarrow{\ +O_2,\ +LH\ } LOO^\bullet + products \qquad e_2 k_{32}$$

$$2\ LOO^\bullet \longrightarrow products \qquad k_t$$

Scheme 3. Kinetic scheme of lipid autoxidation by Kancheva & Belyakov [39].

where: R_{IN} – the rate of chain generation, k_p and k_t – rate constants of chain propagation and termination, respectively. The kinetic scheme 3 is significantly simplified and readily solved assuming a quasi-steady state for LOO•, rapid achievement of equilibrium and neglecting the loss of Q and LOOH since their decomposition rate constants are low. The total concentration of lipid hydroperoxides [T] and concentration of oxygen consumed can be determined by the formulae (1) and (2):

$$[T] = \left(\sqrt{[T_o]} + \frac{1}{2}\frac{k_p}{\sqrt{k_t}}[LH]\sqrt{k_i} \cdot t \right)^2 \tag{1}$$

$$[O_2] = \frac{k_p}{\sqrt{k_t}}[LH]\sqrt{k_i}\sqrt{[T_o]} \cdot t + \frac{1}{4}\left(\frac{k_p}{\sqrt{k_t}}[LH] \right)^2 \cdot k_i \cdot t^2 \tag{2}$$

It is established that lipid hydroperoxides decay is in agreement with a first order reaction and pseudo-monomolecular mechanism (a reaction between hydroperoxides and non-oxidized lipid substrate; LOOH + LH). More detailed information about the mechanism of lipid autoxidation with different mechanisms of lipid hydroperoxides decomposition is published recently by Kancheva & Kasaikina [32].

2.3. Isomerization of Lipid Peroxyde Radicals with Intramolecular Cyclization

Peroxyl radicals are important intermediates in the peroxidative destruction of cell membranes, the latter being implicated in a number of degenerative diseases. The structures of cyclic peroxides produced during the oxidation of lipids were discussed for many years, but only some of these compounds have been adequately characterized and their structures determined [37]. The compounds were isolated from a mixture of products obtained by oxygenation with singlet oxygen of methyllinoleate hydroperoxides and the identified 9-hydroperoxy-10,13-epidioxy-11-octadecanoate (1) and 13-hydrooperoxy of lipid -9,12-epidioxy-10-octadecenoate (2) are presented in Figure 1:

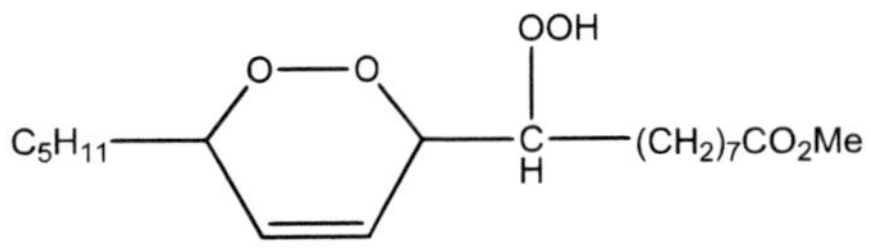

Figure 1. Isomeric forms of cyclic peroxides (1) and (2) produced during lipid oxidation.

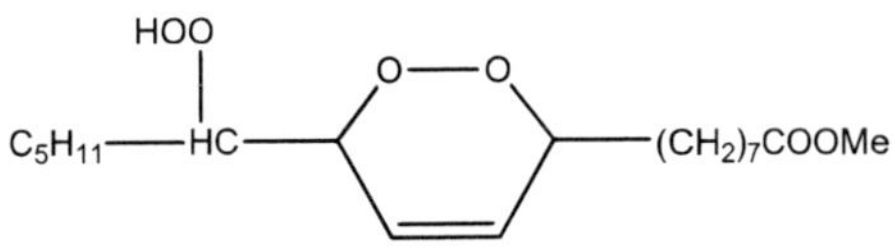

Two isomeric forms of each of these products were obtained and separated. It is clear that lipid oxidation results in different peroxidic species among which are monohydro-peroxides and hydroperoxy epidioxides, both of them existing in several OOH-position and geometrical isomeric forms [37].

Many classical mechanistic concepts of lipid oxidation were formulated on the basis of kinetic studies. Later, the general free radical mechanism of oxidation was supported by the results of structural studies on primary hydroperoxide products.

To simplify the kinetics of linoleate oxidation reaction, Kortenska & Vasilév [40] studied the reaction at early stages, low conversion depths and low temperatures and in presence of an appropriate initiator. Under these conditions, the propagation reactions producing hydroperoxides in high yields are dominating whereas decomposition of hydroperoxides is minimized or made insignificant.

However, the kinetics becomes much more complex when autoxidation is carried out to high conversion, or at elevated temperatures, or in presence of metals. Decomposition of hydroperoxides becomes significant either at the advanced levels of oxidation of linoleate or at the earlier stages in the case of linoleate and other polyunsaturated fatty acids containing more than three double bonds.

Table 1 presents kinetic data on the kinetics of oxygen consumption for different [LH] and R_{IN}. The rate of initiation was measured by the induction period method using inhibitor Chroman C1 (CrC1- a synthetic analogue of α-tocopherol), which is known to have a n value of 2.0 (n - is the number of radicals trapped by each molecule of the antioxidant).

Table 1. Kinetic parameters of initiated methyl linoleate (LH) oxidation at T = 333K, different LH concentrations and [AIBN] = 3.84 10^{-3}M

[LH], M	[CrC1], 10^{-5} M	IP s	R_{IN}, 10^{-8} M/s	R_{ox}, 10^{-6} M/s	$k_p/(2k_t)^{1/2}$, 10^{-2} $M^{-1}s^{-1}$	nk_0, 10^{-5} s^{-1}
0.15	1.92	720	5.34	1.28	3.64	1.39
0.29	1.92	750	5.13	2.38	3.66	1.33
0.59	2.38	936	5.09	4.58	3.30	1.33
0.88	1.92	828	4.64	5.93	3.13	1.20
1.18	1.92	1056	3.64	6.78	3.00	0.95
1.44	1.92	1152	3.34	6.98	2.66	0.87
1.62	1.92	1380	2.79	7.29	2.69	0.72

IP – the induction period, k_0 – the rate constant of $LO_2\bullet$ generation.

Table 2. Kinetic parameters of initiated linileate (LH) oxidation, 333K, at different rates of initiation; [LH] = 1.7M and 0.3M

[LH], M	[AIBN], mM	[CrCl], M	IP s	R_{IN}, 10^{-8} M/s	R_{ox}, 10^{-6} M/s	$k_p/(2k_t)^{1/2}$, 10^{-2} $M^{-1}s^{-1}$	nk_0, 10^{-5} s^{-1}
1.71	0.1	$4.95\ 10^{-7}$	756	0.13	1.50	2.43	1.32
1.71	0.4	$2.26\ 10^{-6}$	1056	0.43	2.66	2.37	1.08
1.71	1.0	$4.50\ 10^{-6}$	705	1.13	4.70	2.60	1.14
1.70	2.0	$9.80\ 10^{-6}$	1458	1.34	5.03	2.57	0.68
1.62	4.0	$19.2\ 10^{-6}$	1380	2.79	7.29	2.69	0.72
0.29	8.0	$7.69\ 10^{-7}$	780	0.20	0.49	3.85	2.56
0.30	1.0	$7.39\ 10^{-7}$	780	1.89	1.73	4.10	1.93
0.29	4.0	$1.92\ 10^{-5}$	750	5.13	2.38	3.66	1.33
0.28	9.0	$4.13\ 10^{-5}$	735	11.24	3.24	3.52	1.36
0.29	16.0	$9.80\ 10^{-5}$	1020	19.20	4.85	3.76	1.22

Scheme 4 is the simplest kinetic scheme of initiated lipid oxidation. Hydroperoxides (LOOH) are the main products of the low temperature lipid oxidation:

$$\text{Initiation} \xrightarrow{+O_2;\ +LH} LO_2^{\cdot}$$

$$LO_2^{\cdot} + LH \xrightarrow{+O_2;} LOOH + LO_2^{\cdot}$$

$$2LO_2^{\cdot} \longrightarrow \text{products}$$

$$LOOH \longrightarrow LO_2^{\cdot} + \text{products}$$

$$R_{IN} = nk_0[AIBN] \qquad ; nk_0 - \text{effectiveness of the initiator}$$

Scheme 4. The simplest kinetic scheme of initiated lipid oxidation.

The corresponding rate of oxygen consumption (R_{ox}) is expressed by equation (3) which demands proportionality between R_{ox} and R_{IN}

$$R_{ox} = R_{O2} = k_p[LH](R_{IN}/2k_t)^{0.5} \tag{3}$$

However, the dependence of R_{ox} on [LH] is not linear may be as a result of a decrease of $\underline{n}$ value (and correspondingly, R_{IN}) on addition of viscous LH into the reacting solution. Indeed the dependence $\underline{n}k_0 = f([LH])$ shows that it is the case. So, we assumed that the complication could be avoided by plotting the $R_{ox}/(R_{IN}^{1/2}$ ratio (rather than R_{ox}) against [LH]. However, instead of a pure proportional function we obtained a linear dependence of $R_{ox}/R_{IN}^{1/2}$ on [LH]:

$$R_{ox} = R_{O2} = (k'_p + k_p[LH])R_{IN}^{1/2}/2k_t^{1/2} \tag{4}$$

We explain these features by cyclo-izomerization (Scheme 5) of the pentadienyl radical LOO• proceeding by intramolecular attack to the double bond by the radical center. The product is a C-centered cycloperoxide radical (R•), which easily turns into a new peroxyl radical (ROO•). Taking into account this additional channel of oxygen consumption (with an overall unimolecular rate constants k_p') and assuming that ROO• does not contribute to the termination rate (so $k_p' = 2k$) [39], we modify equation (1) into equations (2) and (3) and obtain from experimental data:

$$R_{ox}/R_{IN}^{1/2} = a + b[LH] \qquad (5)$$

where $a = k_p'/(2k_t)^{1/2}$; $b = k_p/(2k_t)^{1/2}$.

Then, parameters $\underline{a}$ and $\underline{b}$ in Eq. 5 are $a = 2k_m/(2k_t)^{1/2} = k_p'/(2k_t)^{1/2}$; $k_p' = 14.8$ s^{-1}; $k_p' = 2k_m$; k_p 74.2 dm^3 mol^{-1}s^{-1}; $2k_t = 8.8 \times 10^6$s^{-1}.

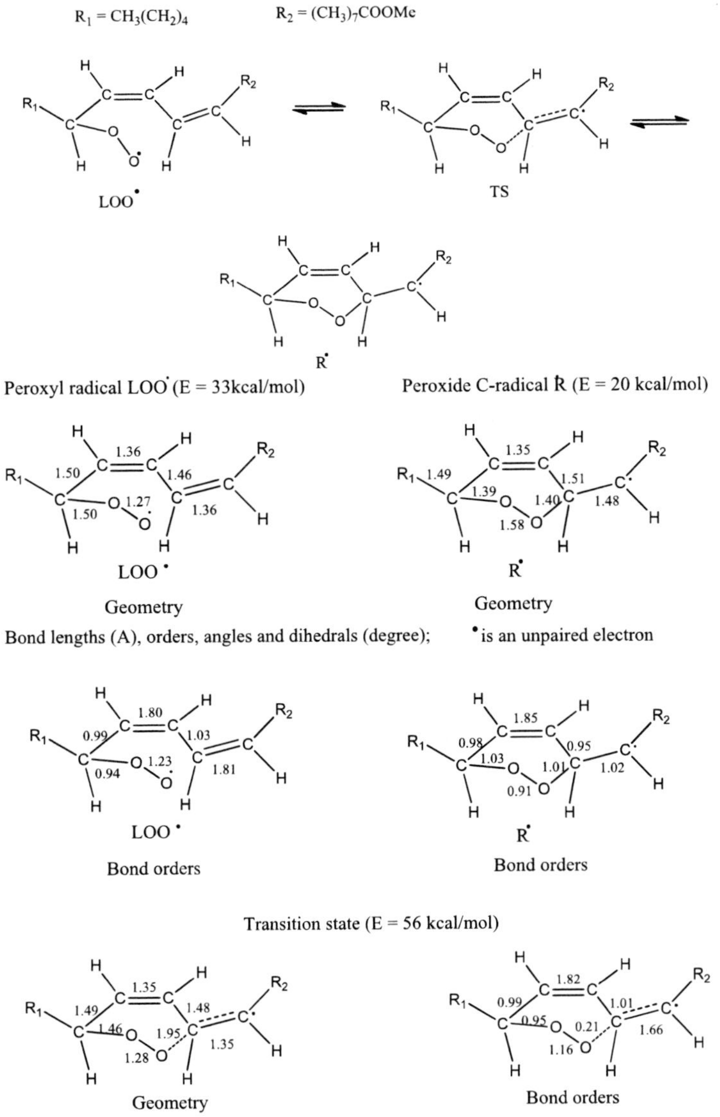

Scheme 5. Cyclo-izomerization of the pentadienyl radical LOO•.

These isomeric conjugated dienoic hydroperoxides are formed in equal concentrations at different autoxidation levels and over a wide range of temperatures. We found the following heats of formation (kcal/mol): for *trans* - LOO• : 39 (CI = 0), 37 (CI = 4), 33 (CI = 5); for *cis*- LOO• : 44 (CI = 0), 43 (CI = 2), 41 (CI = 5); for R•: 20 (CI = 0), 17 (CI = 5); for a transition state: 54-56 (CI = 5). Therefore, the reaction considered is exotermal by 13-20 kcal/mol.

The activation energy of the linoleate peroxyl isomerization is 17-23 kcal/mol, which is compatible with the experimental rate constant, 7.4 s^{-1} at 333 K. The data obtained show that the postulated reaction is quite probable [40].

2.4. Factors, Affecting the Lipid Oxidation Kinetics [2, 12,29,32]

Physical factors – contact surface of oxygen, oxygen partial pressure, temperature, irradiation.

Substrate factors – fatty acids composition – saturated, monoenic and polienic fatty acids; antioxidants (natural or synthetic) – individual or mixtures; prooxidants – surface active compounds.

Linoleate is 40 times more reactive than oleate [37] because it has an active bis-allylic methylene group on carbon-11 between two double bonds (Scheme 5) that can lose a hydrogen atom very readily.

Hydrogen abstraction at the carbon-11 position of linoleate produces a hybrid pentadienyl radical, which reacts with oxygen at the end carbon-9 and carbon-13 positions to produce a mixture of two conjugated diene 9- and 13-hydroperoxides.

A greater reactivity of linoleate is due to the formation of a pentadienyl radical intermediate which is more effectively stabilized by resonance, and of the resulting dienoic hydroperoxides that are stabilized by conjugation.

Structural factors - binding of the fatty acids as methyl esters, such as ME or acylglycerols (monoacylglycerols, MG, diacylglycerols, DA, triacylglycerols, TG)

Role of Lipid Micro Components on Non-Inhibited Lipid Oxidation Kinetics (Mono- and Diacyl Glycerols, Fatty Alcohols)

Application of different combinations of kinetically, spectral and theoretical approaches leads to new results and clarified the peculiarities of the mechanism of lipid oxidation in absence and in presence of various lipid hydroxy components (higher fatty alcohols of different chain length (carbon atoms = 12 - 20), mono- and diacylglycerols). This study was made: a) in presence of an initiator, i.e., initiated oxidation with constant rate of free radicals generation, and b) during lipid autoxidation, i.e., for real lipid oxidation. It has been proved that lipid hydroxyl components cannot change oxidizability of the lipid substrate; however they can accelerate the lipid hydroperoxides decomposition into free radicals during lipid autoxidation [32, 39, 41, 42].

Kinetic modeling of lipid hydroperoxides accumulation and decomposition according to different mechanism of decomposition in absence and in presence of lipid hydroxy components was presented and analyzed [32, 39]. On this base the mechanism of action of lipid hydroxy components was clarified.

$$LOOH + ROH \underset{}{\overset{K_S}{\rightleftharpoons}} S$$

$$[S] = K_s[LOOH][ROH]$$

$$S \xrightarrow{+O_2} LOO^\cdot + products \qquad e_s k_s$$

$$[T] = [LOOH] + [Q] + [S] = [LOOH](1 + K_1[[LH] + K_s[ROH])$$

$$[LOOH] = [T]/(1 + K_1[LH] + K_s[ROH])$$

$$[Q] = K_1[LH] \, [T]/(1 + K_1[LH] + K_s[ROH]$$

$$[S] = K_s[ROH] \, [T] \, /(1 + K_1[LH] + K_s[ROH])$$

Scheme 6. Kinetic scheme of lipid hydroperoxides (LOOH) decay in presence of ROH.

where: Ks: is the equilibrium constant for complex S, initial rate of decomposition of complex S ($e_s k_s$)

It is shown that in presence of a lipid hydroxyl compound k_i^{ROH} strongly increases with the decrease of MeLi (LH) concentration. This is explained with the competition of reactions (LOOH + LH and LOOH + ROH). Eqs 6-7 show us how to calculate the rate constants of initiation k_i and the total hydroperoxides concentration $[T_0]$

$$A = \frac{1}{4}\left(\frac{k_p}{\sqrt{k_t}}[LH]\right)^2 \cdot k_i$$

$$B = \frac{k_p}{\sqrt{k_t}}[LH]\sqrt{k_i} \cdot \sqrt{[T_o]} \tag{6, 7}$$

$$k_i = \frac{4A}{\left(\frac{k_p}{\sqrt{k_t}}[LH]\right)^2}$$

$$[T_o] = \left(\frac{B}{\frac{k_p}{\sqrt{k_t}}[LH]\sqrt{k_i}}\right)^2 \tag{8, 9}$$

Lipid hydroxy compounds (LOH) from the oxidized lipid substrate(LH) are formed during the whole oxidation process:

- LOH and H_2O with a rate of $e_0 k_{30}$ [LOOH] from the hydroperoxides of substrate LH
- LOH and H_2O with a rate of $e_1 k_{31}$ [Q] from the Q
- LOH and H_2O with t a rate of $e_3 k_{33}$ [S] from the S

There are presented some different mechanisms of the interaction between lipid hydroperoxides (LOOH) and hydroxy compounds (ROH):

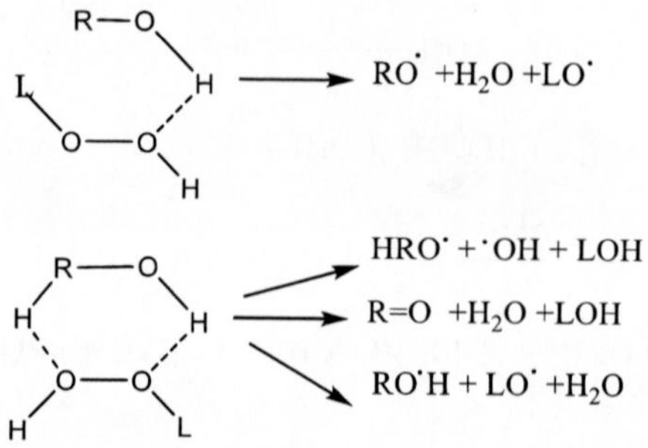

Scheme 7. Different mechanisms of interaction between LOOH and ROH.

2.5. Inhibited Lipid Oxidation

Plant (poly) phenolics are multifunctional antioxidants and act as: reducing agents (free radical terminators), metal chelators, and singlet oxygen quenchers. The activity of antioxidants depends on complex factors including: the nature of antioxidants, the conditions of oxidation, the properties of the oxidizing substrate and the stage of oxidation [27, 29, 30, 38]. An ideal antioxidant as a food additive or for the therapy of human diseases must be colorless, with no taste, and odor; be effective at low concentrations, easy to produce, stable, and with a low price [28, 30, 31, 37].

It must be noted that the radical scavenging activity towards different model radicals like DPPH gives information only about the H donating capacity of the studied compounds and some preliminary information for their possibility to be used as antioxidants. However, antioxidant activity is capacity of the compounds to inhibit lipid oxidation and thus to shorten the oxidation chain length as a result of its reaction with peroxide radicals. For that reason the antioxidant activity means the chain-breaking activity of the compounds [12].

2.5.1. Main Inhibiting and Side Reactions of Inhibited Lipid Oxidation
Reactions of inhibiting

(7) $LO_2• + AH \rightarrow LOOH + A•$ k_A (key inhibiting reaction)
(8) $LO_2• + A• \rightarrow A\text{-}OOL(QP)$ k_A (cross-recombination reactions)
(9) $A• + A• \rightarrow A - A$ k_R (recombination reaction)
(9a) $A• + A• \rightarrow AH + A(\text{-}H)$ k_D (disproportionation reaction)

Side reactions, decreasing the antioxidant potential

(-7) $LOOH + A• \rightarrow LO_2• + AH$ k_{-A} (reverse inhibiting reaction)
(10) $A• + LH (O_2) \rightarrow AH + LO_2•$ k_{10} (generation of $LO_2•$ radicals)
(11) $QP \rightarrow \delta LO_2• + P$ k_{11} (quinolide peroxides decomposition)
(12) $AH + LOOH \rightarrow A• + LO• + H_2O$ k_{12} (hydroperoxides decomposition)
(13) $AH + O_2 \rightarrow A• + HO_2•$ k_{13} (oxidation of the antioxidant)
(14) $2 A• + O_2 \rightarrow A\text{-}OOA (QP)$ k_{14} (oxidation of the phenoxyl radicals)

Scheme 8. Basic kinetic scheme of inhibited lipid oxidation.

According to Roginsky [30, 31], reactions of inhibited oxidation can be separated into three main groups:

a)   Reactions, characteristic of all types of antioxidants and at all oxidizing conditions: 0, 2, 3, 6 (chain generation, propagation, branching and termination);

b)   Depending on the mechanism of phenoxyl radical's recombination reactions 9 and 9a or 8 and 11 are taken in consideration. Reaction 9a is characteristic for the phenoxyls with n-alkylic substituents or OH groups in positions 2, 4 or 6. It is this reaction, not 9 that is the main road to the decay of phenoxy radicals of most industrial antioxidants. This reaction is crucial for the theory of inhibited oxidation, since it leads to regeneration of the starting phenol, therefore, to increase in its effectiveness.

c)   The rest of reactions are considered as marginal or side reactions. Their contribution varies depending on the structure of the antioxidant and the oxidation conditions.

The rate of inhibited lipid oxidation is presented by the equation:

$$R_A = k_p[LH]R_{IN}/nk_A[AH]_0 \tag{10}$$

where n – is the stoichiometric coefficient of inhibition, meaning how many radicals are trapped by one antioxidant molecule (for the classic antioxidant n = 2), $[AH]_0$ – initial concentration of the antioxidant.

Since the rate of inhibited oxidation is directly proportional to the R_{IN}, the efficient delay of the oxidation process is possible only in cases where, in the absence of AH, chain length is sufficiently large. Even when $2k_A[AH] \gg k_p[LH]$, hydroperoxides of the oxidizable substrate are formed by reaction 7 with a rate R_{IN}. In linear chains break the antioxidant has been consumed in a zero order rate $R_{IN}/2$. The time in which the antioxidant is fully consumed is called an induction period. Reaction 7 is reversible. Decreasing the substituents' volume in *ortho*-position resulted in an increase of the rate constant of the reversible reaction for phenolic antioxidants. In case of sterically hindered phenolic antioxidant (BHT, TBHQ) , reaction 7 is not reversible.

Roginsky [30, 31] concluded on the base of kinetic analysis that phenolic antioxidant has the higher efficiency, when the level of its side reactions is very low. A real criterion is the rate constant k_9, which gives information about the reaction mechanism of phenoxyl radicals, i.e reaction with a regeneration (disproportionation of phenoxyl radicals) or without regeneration (recombination of phenoxyl radicals) of the antioxidant molecule. The greater k_9, the smaller proportion of side reactions. The study on the relationship between structure and reactivity of the various phenolic antioxidants leads to boost the synthesis of a number of antioxidants with desirable properties. The isolation of antioxidants from natural products allows the use of a safe and in many instances significantly more effective antioxidants compared with synthetic ones. One of the most important objectives of the theory of inhibited oxidation now is studying the reactions in which it is possible to regenerate the phenolic antioxidant and thus to increase its effectiveness.

Role of ROH Types on the Rate Constants of Initiated Inhibited Lipid Oxidation

Our studies with kinetically pure lipid substrates (free of pro-and antioxidants) indicate the blocking action of ROH on the phenolic antioxidant, furthermore at high concentrations the process proceeds as non-inhibited. The observed effect may be due to the blocking action of ROH and also to accelerating the lipid hydroperoxides decomposition [43].

Determination of the main kinetic parameter k_A/k_p by volumometric method is a real criterion which reaction predominates – whether ROH blocks the AH or accelerates LOOH decomposition.

Taking into account that the rate of oxygen consumption R_{ox} in absence of an antioxidant is given by Eq. 3, the processing of the kinetic curves in presence of AH are made based on the following dependence:

$$F = \frac{1 + R_A/Rox}{1 - R_A/Rox} - \frac{Rox}{R_A} = \left(\frac{k_A R_{ox}}{k_p[LH]} \right) t + C$$

(11)

where: R_{ox} and R_A are rates of oxygen consumption in absence and in presence of an inhibitor, M/s; C – an integral constant. From the slope of this linear curve kinetic parameters $k_A R_{ox}/k_p$ [LH], and further k_A/k_p are calculated/determined. The concentration of lipid substrate [LH] = 1.5M.

The following values for k_A/k_p are found: in absence of ROH - k_A/k_p = 3.75 10^2; in presence of ROH (1-octadecanol) - k_A/k_p =2.50 10^2; and in presence of 1-monopalmitoyl-glycerol - k_A/k_p =1.65 10^2.

The data obtained show that in this case the addition of 1-octadecanol (1 – OD) and 1-monopalmitoylglycerol (1-MP) drives to 1.5 - or 2.3- fold decrease in the rate constant of the inhibited oxidation. The effect observed is a kinetic evidence for blocking action of the phenolic antioxidant in the presence of ROH as a result of complex formation based on hydrogen bond formation between them.

Data obtained prove the assumption that fatty alcohols and monoacylglycerols participate in the reactions of the interruption of the chain on the inhibitor and lower the rate constant of this reaction. The two hydroxyl groups in the monoacylglycerol molecule are likely to cause a greater degree of blocking the action of the inhibitor as compared to 1-octadecanol [43].

Role of Phenol Antioxidant Type on Kinetics and Mechanism of Lipid Autoxidation in Presence of ROH [44]

Since there is an experimental evidence that the effectiveness of the inhibitor decreases as a result of blocking its action by lipid hydroxy components (ROH), studies with other types of phenolic antioxidants (sterically hindered, BHT) and with a high value of k_{AH} (alpha-tocopherol) in the presence of ROH would allow to clarify their mechanism of action.

Kinetic Analysis of Inhibited Lipid Autoxidation in Presence of Lipid Hydroxycompounds (ROH)

At high concentrations of oxygen (kinetic mode of autoxidation) and phenolic antioxidant when latter is consumed linearly, the interrupting of the oxidation chain is carried out by a reaction between peroxide radicals and the phenolic antioxidant as $k_{AH}[AH] \gg k_t LO_2\bullet]$ and the inhibition rate in the oxidation in absence of ROH is determined according to equation (4).

In presence of ROH is possible the formation of a complex based on hydrogen bonding between ROH and AH:

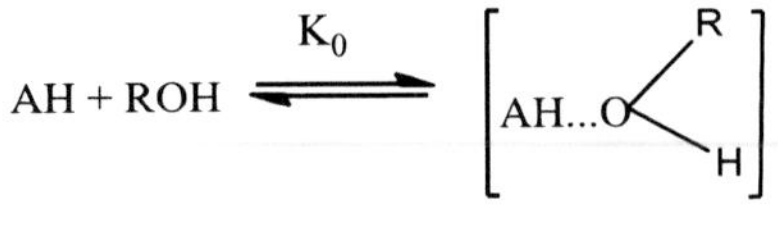

$$AH + ROH \underset{}{\overset{K_0}{\rightleftharpoons}} \left[AH...O \underset{H}{\overset{R}{\diagdown}} \right] \tag{12}$$

The value of K_0 is a quantitative measure of the blocking effect of the ROH to the phenolic antioxidant AH:

$$K_0 = \frac{[AH]_0 - [AH]}{[ROH][AH]} \tag{13}$$

The effective concentration of the antioxidant, [AH], is equal to the free amount of antioxidant, not included in the complex and can be determined by the formula:

$$[AH] = \frac{[AH]_0}{1 + K_0[ROH]} \tag{14}$$

The following method for determining K_0 from the experimental results is proposed. After substitution of [AH] in the equation for the initial rate of the inhibited lipid oxidation, the following equation for the rate of inhibited lipid oxidation in the presence of lipid hydroxy components is obtained:

$$R_{AH}{}^{ROH} = \frac{k_p[LH]R_i{}^{ROH}}{nk_{AH}[AH]_0} (1 + K_0[ROH]) \tag{15}$$

where R_A and $(R_A)^{ROH}$ are initial rates of inhibited lipid autoxidation in absence and in presence of an antioxidant, respectively.

The kinetics of the inhibited lipid autoxidation depends on the participation of ROH both in blocking antioxidant in a complex, and in accelerating the decomposition of hydroperoxides to free radicals, as a result the rate of initiation R_i is growing. There are possible three cases:

First case: ROH blocks the effects of AH, but does not change R_i (i.e., $(R_A)^{ROH} \approx R_A$). Then the relationship of the ratio between the oxidation rate of inhibition in the presence of ROH $(R_A)^{ROH}$ and in its absence R_A and the concentration of ROH is described by a linear equation of first degree:

$$(R_A)^{ROH}/R_A = 1 + K_0[ROH] \tag{16}$$

In this case K_0 determines as the slope of the linear equation.

Second case: ROH cannot block AH (as a result of the sterical hindrance of AH), and participates in the oxidation process only by accelerating the lipid hydroperoxides decomposition.

In this case the ratio $(R_A)^{ROH}/R_A$ can be presented as the ratio between rate constants of initiation in presence $(k_i)^{ROH}$ and in absence of ROH (k_i):

$$(R_A)^{ROH}/R_A = (R_i)^{ROH}/R_i = (k_i)^{ROH}/k_i \tag{17}$$

$$(R_i)^{ROH} = (k_i)^{ROH}[LOOH]; \quad R_i = k_i[LOOH] \tag{18}$$

Third case: ROH participates in both reactions of the oxidation process: i) blocking the effect of the antioxidant and ii) accelerating the hydroperoxides decomposition. In this case the dependence $(R_A)^{ROH}/R_A = f([ROH])$ is non-linear and its kinetic analysis gives a possibility to clarify the mechanism of action of ROH in the oxidation process, as well as to determine the equilibrium constants K_0 and the effective antioxidants concentration [AH].

The following kinetic model describes the lipid hydroperoxides (LOOH) decomposition, taking into account their mono- and pseudo-monomolecular mechanisms, as well as the presence of a lipid compound (ROH) and of phenolic antioxidant (AH):

$$LOOH \xrightarrow[LH, O_2]{kio} LO_2^{\bullet}$$

$$LOOH + LH \underset{}{\overset{K_1}{\rightleftharpoons}} Q \xrightarrow[LH, O_2]{ki1} LO_2^{\bullet} \qquad K_1 = \frac{[Q]}{[LOOH][LH]}$$

$$LOOH + ROH \underset{}{\overset{K_S}{\rightleftharpoons}} S \xrightarrow[LH, O_2]{kis} LO_2^{\bullet} \qquad K_S = \frac{[S]}{[LOOH][LH]}$$

$$LOOH + AH \underset{}{\overset{K_P}{\rightleftharpoons}} P \xrightarrow[LH, O_2]{P} LO_2^{\bullet} \qquad K_P = \frac{[P]}{[LOOH][LH]}$$

Scheme 9. Kinetics of lipid hydroperoxides decomposition in presence of lipid hydroxyl compound (ROH) and an antioxidant (AH).

where: K_s and K_p – are the equilibrium constants for the complexes, S and P, respectively, k_{is} and k_{ip} – are the corresponding rate constants of initiation at monomolecular decomposition of LOOH, of the complexes S and P.

When the total concentration of lipid hydroperoxides is presented by $[LOOH]_{\Sigma}$, than from Scheme 9 followed:

$$[LOOH]_{\Sigma} = [LOOH] + [Q] + [S] + [P] = [LOOH](1 + K_1[LH] + K_S[ROH] + K_P[AH]) \tag{19}$$

and for the rate constants of initiation in presence and in absence of ROH:

$$ki^{ROH} = \frac{kio + ki1K1[LH] + kisKs[ROH] + kipKp[AH]}{1 + K1[LH] + Ks[S] + Kp[AH]}$$

$$ki = \frac{kio + ki1K1[LH] + kipKp[AH]}{1 + K1[LH] + Kp[AH]} \tag{20, 21}$$

It has been obtained that the phenolic antioxidants' efficiency decreases in presence of ROH. The effect of monoacylglycerols on the inhibition rate constant decrease is higher in comparison with that of 1-octadecanol. Based on this kinetic analysis of the inhibited lipid oxidation it could be concluded that ROH decreases the efficiency of hydroquinone alpha-tocopherol (phenolic antioxidants with free OH groups) as a result of the complex formation (i.e., blocking action), but for BHT (strically hindered OH group) - as a result of accelerating lipid hydroperoxides decomposition [44].

3. BIO-ANTIOXIDANTS [11, 12, 45]

Biologically active compounds with antioxidant potential, i.e., bio-antioxidants (natural and their synthetic analogues) have a wide range of applications. They are important drugs, antibiotics, agrochemical substances, and food preservatives. Many of the drugs today are synthetic modifications of naturally obtained substances with both activities – biological and antioxidant. The most known bio-antioxidants are flavonoids and cinnamic acids. A criterion for a good antioxidant is that the compound should contain a highly labile hydrogen atom forming a radical, the radical formed should be stable and non-reactive so that it will not participate in the propagation step. Sterically hindered phenolic compounds satisfy most of the above-mentioned requirements. Thus, the antioxidant and radical scavenging effects of polyphenols are highly cited.

Determination of the Main Kinetic Parameters of the Studied Compounds

Antioxidant efficiency means the potency of antioxidant to increase the oxidation stability of the lipid sample by blocking the radical chain process. It could be presented with *induction period* (IP) *and protection factor* (PF). IP, i.e., the time, in which the concentration of antioxidant is fully consumed, was determined as a cross-point for the tangents to the two parts of the kinetic curves of lipid autoxidation; IP_A in the presence of antioxidant and IP_C for the control lipid sample without antioxidant. PF means how many times the antioxidant increases the oxidation stability of the lipid sample and was determined as a ratio between the induction periods in presence (IP_A) and in absence (IP_C) of an antioxidant, i.e., PF = IP_A/IP_C. *Antioxidant reactivity*, expressing the possibility of the antioxidant to take part in side reactions of the oxidation process, i.e., to change the initial oxidation rate can be presented with the following kinetic parameters: initial rate of lipid autoxidation, inhibition degree and/or oxidation rate ratio. *Initial rate of lipid autoxidation* in absence (R_C) and in presence (R_A) of antioxidant was found from the tangent at the initial phase of the kinetic curves of hydroperoxides accumulation. *Inhibition degree* (ID) is a measure of the antioxidant reactivity, e.g., how many times the antioxidant shortens the oxidation chain length, i.e., ID = R_C/R_A, and for that reason is one of the most important kinetic parameters. *Antioxidant capacity* can be presented with the following kinetic parameters: main rate of antioxidant consumption and relative mean rate of antioxidant consumption. *Main rate of antioxidant consumption* (R_m), means the main rate of inhibitor consumption during the induction period of the inhibited lipid autoxidation, i.e., $R_m = [AH]/IP_A$.

3.1. Design of New Bio-Antioxidants

- *Individual* – the idea is to combine in one molecule by a specific synthetic way various functional fragments, responsible for biological and antioxidant activities [11].
- *Compositions* – by mixtures (double or triple) of biologically active compounds, antioxidants and synergists [12]

3.2. Synergism, Additivizm and Antagonism of Equimolar Binary and Triple Mixtures of Bio-Antioxidants with Alpha-Tocopherol and Ascorbic Acid/Palmitate

In this study different effects of binary and triple mixtures of various phenolic antioxidants - synthetic and of natural origin - were compared and discussed. Binary mixtures with alpha-tocopherol (TOH) of flavonoids, standard antioxidants and cinnamic acids, simple hydroxy-coumarins and bis-coumarins, benzo[kl]xanthene lignans and dihydrobenzofuran neolignans biphenyls and their monomers were selected for this study. Triple mixtures with TOH and ascorbic acid (AscH) were created with those compounds which showed a synergism in binary mixtures with TOH. If two or more antioxidants are added to oxidizing lipid substrates, their combined inhibitory effect can be additive, antagonistic, or synergistic [27, 37, 38].

Synergism - the inhibiting effect of the binary mixtures (IP_{1+2}) is higher than the sum of the induction periods of the individual phenolic antioxidants ($IP_1 + IP_2$) i.e., $IP_{1+2} < IP_1 + IP_2$. The percent of synergism was calculated according to the formulae for the binary mixtures [37]:

%Synergism = 100 {[IP_{1+2} - ($IP_1 + IP_2$)]/($IP_1 + IP_2$)}.

Additivism - the inhibiting effect of the binary mixtures (IP_{1+2}) is equal to the sum of the induction periods of the individual phenolic antioxidants, i.e., $IP_{1+2} = IP_1 + IP_2$.

Antagonism - the inhibiting effect of the (IP_{1+2}) is lower than the sum of the induction periods of the individual phenolic antioxidants, i.e., $IP_{1+2} < IP_1 + IP_2$.

As analogy with the formula of synergism, we created a new formula for calculation of % *Antagonism* = 100 {[($IP_1 + IP_2$)-IP_{1+2}]/ IP_{1+2} }.

Formulae for the triple mixtures were created also from us by analogue with the binary mixtures:

$\%Synergism = 100 \, [(IP_\Sigma - \Sigma IP_i)]/ \Sigma IP_i]$; and

$\% \, Antagonism = 100 \, [(\Sigma IP_i - IP_\Sigma)]/IP_\Sigma]$, where IP_Σ is the induction period of triple mixture; ΣIP_i, where i=1,2,3, is the sum of induction periods of components 1,2, and 3 of triple mixture.

On the basis of results obtained new effective powerful complex bio-antioxidants can be created for practical purposes.

A. Flavonoids [46]

Flavonoids constitute a family of aromatic molecules that are derived from phenyl- and malonyl-coenzyme A: they are generally classified into several groups, e.g., flavones, flavonols, chalcones, flavanones, isoflavones, anthocyanidins and others, according to the chemical features of rings A and B, and the oxidation of the C-ring.

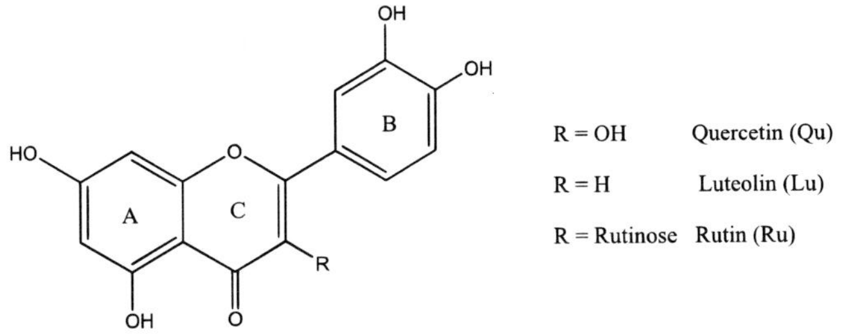

Figure 2. Structures of flavonoids: quercetine (Qu), luteoline (Lu) and rutine (Ru).

While flavanones and flavanols have a single bond between the atoms 2 and 3 of the C-ring, flavones, flavonols, isoflavones and anthocyanidins have a double or aromatic bond there. Ring B is normally attached to position 2 of ring C except in the case of isoflavonoids. Naturally, about 97% of flavonoids exist as aglycons. Flavonoids are unique natural bio-antioxidants, because they are powerful antioxidants and possess various biological activities. A lot of studies of scientists are focused on the structure-activity relationship of these interesting compounds [47, 48].

Bors et al. [47] postulated the main structural fragments in flavonoids responsible for their strong antioxidant activity, and capacity to scavenge free radicals. Belyakov et al. [48] published very interesting data which evidenced that the prooxidant effect of flavonoids is due to the non-classical kinetics of reaction with peroxide radicals and intramolecular reaction of radicals formed. Later Vasil'ev et al. [49] published data explaining the mechanism of action of different classes of phenolic antioxidants with a catecholic structure. Vasil'ev et al. demonstrated [50] that the prooxidant effect of chalcones with a catecholic structure is due to the formation of dioxiethanes. These reactions with dioxiethane formation can explain the prooxidant properties of flavonoids too.

In order to study the possible synergism between two flavonoid aglicones Qu and Lu binary mixtures with equimolar concentrations (0.1mM) were prepared and their effect on the kinetics of lipid autoxidation was studied (Figure 3a and Table 3).

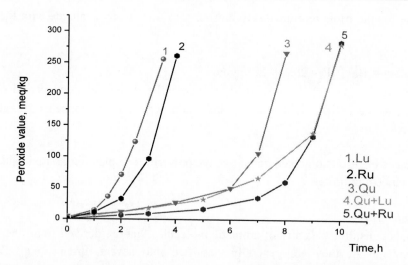

Figure 3a. Kinetic curves of lipid hydroperoxides accumulation during TGSO autoxidation at 80°C in presence of 0.1mM Luteolin (Lu), Rutin (Ru), Quercetin (Qu) and of their equimolar (1: 1) binary mixtures (Lu+Qu) and (Qu+Ru).

The mixtutre of Qu+Lu showed almost 7-fold higher inhibiting effect than Lu and 1.4-fold higher inhibiting effect than Qu. The mixture of Qu + Ru showed a lower oxidation stability of lipid substrate than of Qu alone, however, almost 3-fold higher effect than Ru. Evidently, the addition of Ru to Qu not only didn't improve the antioxidant efficiency of Qu but even led to a decrease of the antioxidant potential of the aglycon. Consequently, the both mixtures of Qu+Lu and Qu+Ru show no synergism; furthermore they showed an antagonism between flavonoids. These results manifested that these flavonoid aglycons must be used as individual antioxidants, not in mixtures.

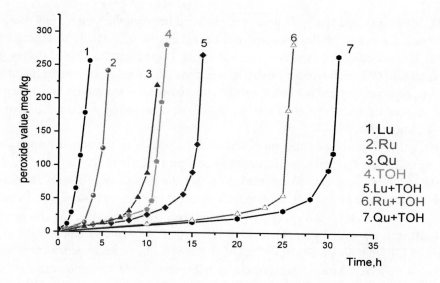

Figure 3b. Kinetic curves of lipid hydroperoxides accumulation during TGSO autoxidation at 80°C in presence of 0.1mM Luteolin (Lu), Rutin (Ru), Quercetin (Qu), α-Tocopherol (TOH) and of their equimolar (1:1) binary mixtures(Lu+TOH), (Qu+TOH) and (Ru+TOH).

Table 3. Inhibiting efficiency of various binary mixtures of two (1 and 2) antioxidants in equimolar concentrations (0.1mM) and 1:1 ratio, 80°C, during TGSO autoxidation (IP_c=1.7±0.2)h, R_c=1.2 10^{-6} M/s)

Binary mixtures	IP_{1+2}	IP_1	IP_2	Synergism/Additivism/Antagonism	%Syn	Refs
Quercetin (1) + Luteolin (2) (Qu+Lu)	7.5±0.8	9.9±0.9	2.2±0.2	Ant IP_{1+2}< (IP_1+ IP_2)	-	[32,46]
Quercetin (1)+Rutin (2) (Qu+Ru)	8.3±0.8	9.9±0.9	2.7±0.2	Ant IP_{1+2}< (IP_1+ IP_2)	-	[32,46]
Quercetin (1) + Tocopherol (2) (Qu+TOH)	29.7±1.5	9.9±0.9	10.5±0.9	Sin IP_{1+2}> (IP_1+ IP_2)	46%	[32,46]
Luteolin (1) + Tocopherol (2) (Lu+TOH)	15.1±0.9	2.4±0.2	10.5±0.9	Sin IP_{1+2}> (IP_1+ IP_2)	19%	[32,46]
Rutin (1)+ Tocopherol (2) (Ru+TOH)	24.9±1.5	2.7±0.2	10.5±0.9	Sin IP_{1+2}> (IP_1+ IP_2)	87%	[32,46]
Caffeic acid (1) + Tocopherol(2) (CA+TOH)	20.4±1.5	9.8±0.9	10.5±0.9	Add IP_{1+2}= (IP_1+ IP_2)	-	[29,32]
Sinapic acid (1) + Tocopherol (2) (SA+TOH)	16.1±0.9	5.3±0.5	10.5±0.9	Sin IP_{1+2}> (IP_1+ IP_2)	1.9%	[29,32]
BHT (1) + Tocopherol (2) (BHT + TOH)	21.5±1.5	7.5±0.5	10.5±0.9	Sin IP_{1+2}> (IP_1+ IP_2)	19.4%	[29,32]
TBHQ (1)+ Tocopherol (2) (TBHQ + TOH)	26.1±1.5	7.9±0.5	10.5±0.9	Sin IP_{1+2}> (IP_1+ IP_2)	44.2%	[29,32]
6,7-diOH-Cumarin(1) +TOH (2) (Cum$_2$+TOH)	12.7±0.9	7.1±0.5	10.5±0.9	Ant IP_{1+2}< (IP_1+ IP_2)	-	[32,59]
7,8-diOH-Cumarin(1) +TOH (2) (Cum$_1$+TOH)	14.2±0.9	2.0±0.2	10.5±0.9	Sin IP_{1+2}> (IP_1+ IP_2)	14%	[32,59]
7-OH-Cumarin(1) +TOH(2) (Cum3+TOH)	11.8±0.9	1.5±0.2	10.5±0.9	Add IP_{1+2}= (IP_1+ IP_2)	-	[32,59]
Sinapic acid (1)+TOH (2) (SA+TOH)*	45.0±1.0	8.5±0.5	21.0±1.5	Sin IP_{1+2}> (IP_1+ IP_2)	52%	[29,32]
M$_1$OH (1) + TOH (2)	14.8±0.8	1.3±0.2	10.5±0.9	Sin IP_{1+2}> (IP_1+ IP_2)	25.4%	[60,61]
D$_1$(OH)$_2$ (1) + TOH (2)	13.2±0.8	3.2±0.2	10.5±0.9	Add IP_{1+2}= (IP_1+ IP_2)	-	[60,61]
M$_2$OH (1) + TOH (2)	10.3±0.8	1.3±0.2	10.5±0.9	Ant IP_{1+2}< (IP_1+ IP_2)	15.5%	[60]
D$_2$(OH)$_2$ (1) + TOH (2)	10.9±0.8	2.0±0.2	10.5±0.9	Ant IP_{1+2}< (IP_1+ IP_2)	8.7%	[60]
FA(1) + TOH(2)	18.5±0.8	1.9±0.3	10.5±0.9	Sin IP_{1+2}> (IP_1+ IP_2)	49.2%	[60]
DFA(1) + TOH (2)	21.5±0.8	2.0±0.3	10.5±0.9	Sin IP_{1+2}> (IP_1+ IP_2)	71.4%	[60]

* for SA+TOH, TGL autoxidation, 100°C [29,32].

As we can see from the Figure 3b and Table 3 the equimolar binary mixtures of flavonoids and TOH demonstrated a synergism between the components: 47% for Qu+TOH, 19% for Lu+TOH and 87% for Ru+TOH.

It is found that the lipid oxidation stability (presented as protection factor, PF, in presence of flavonoids studied) decreases in the order: PF: 22.8 (Qu+TOH) > 19.2 (Ru+TOH) > 15.1 (Lu+TOH) > 8.1 (TOH) > 7.6 (Qu) > 2.1 (Ru) > 1.7 (Lu). The following reactions of binary mixtures of flavonoids (for example quercetin) Qu(OH)$_2$, α-tocopherol, TOH) and of their radicals - tocopheryl radical (TO•) and semiquinone radicals Qu(OH)O• with lipid peroxide radicald (LO$_2$•) and reactions of homo- and cross-recombination and disproportionation rections, responsible for different effects observed are presented:

Reactions of Quercetin (Qu(OH)$_2$ and its radicals

Qu(OH)$_2$ + LO$_2^\bullet$ → Qu(OH)O$^\bullet$ + LOOH (H-atom transfer)

Qu(OH)O$^\bullet$ + LO$_2^\bullet$ → Qu(OH)O-OOL (cross-recombination with quinolide peroxides formation)

Qu(OH)O-OOL+ LO$_2^\bullet$ → Qu(O•)O-OOL + LOOH (H-atom transfer)

Qu(O•)O-OOL+ LO$_2^\bullet$ → Qu(OOOL)$_2$ (cross-recombination with quinolide peroxides forming)

2 Qu(OH)O$^\bullet$→ Qu(OH)$_2$+QuO$_2$ (homo-disproportionation with Qu(OH)$_2$ regeneration and ortho-quinone formation QuO$_2$)

Reactions of α-Tocopherol (TOH) and its phenoxyl radical

TOH + LO$_2^\bullet$ → TO$^\bullet$ + LOOH (H-atom transfer)

TO$^\bullet$ + LO$_2^\bullet$ → TO-OOL (cross-recombination with quinolide peroxides forming)

2 TO$^\bullet$ → TOH + (homo-disproportionation with TOH regeneration and tocopheryl-methylene-quinone formation T=O)

Reactions between Qu(OH)$_2$ and TOH and between their radicals

Qu(OH)O$^\bullet$ + TOH → Qu(OH)$_2$ + TO$^\bullet$ (H-atom transfer with Qu(OH)$_2$ regeneration)

TO$^\bullet$ + Qu(OH)$_2$ → TOH + Qu(OH)O$^\bullet$ (H-atom transfer with regeneration of TOH)

TO$^\bullet$ + Qu(OH)O $^\bullet$ → TOH + QuO$_2$ (cross-disproportionation with regeneration of TOH and ortho-quinone formation)

TO$^\bullet$ + Qu(OH)O $^\bullet$ → Qu(OH)$_2$+ T=O (cross-disproportionation with regeneration of Qu(OH)$_2$ and tocopheryl-methylene-quinone formation T=O)

TO$^\bullet$ + Qu(OH)O $^\bullet$ → products (cross-recombination without regeneration)

Reactions of H-atom transfer and cross-disproportionation reactions are responsible for the synergism obtained; however, reaction of cross-recombination is responsible for the antagonism observed. Table 4 presents results about differences in O-H bond dissociation enthalpies (BDE) of Qu, Lu and Ru and TOH, which are the suitable theoretical descriptors for explanation (and probably for prediction) of the effects of binary mixtures.

Table 4. Binary mixtures of bi-phenolic and polyphenolic antioxidants with TOH

$Q(OH)_2$	$Q(OH)_2+TOH$	BDE_{QH2} ΔBDE_{O-H}	$QH2$ regeneration	TOH regeneration	Side reactions
CA	Additivism	$=BDE_{TOH}$ $\Delta BDE = 0$	yes	H-atom transfer Cross-disproport	No
7,8-di-OHCum $Cum_1(OH)_2$	Synergism	$\uparrow BDE_{TOH}$ $\Delta BDE > 0$	yes	H-atom transfer Cross-disproport	No
6,7-di-OHCum $Cum_2(OH)_2$	Antagonism	$\downarrow BDE_{TOH}$ $\Delta BDE < 0$	yes	H-atom transfer	Cross-recombination
FLAVONOIDS					
Qu + Lu	Antagonism	$BDE < 0$	yes	-	Cross-recombination
Qu + Ru	Antagonism	$BDE < 0$	yes	-	Cross-recombination
Qu + TOH	Synergism 46%	$\uparrow BDE_{TOH}$ $BDE > 0$	yes	H-atom transfer Cross-disproport	No
Lu + TOH	Synergism 19%	$\uparrow BDE_{TOH}$ $BDE > 0$	yes	H-atom transfer Cross-disproport	No
Ru + TOH	Synergism 89%	$\uparrow BDE_{TOH}$ $BDE > 0$	yes	H-atom transfer Cross-disproport	No

It is seen that in case when $\Delta BDE > 0$ it is observed a synergism, and in case of $\Delta BDE < 0$, an antagonism was observed (Tables 3 & 4).

B. Cinnamic Acids and Standard Antioxidants

Cinnamic acids are biological precursors of coumarins and chalcones and are widely distributed in the plant kingdom. Bors et al. [51] reported interesting paper concerning structure and kinetic modeling of phenoxyl radicals of several phenols and phenolic acids with *ortho*-methoxy groups generated by pulse-radiolytic oxidation. Structures of the phenoxyl radicals were obtained with EPR spectroscopy and the experimental isotropic coupling constants were confirmed by hybrid DFT calculations with B3LYP functional theory and a variety of basis sets, and with consideration of the solvent. With regard to the stability of phenoxyl radicals, which is of particular interest for the accompanying EPR experiments, authors observed a consistently lower decay rate for all di-methoxy compounds as compared to the mono-methoxy substances, both for neutral phenoxyl radicals and dissociated phenolic acids. Nevertheless, kinetic arguments may explain the EPR results; i.e., phenoxyl radicals shielded by two adjacent methoxy groups are more stable than those with only one methoxy group. One has to keep in mind, however, that the time scale of the EPR experiments is about three orders of magnitude longer than that of the pulse radiolysis studies and that *in situ* generation of the radicals by HRP/H_2O_2 may result in secondary species, not only in the initially present phenoxyl radical exclusively [51].

Nenadis et al. [52, 53] reported data concerning the antioxidant activity of cinnamic acids by applying combination of experimental and theoretical approaches, especially on the effect of side chain. Synthetic analogues of naturally occurred mono- and di-prenyl detrivatives of 4-hydroxy-coumaric acids, found in Brazilian propolis (PHC and DPHC), showed moderate antioxidant activity [54]. Yanishlieva [55] published data about different factors affecting the antioxidant effectiveness and strength of cinnamic acid derivatives. Kancheva [56], Kasaikina et al. [57] and Rusina et al. [58] reported on the structure-antiradical relationship and antioxidant activity of a series of cinnamic acid derivatives.

We studied the effects of equimolar binary mixtures at 0.1mM concentration of cinnamic acids – caffeic (CA), sinapic (SA) and ferulic (FA) as well as of standard antioxidants - butylated hydroxyl toluene (BHT) and *tert*-butylhydroquinone (TBHQ) with tocopherol (TOH).

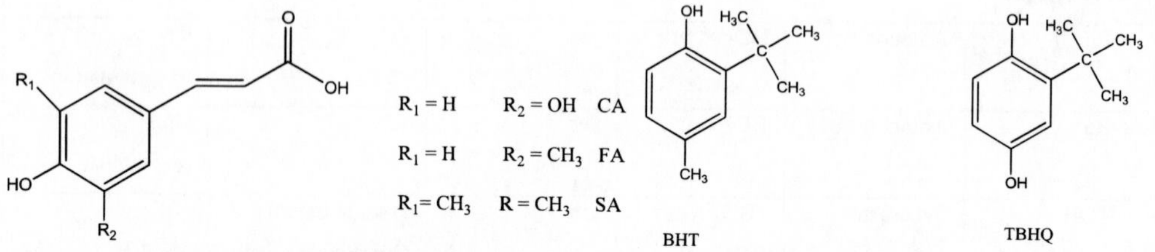

R₁ = H   R₂ = OH CA

R₁ = H   R₂ = CH₃ FA

R₁ = CH₃   R = CH₃ SA

BHT

TBHQ

Figure 4. Structures of cinnamic acids, studied: caffeic acid (CA), ferulic acid (FA) and synaptic acid (SA); and of standard antioxidants studied: butylated hydroxytoluene (BHT) and tert-butyl-hydro-quinone (TBHQ).

Figure 5 presents the kinetics of lipid autoxidation in presence of studied cinnamic acids and standard antioxidants as individual compounds and in equimolar binary mixtures with TOH.

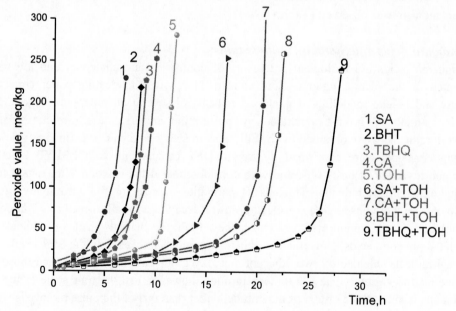

1.SA
2.BHT
3.TBHQ
4.CA
5.TOH
6.SA+TOH
7.CA+TOH
8.BHT+TOH
9.TBHQ+TOH

Figure 5. Kinetic curves of lipid hydroperoxides accumulation during TGSO autoxidation at 80°C in presence of 0.1mM sinapic acid (SA), butylated hydroxytoluene (BHT), tert-butylated hydroquinone (TBHQ), caffeic acid (CA), α-tocopherol (TOH) and of their equimolar (1:1) binary mixtures (SA+TOH), (BHT+TOH), (TBHQ+TOH), and (CA+TOH).

The following order of lipid oxidation stability was found:

(TBHQ+TOH) > (BHT+TOH) > (CA+TOH) > (SA+TOH) > TOH > CA > TBHQ ≥
BHT > SA

Table 3 presents the result of effects observed in binary mixtures. It is seen that all compounds demonstrated synergism with TOH, only CA manifested additivism with TOH. The strongest inhibiting effects and synergism obtained of the binary mixtures (TBHQ+TOH) and (BHT+TOH) can be explained by the following mechanism (Scheme 8). It is seen that both components of the mixture – BHT (or TBHQ) and TOH can be regenerated during the homo-disproportionation reactions of phenoxyl radicals from BHT (or TBHQ) and TOH formed, as well as during the reactions of cross-disproportionation between their radicals:

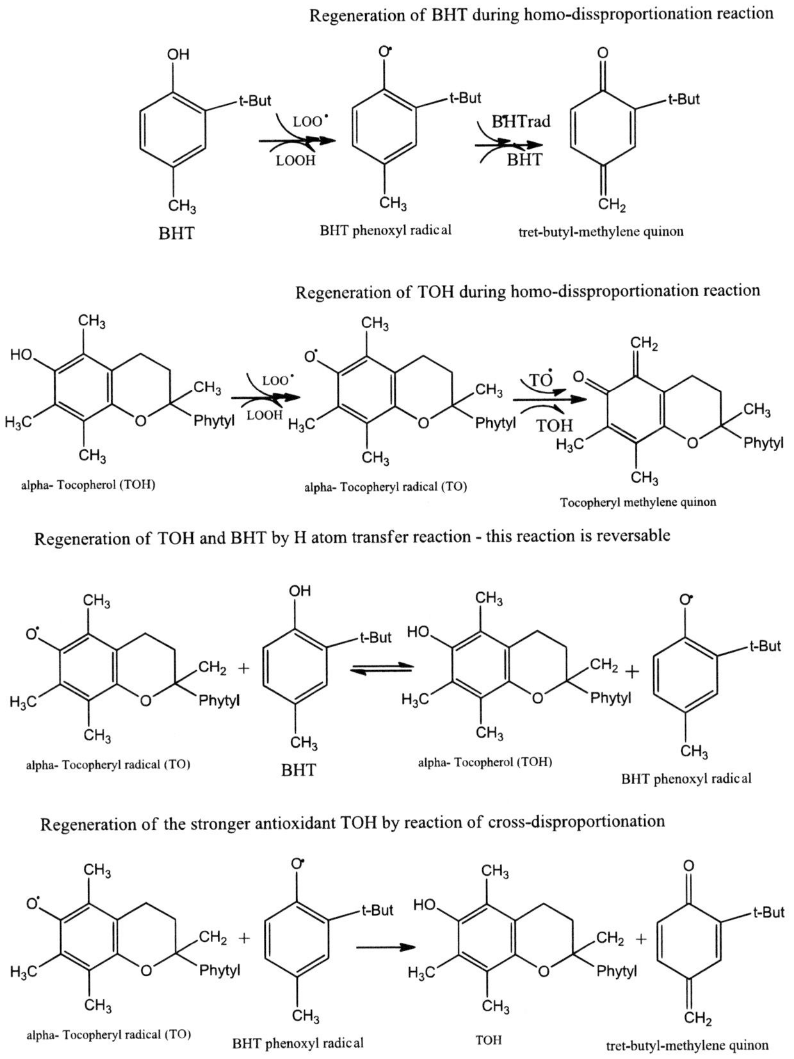

Scheme10. Mechanism of BHT and TOH action in binary mixture with possible regeneration of BHT and TOH.

In this binary mixture TOH is the stronger antioxidant and its regeneration from H-atom transfer and cross-disproportionation is of importance for the synergism obtained.

In this case both antioxidants are able to be regenerated during the H-atom transfer and by cross-disproportionation reaction of their radicals and as a result this binary mixture showed the strongest inhibiting effect and synergism (Table 5).

It has been found that CA+TOH didn't show synergism, only additivism between the components. Its mean that both strong antioxidants (CA and TOH have similar inhibiting activity, see Table 3) work as individual antioxidants not in tandem.

Table 5. Binary mixtures of monophenolic antioxidants AH with TOH

AH	AH+TOH	BDE $_{A-H}$	AH regeneration	TOH regeneration	Side reactions
BHT	Synergism	↑BDE $_{TOH}$ Δ BDE > 0	yes	H-atom transfer, cross-dispropor.	No t-But
SA	Synergism	↑BDE $_{TOH}$ Δ BDE > 0	no	H-atom transfer	Yes +
FA	Synergism	↑BDE $_{TOH}$ Δ BDE > 0	no	H-atom transfer	Yes +
M$_1$OH	Synergism	↑BDE $_{TOH}$ Δ BDE > 0	no	H-atom transfer	Yes +
M$_2$OH	Antagonism	↑BDE $_{TOH}$ Δ BDE > 0	no	H-atom transfer	Yes +++
7-OH-Cum Cum3OH	Additivism	↑BDE $_{TOH}$ Δ BDE > 0	no	H-atom transfer	Yes +++

C. Hydroxy-coumarins [59]

Coumarins are important class of oxygen heterocycles, widespread in plant kingdom. They have attracted intense interest recently due to their presence in natural sources, and to their possession of diverse pharmacological properties. 4-Methylcoumarins have been found to possess choleretic, analgesic, anti-spermatogenic, anti-tubercular and diuretic properties. Polyphenolic coumarins are known to act as antioxidants in biological systems, but it is difficult to distinguish their antioxidant activity from the many other effects they produce in cells.

In order to study the possible synergism between two phenolic antioxidants, the antioxidant efficiency and reactivity of three binary mixtures of coumarins and TOH (Cum$_1$+TOH, Cum$_2$+TOH and Cum$_3$+TOH) were tested and compared. Figure 6 and Table 3 present results obtained. It is found a higher oxidation stability of the lipid substrate in presence of all binary mixtures in comparison with individual compounds.

Regeneration of TBHQ during homo-dissproportionation reaction

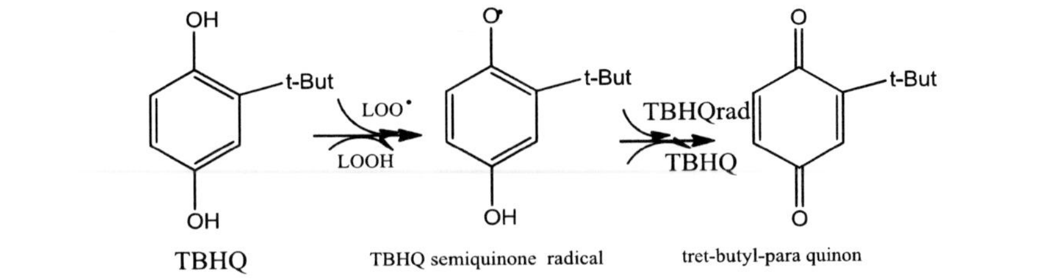

Regeneration of TOH during homo-dissproportionation reaction

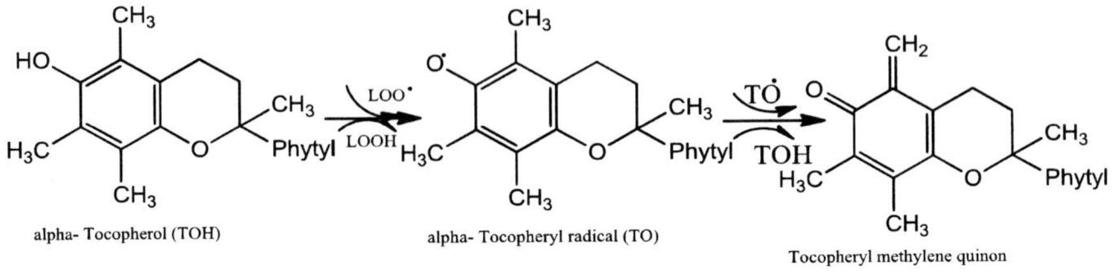

Regeneration of TOH and TBHQ by H atom transfer reaction - this reaction is reversable

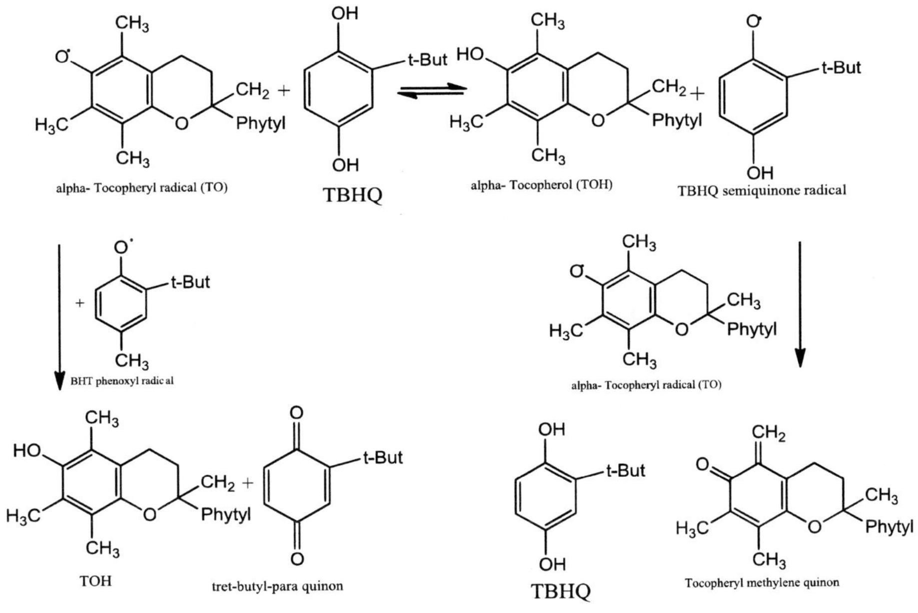

Regeneration of TOH and TBHQ by reaction of cross-disproportionation

Scheme 11. Mechanism of TBHQ and TOH action in binary mixture with possible regeneration of TBHQ and TOH.

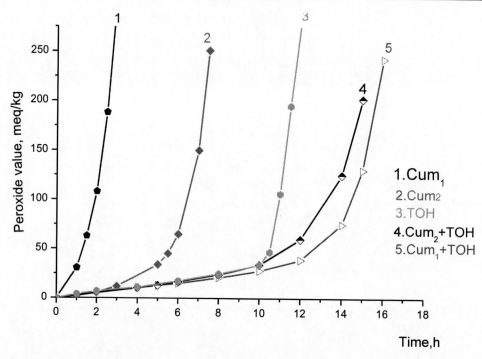

Figure 6. Kinetic curves of lipid hydroperoxides accumulation during TGSO autoxidation at 80°C in presence of 0.1mM 7,8-dihydroxy-4-methyl-coumarin (Cum$_1$), 6,7-dihydroxy-4-methyl-coumarin (Cum$_2$), α-tocopherol (TOH) and of their equimolar (1:1) binary mixtures (Cum$_1$+TOH) and (Cum$_2$+TOH).

The synergism was observed only for the binary mixture of 7,8-dihydroxy-4-methyl coumarin (Cum$_1$) with α-tocopherol (TOH) Cum$_1$+TOH:

$$IP_{1+2}(14.2) > IP_{Cum1}(2.0) + IP_{TOH}(10.5) \text{ and 14 \% synergism.}$$

In case of 6,7-dihydroxy-4-methyl-coumarin(Cum$_2$) with α-tocopherol (TOH) Cum$_2$+TOH it was found an antagonism between the two antioxidants:

$$IP_{1+2}(12.7) < IP_{Cum2}(7.1) + IP_{TOH}(10.5).$$

In case of 7-hydroxy-4-methyl-coumarin (Cum$_3$) with α-tocopherol (TOH) Cum$_3$+TOH an additivism was observed: $IP_{1+2}(11.8) = IP_{Cum3}(1.7) + IP_{TOH}(10.5)$.

The highest oxidation stability of TGSO in presence of all binary mixtures with α-tocopherol (TOH) may be explained taking into account that the both antioxidants may be regenerated during the oxidation process. It is known that the catecholic moiety of coumarine molecules allows formation of semiquinone radicals. These semiquinone radicals may regenerate the initial antioxidant molecule during reaction of bimolecular recombination with homo- and cross-disproportionation of semiquinone radicals [27, 33]:

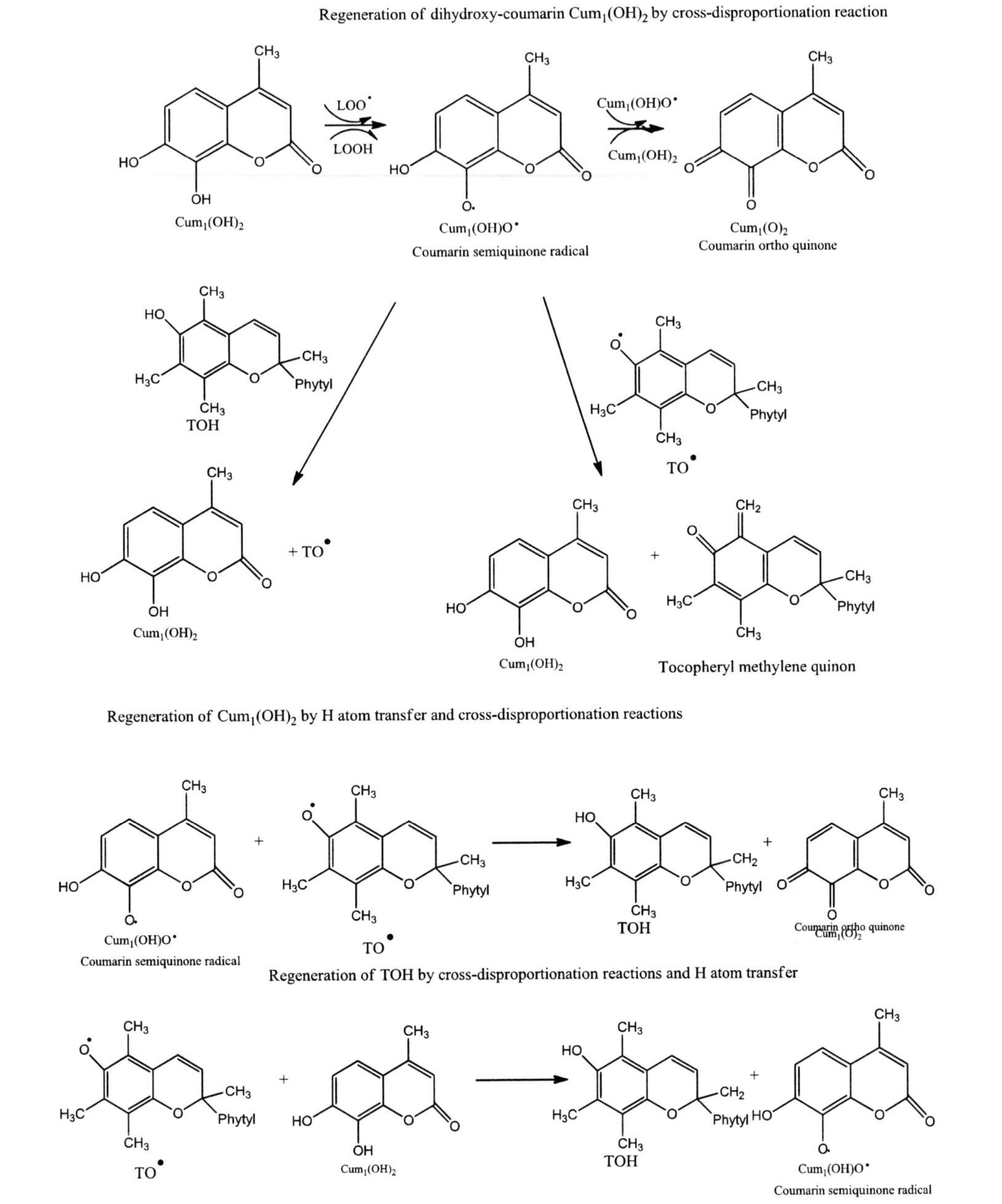

Regeneration of dihydroxy-coumarin Cum$_1$(OH)$_2$ by cross-disproportionation reaction

Regeneration of Cum$_1$(OH)$_2$ by H atom transfer and cross-disproportionation reactions

Regeneration of TOH by cross-disproportionation reactions and H atom transfer

Scheme 12. Mechanism of synergistic effect of binary mixture of 7,8-dihydroxy-4-methyl-coumarin, Cum$_1$(OH)$_2$ with α- tocopherol (TOH).

These reactions demonstrate that during lipid oxidation process the initial molecules of 7,8-dihydroxy-4-methyl coumarin, Cum$_1$(OH)$_2$ and TOH are regenerated by different mechanisms and that makes this binary mixture the most powerful antioxidant composition. It could be seen that the positions of both phenolic groups in coumarin molecule plays an important role in their mechanism of action. In case of 7-hydrpxy-4-methyl-coumarin, Cum$_3$OH, the observed additivism of the binary mixture (Cum$_3$+TOH) may be explained with the possible reactions of homo-disproportionation of TO• and cross-disproportionation of phenoxyl radical (Cum₃O•) from monohydroxy coumarin, and tocopheryl radical (TO•) with regeneration of TOH.

Considering that 4-methylcoumarins, in contrast to many other coumarins, are not metabolized to toxic epoxide intermediates, the results indicate the possible application of these compounds as individual antioxidants and/or in complex binary mixtures.

D. Monomers and Dimers [60,61]

Dehydrozingerone (M_1OH) is a half molecule of curcumin – one of the most powerful antioxidant with a wide spectrum of its biological activity. Ginger and curcumin are well known spices. Recently the synthesized natural-like C2-symmetry hydroxylated biphenyls (dimers) of their corresponding monomers (dehydrozingerone, M_1OH, zingerone, M_2OH and ferulic acid, FA) were selected for this study, because of their interesting biological activity against neuro-degenerative diseases and melanoma cancer.

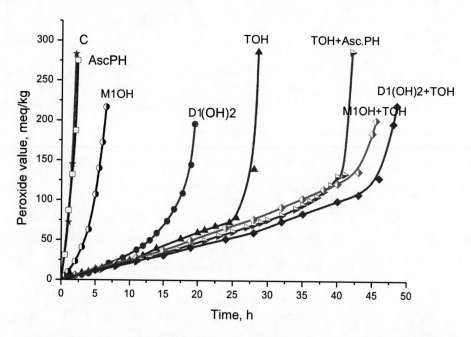

Figure 7a. Kinetic curves of lipid hydroperoxides accumulation during TGSO autoxidation at 80°C in absence (control, c) and in presence of 0.1mM monomer M_1OH (dehydro-zingerone), of dimer [$D_1(OH)_2$] of dehydro-zingerone, ascorbyl palmitate (AscPH), α-tocopherol (TOH) and their equimolar binary mixtures ($M_1OH+TOH$), [$D_1(OH)_2+TOH$)] and (TOH+AscPH).

It is seen that the dimer of dehydrozingerone ($D_1(OH)_2$) is able to ensure higher oxidation stability of lipid substrate, i.e., it has better protective effect in comparison with the corresponding monomer (M_1OH). TOH manifested the best protective effect on lipid autoxidation in comparison with other individual compounds. However, it is evident that AscPH didn't show any antioxidant activity (potential). The kinetic curve in presence of AscPH is the same as for the control sample. New orders of antioxidant efficiency (as protection factor, PF), antioxidant reactivity (as inhibition degree, ID) and antioxidant capacity (R_m) were found for the individual compounds [60]:

PF: TOH (21.2) > $D_1(OH)_2$ (13.5) > M_1OH (3.5) > AscPH (1.0)
ID: TOH (29.3) = $D_1(OH)_2$ (29.3) >> M_1OH (6.3) > AscPH (1.0)
R_m, 10^{-8} M/s: TOH (1.0) < $D_1(OH)_2$ (1.6) < M_1OH (6.0) <<AscPH (21.4)

The observed lower antioxidant activity of M_1OH and $D_1(OH)_2$ with respect to TOH can be due to the higher bond dissociation enthalpy (BDE) of OH groups of M_1OH and $D_1(OH)_2$ in comparison with those of TOH (ΔBDE_{M1OH} = 9.6 and $\Delta BDE_{D1(OH)2}$ = 9.0 kcal/mol, respectively). Another reason for the lower antioxidant activity of M_1OH and $D_1(OH)_2$ with respect to TOH can be explained with the impossibility of their phenoxyl radicals to be regenerated like TOH during homo-disproportionation reaction.

Data obtained (Figure 7a and Tables 3&6) showed that both binary mixtures ($M_1OH+TOH$ and $D_1(OH)_2+TOH$) lead to a maximal oxidation stability of lipid substrate in comparison with the corresponding individual components. The latest is of importance for the practice, because these binary mixtures are able to ensure the best protective effect on the lipid substrate being oxidized.

PF: $D_1(OH)_2+TOH$(35.4)> $M_1OH+TOH$(32.7) > TOH(21.2) > $D_1(OH)_2$ (13.5) >> M_1OH(3.5)

ID: $D_1(OH)_2+TOH$ (29.3)=TOH (29.3)=$D_1(OH)_2$(29.3) > $M_1OH+TOH$ (25.9) >> M_1OH (6.3)

R_m, 10^{-8} M/s: $D_1(OH)_2+TOH$ (0.60) ≤ $M_1OH+TOH$ (0.65)< TOH(1.0)<$D_1(OH)_2$(1.6)<< M_1OH (6.0).

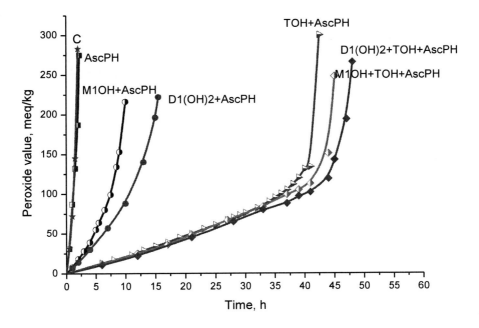

Figure 7b. Kinetic curves of lipid hydroperoxides accumulation during TGSO autoxidation at 80°C in absence (control, c) and in presence of 0.1mM ascorbyl palmitate (AscPH), of equimolar (1:1) binary mixtures with AscPH of monomer $M_1OH+AscPH$ and of dimer $D_1(OH)_2+AscPH$, and of their triple (1:1:1) equimolar mixtures with TOH and AscPH of monomer $M_1OH+TOH+AscPH$) and of dimer $D_1(OH)_2+TOH+AscPH$).

Effect of equimolar (1:1) binary mixtures of studied compounds with ascorbyl palmitate (AscPH)

Figure 7b and Table 6 showed the data observed for the equimolar binary mixtures of M_1OH, $D_1(OH)_2$ and TOH with AscPH. New orders of antioxidant properties were obtained:

PF: TOH+AscPH (31.5) >> $D_1(OH)_2$+AscPH (10.4) > M_1OH + AscPH (6.2) > AscPH (1.0)

ID: TOH+AscPH (29.3) >> $D_1(OH)_2$+AscPH (8.8) > M_1OH+AscPH (6.8) > AscPH (1.0)

Rm, 10^{-8} M/s: TOH+AscPH(0.68) < $D_1(OH)_2$+AscPH (2.1) < M_1OH +AscPH (3.5) <<AscPH (21.4)

The highest antioxidant efficiency (PF) was found for binary mixture of TOH + AscPH, which is 3-fold higher than that of $D_1(OH)_2$+AscPH and 5-fold higher than that of M_1OH+AscPH. $D_1(OH)_2$ in binary mixture with AscPH leads to a higher oxidation stability of lipid substrate than in case of M_1OH+AscPH.

The binary mixtures of studied compounds (M_1OH+AscPH and $D_1(OH)_2$+AscPH) showed higher protective effect than that of AscPH. The latest is due to the possible regeneration of M_1OH and $D_1(OH)_2$ from AscPH during the oxidation process:

$M_1O\cdot$ + AscPH → M_1OH + AscP· reaction of H-atom transfer with monomer regeneration

$M_1O\cdot$ + AscP· → M_1OH + DHAP (dehydroascorbyl palmitate) cross-disproportionation reaction with monomer regeneration

Both reactions with monomer regeneration are of importance for the synergism of M_1OH+AscPH mixture obtained, because M_1OH is the stronger antioxidant in comparison with AscPH. Our results confirm again AscPH as a synergist, but not as antioxidant during bulk lipid autoxidation.

Antagonism was detected only for $D_1(OH)_2$ +AscPH binary mixture that evidenced the lower level of dimer regeneration from AscPH. This result can be explain with the reverse character of H atom transfer reaction:

$D_1(OH)O\cdot$ + AscPH ⇔ $D_1(OH)_2$ + AscP·

Probably it is a result of the possible AscPH regeneration in reaction between AscP· and $D_1(OH)_2$ and thus reduces its activity.

Another reason for antagonism obtained is the possible cross-recombination reaction between AscP· and $D_1(OH)O\cdot$ to inactive product. The latest reduced the concentration of dimer phenoxyl radical which could be regenerated by H-atom transfer from AscPH.

We expected to increase significantly the efficiency of antioxidant compositions, due to the regeneration by different reactions of TOH and M_1OH /or $D_1(OH)_2$ during the oxidative process by preparing ternary mixtures M_1OH+TOH+AscPH and $D_1(OH)_2$ +TOH+AscPH. The protective action of triple mixtures of M_1OH and $D_1(OH)_2$ with TOH and AscPH is presented at Figure 7b and Table 6.

PF: $D_1(OH)_2$ + TOH + AscPH (35.4) > M_1OH + TOH + AscPH (33.1)

ID: $D_1(OH)_2$ + TOH + AscPH (35.2) > M_1OH + TOH + AscPH (29.3)

R_m, 10^{-3} M/s: $D_1(OH)_2$ + TOH + AscPH (0.60) > M_1OH + TOH + AscPH (0.65)

Table 6. Lipid hydroperoxides concentration [LOOH] and α-tocopherol (TOH) content determined during lipid autoxidation of triglycerides of sunflower oil (TGSO) at $80^{\circ}C$

Abbrev. of mixtures	Time, h	[LOOH] average, mM	TOH content, mg/g
$(TOH)_5$	5	4.9 ± 1.1	0.458 ± 0.018
$(TOH)_{10}$	10	11.8 ± 1.2	0.452 ± 0.018
$(TOH)_{15}$	15	18.0 ± 2.0	0.451 ± 0.018
$(TOH)_{20}$	20	25.2 ± 4.3	0.380 ± 0.015
$(TOH)_{25}$	25	33.5 ± 5.5	0.258 ± 0.010
$(TOH)_{30}$	30	143.0 ± 5.0	0.016 ± 0.001
Equimolar binary mixtures	with	AscPH	
$(TOH+AscPH)_5$	5	2.7 ± 2.5	0.466 ± 0.019
$(TOH+AscPH)_{10}$	10	5.4 ± 4.6	0.454 ± 0.018
$(TOH+AscPH)_{15}$	15	10.2 ± 6.4	0.445 ± 0.018
$(TOH+AscPH)_{20}$	20	14.7 ± 8.8	0.442 ± 0.018
$(TOH+AscPH)_{30}$	30	28.0 ± 12.0	0.440 ± 0.018
$(TOH+AscPH)_{45}$	45	152.0 ± 3.0	0.059 ± 0.002
Equimolar binary mixtures	with	TOH	
$(M_1OH+TOH)_5$	5	6.3 ± 1.5	0.466 ± 0.019
$(M_1OH +TOH)_{10}$	10	11.0 ± 2.0	0.449 ± 0.018
$(M_1OH +TOH)_{15}$	15	16.2 ± 1.8	0.442 ± 0.018
$(M_1OH +TOH)_{20}$	20	21.6 ± 2.3	0.366 ± 0.015
$(M_1OH +TOH)_{30}$	30	39.2 ± 1.2	0.288 ± 0.012
$(M_1OH +TOH)_{45}$	45	86.0 ± 20.0	0.047 ± 0.002
$(D_1(OH)_2+TOH)_5$	5	5.7 ± 0.9	0.462 ± 0.018
$(D_1(OH)_2+TOH)_{10}$	10	11.3 ± 1.3	0.459 ± 0.018
$(D_1(OH)_2+TOH)_{15}$	15	15.7 ± 2.6	0.452 ± 0.018
$(D_1(OH)_2+TOH)_{20}$	20	23.0 ± 1.0	0.396 ± 0.016
$(D_1(OH)_2+TOH)_{30}$	30	39.4 ± 4.5	0.296 ± 0.012
$(D_1(OH)_2+TOH)_{45}$	45	64.7 ± 2.3	0.049 ± 0.002
Equimolar triple mixtures	with	TOH and AscPH	
$(M_1OH+TOH+AscPH)_5$	5	2.0 ± 2.0	0.468 ± 0.019
$(M_1OH+TOH+AscPH)_{10}$	10	4.8 ± 4.8	0.467 ± 0.019
$(M_1OH+TOH+AscPH)_{15}$	15	9.5 ± 9.5	0.458 ± 0.018
$(M_1OH+TOH+AscPH)_{20}$	20	13.0 ± 7.0	0.449 ± 0.018
$(M_1OH+TOH+AscPH)_{30}$	30	28.0 ± 7.0	0.329 ± 0.013
$(M_1OH+TOH+AscPH)_{45}$	45	91.0 ± 33.0	0.114 ± 0.005
$(D_1(OH)_2+TOH+AscPH)_5$	5	2.0 ± 2.0	0.468 ± 0.019
$(D_1(OH)_2+TOH+AscPH)_{10}$	10	4.8 ± 4.8	0.466 ± 0.019
$(D_1(OH)_2+TOH+AscPH)_{15}$	15	8.5 ± 4.5	0.462 ± 0.018
$(D_1(OH)_2+TOH+AscPH)_{20}$	20	12.3 ± 6.8	0.459 ± 0.018
$(D_1(OH)_2+TOH+AscPH)_{30}$	30	24.0 ± 10.0	0.426 ± 0.017
$(D_1(OH)_2+TOH+AscPH)_{45}$	45	54.0 ± 17.0	0.379 ± 0.015

M_1OH - dehydrozingerone (monomer), $D_1(OH)_2$ - dimer of dehydrozingerone.
TOH - α-Tocopherol, AscPH - ascorbyl palmitate.

Triple mixture of $D_1(OH)_2$ with TOH and AscPH manifested also a higher antioxidant efficiency and reactivity than the corresponding triple mixture of M_1OH. However, triple mixture of M_1OH + TOH + AscPH showed similar PF as for double mixture of M_1OH + AscPH.

PF: $M_1OH+TOH+AscPH$ (33.1)   > $M_1OH+TOH(32.7)$ >   TOH(21.2)>>
$M_1OH+AscPH(6.2) > M_1OH$ (3.5)

PF:=$D_1(OH)_2+TOH+AscPH(35.4)=D_1(OH)_2+TOH(35.4)$>>$D_1(OH)_2(13.5)$>$D_1(OH)_2+As$
cPH (10.4)

We prove by HPLC monitoring of the TOH content during the process of lipid autoxidation [61] that the mechanism of synergistic action of binary and triple mixtures of M_1OH and $D_1(OH)_2$ with TOH and AscPH is due to the regeneration of TOH (Table 6).

Complex mechanisms of TOH regeneration in binary and triple mixtures are presented at Figure 8 (a-d).

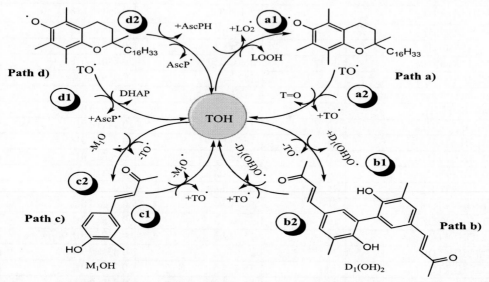

Path a):   a1) H-atom transfer from TOH to $LO_2\bullet$ (the key reaction of inhibited oxidation);
           a2) Homo-disproportionation of tocopheryl radicals (TO•) with TOH regeneration;
Path b):   b1) H-atom transfer from TOH to $D_1(OH)O\bullet$ with regeneration of $D_1(OH)_2$;
           b2) H-atom transfer from $D_1(OH)_2$ to TO• with regeneration of TOH;
Path c):   c1) H-atom transfer from M_1OH to TO• with regeneration of TOH;
           c2) H-atom transfer from TOH to $M_1O\bullet$ with regeneration of M_1OH;
Path d):   d1) Cross-disproportionation between TO• and AscP• with regeneration of TOH and DHAP – dehydroascorbylpalmitate formation;
           d2) H-atom transfer from AscPH to TO• with regeneration of TOH.

Figure 8a. Complex mechanism of TOH regeneration during lipid autoxidation added what??? as individual antioxidant (Path a) and in double mixtures with $D_1(OH)_2$ (Path b), M_1OH (Path c), and AscPH (Path d).

Observed synergism of $M_1OH+TOH$ (32.3 %) is due to the possible regeneration of TOH, as the strongest antioxidant, by reaction of H-atom transfer from M_1OH to the tocopheryl radical, TO•.

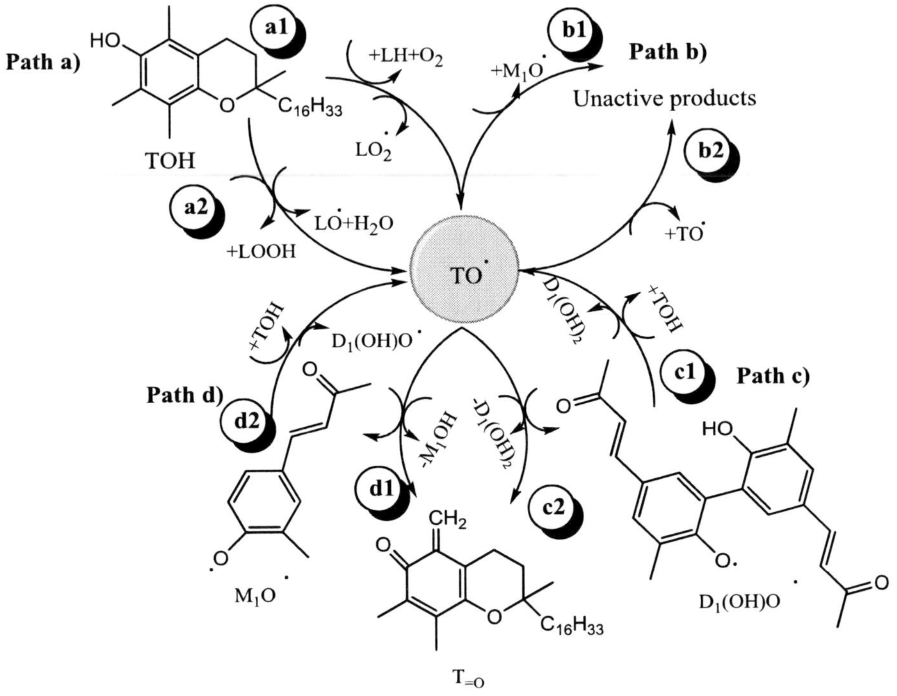

Path a): **a1)** Additional generation of free radicals ($LO_2^\bullet$) from TOH in reaction with lipid substrate (LH); (at high TOH concentration - activity of TOH decreases);

  a2) TOH increases decomposition of LOOH into free radicals (side reaction, reducing activity of TOH);

Path b): **b1)** Cross-recombination of tocopheryl radical ($TO^\bullet$) and $M_1O^\bullet$ (formation of inactive products);

  b2) Homo-recombination of two tocopheryl radicals ($TO^\bullet$) to inactive products;

Path c): **c1)** H-atom transfer from TOH to $D_1(OH)_2^\bullet$ with regeneration of $D_1(OH)_2$;

  c2) Cross-disproportionation reaction between $TO^\bullet$ and $D_1(OH)_2^\bullet$ with regeneration of $D_1(OH)_2$;

Path d): **d1)** Cross-disproportionation reaction between $TO^\bullet$ and $M_1O^\bullet$ with regeneration of M_1OH.

Figure 8b. Complex mechanism of possible side reactions of tocopherol ??? (TOH) and its tocopheryl radical ($TO^\bullet$) resulting to decrease of TOH activity.

CONCLUSION

Antioxidant activity is capacity of the compound to shorten the oxidation chain length as a result of its reaction with peroxyl radicals. For that reason we mean as antioxidant activity the chain-breaking activity of the compounds.

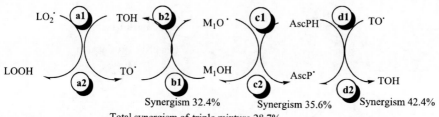

Synergism 32.4%

Synergism 35.6%

Synergism 42.4%

Total synergism of triple mixture 28.7%

Main reactions, responsible to the synergism obtained:
a1) H-atom transfer from TOH to $LO_2\bullet$ (the key reaction of inhibited oxidation)
b1) H-atom transfer from M_1OH to TO• with regeneration of TOH;
c1) H-atom transfer from AscPH to M_1O• with regeneration of M_1OH;
d1) H-atom transfer from AscPH to TO• with regeneration of TOH;
Additional reactions:
a2) Decomposition of LOOH by tocopheryl radical (TO•) to $LO_2^\bullet$ (decreasing TOH activity)
b2) H-atom transfer from TOH to M_1O• with regeneration of M_1OH;
c2) H-atom transfer from AscPH to M_1O• with regeneration of M_1OH;
d2) H-atom transfer from TOH to AscP• with regeneration of AscPH.

Figure 8c. Complex mechanism of synersism obtained between components in triple mixture M_1OH + TOH + AscPH.

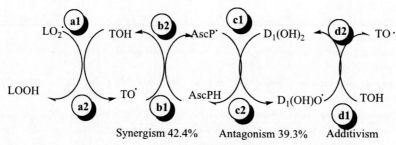

Synergism 42.4%   Antagonism 39.3%   Additivism

Total effect of triple mixture - additivism

Main reactions, responsible for the synergism obtained:
a1) H-atom transfer from TOH to $LO_2\bullet$ (the key reaction of inhibited oxidation)
b1) H-atom transfer from AscPH to TO• with regeneration of TOH;
c1) H-atom transfer from $D_1(OH)_2$ to AscPH with regeneration of AscPH;
d1) H-atom transfer from TOH to $D_1(OH)O$• with regeneration of $D_1(OH)_2$;
Additional reactions:
a2) Decomposition of LOOH by tocopheryl radical (TO•) to $LO_2^\bullet$ (decreasing TOH activity)
b2) H-atom transfer from TOH to AscPH• with regeneration of AscPH;
c2) H-atom transfer from AscPH to $D_1(OH)O$• with regeneration of $D_1(OH)_2$;
d2) H-atom transfer from TOH to $D_1(OH)O$• with regeneration of $D_1(OH)_2$.

Figure 8d. Complex mechanism of additivism obtained between components in triple mixture $D_1(OH)_2$ + TOH + AscPH.

Synergism between individual components in binary mixtures is explained with differences in BDEO-H and by H-atom abstraction and cross-disproportionation reaction, leading to regeneration of the most powerful antioxidant.

Additivism is found for antioxidants with close BDE O-H and similar power. Antagonism is found for antioxidants with lower BDE O-H than of TOH and when regeneration of antioxidants is not possible during the reaction of cross-recombination of both phenoxyl radicals. Structural characteristics of the complex system: oxidizing substrate-antioxidant must be considered. On the basis of this comparable analysis, the most effective individual antioxidants and binary mixtures were proposed for the highest and optimal lipid oxidation stability.

FUTURE TRENDS

Nature creates a molecular diversity under the principles of usability and economy that selects only those structures that are necessary for some specific functions. However, this process of natural molecular evolution takes thousands of years in production of this limited but effective molecular diversity.

We can learn from the nature about what kind of molecular structures are useful, for one practical purpose. Then we can use rational approaches to generate a great diversity from these structures in a fast and efficient way.

The relation of structure to antiradical, antioxidant and/or biological activities of individual compounds from different extracts will be studied in the future also by using different theoretical models which allow to predict the new structures of bio-antioxidants with known properties.

Synthetic analogues of natural bio-antioxidants – plants have been an important source for discovery and development of new drugs especially for anticancer and anti-inflammatory diseases. Nowadays, more than 500 of the prescribed drugs are derived or synthesized, taking examples from natural products. The role of organic synthesis is crucial for the development and production of new synthetic drugs, based on natural products templates.

REFERENCES

[1]   Halliwell, B. (2007) Biochemistry of oxidative stress, *Biochem. Soc. Trans*, 35, 1147-50.

[2]   Kancheva, V. (2010) *Oxidative Stress and Lipid Oxidation*. In: "Antioxidants - Prevention and Healthy Aging", Ed. by F.Ribarova, SIMELPRESS Publ., Sofia, Bulgaria, Chapter 3, 233-238.

[3]   Hristakieva, E. & Gadjeva, V. (2001) Oxidative stress in patients with vitiligo. *J. Eur. Academy of Dermatol. And Venerol.* 15 (2P), 23-39.

[4]   Hristozov, D., Gadjeva, V., Vlaykova, T., Dimitrov, G. (2001) Evaluation of oxidative stress in patients with cancer. *Arch. Physiol. Biochem.* 109, 331-336.

[5]   Hartmann, J.T., Nickols, C.R., Droz, J. P.(2000) Hematologic disorders associated with primar mediastinal nonseminomatous germ cell tumors. *Journal of the National Cancer Institute*, 92, 54-61.

[6]   Griendling, K. K., Sorescu, D., Lasseque, B., Ushio-Fukai, M. (2000) Modulation of protein kinase activity and gene expression by reactive oxygen species and their role in

vascular physiology and pathophysiology. *Atheroscler Tromb. Vasc. Biol.* 20, 2175-2183.

[7] Kosky, L., Dwarakanath, B. D., Raj, H. G., Chandra, R., Mathew, T. L. (2003) Suicidal oxidative stress induced by certain antioxidants. *Indian J. Exp. Biol.* 41, 391-399.

[8] Komosinska-Vassilev, K. Olczyk, P. Olczyk, K. Wiusz-Szczotka. (2005) Effects of methabolic control and vascular complications on induced of oxidative stress in type 2 diabetic patients. *Diabetes Res. Clin. Pract.* 68 (3), 207-216.

[9] Kesavulu, M. M., Gippi, R., Rao Kameswara, B., Apparao, C. (2000) Lipid peroxidation and antioxidant enzyme levels in type 2 diabetics with microvascular complications. *Diabetes Metab.* 26 (5), 387-392.

[10] Gunawardena, K. (2000) Vitamin E and other antioxidants inhibit human prostate cancer cells through apoptosis. *Prostate*, 44 (4), 287-295.

[11] Burlakova, E.B.(2007) Bioantioxidants. Molecular cell biophysics, *Russ. Chem. J.*, 51, 3-12 (in Russian).

[12] Kancheva, V.D. & Kasaikina, O.T. (2013) Bio-antioxidants - a chemical base of their antioxidant activity and beneficial effect on human health, *Current Medicinal Chemistry*, 20, 4784-4805.

[13] Gadjeva, V. (2006)Role of ROS in the modulation of angiogenesis, antiangiogenic action of antioxidants. *Compt. Rend. Acad. Bulg. Sci.* 59 (4), 443-453.

[14] Gadjeva, V., Kuchukova, D., Georgieva, R. (2005) Influence of polychemotherapy on the antioxidant levels and lipid peroxidation in patients with lymphoproliferative diseases. *Comparative Clinical Pathology*, 14, 13-18.

[15] Gadjeva, V., Lazarova, G., Zheleva, A. 92003) Spin labeled antioxidants protect bacteria against the toxicity of alkylating antitumor drug CCNU. *Toxicol. Lett.* 15, 289-294

[16] Gadjeva, V., Kuchukova, D., Tolekova, A., Tanchev, S. (2005) Beneficial effects of spin-labelled nitrosourea on CCNU-induced oxidative stress in rat blood compared with vitamin E. *Die Pharmacie*, 60, 530-532.

[17] Karamalakova, Y., Georgieva, E., Arora, R., Sharma, R. K., Nikolova, G., Gadjeva, V., Zheleva, A. (2012) Investigations on the levels of oxidative stress biomarkers and organs biodistribution of Psoralea corylifolia linn. *J. BioSci. Biotech. 2012, SE/ONLINE: 67-7*

[18] Nikolova, G. (2013) Oxidative sterss and Parkinson disease, *Trakia Journal of Sciences*, 10 (1), 92-100.

[19] Barnham, K., Masters, C., Bush, A. (2004) Neurodegenerative diseases and oxidative stress, *Nature*, 3, 205-214.

[20] Halliwell, B. (2006) Oxidative stress and neurodegeneration : where are we now? *J. Neurochem*, 97, 1634-1658.

[21] Sanyal, J., Bandyopadhyay, S., Banerjee, T., Mukherjee, S., Chakraborty, D., Ray, B., Rao, V. (2009) Plasma levels of lipid peroxides in patients with Parkinson's disease, *Eur Rev Med and Pharmacol Sci.*, 13, 129-132.

[22] Halliwell, B. (2001) Role of free radicals in the neurodegenerative diseases: therapeutic implications for antioxidant treatment, *Drugs Aging*, 18, 685-716.

[23] Arora, R., Gupta, D., Chawla, R., Sagar, R., Sharma, A., Kumar, R., Prasad, J., Singh, S., Samanta, N., Sharma, R.K. (2005) Radioprotection by plant products: present status and future prospects. *Photother. Res.* 19, 1-22.

[24] Arora, R., Dhaker, A.S., Adhikari, M., Sharma, J., Chawla, R., Gupta, D., Zheleva, A., Karamalakova, Y., Kumar, R., Sharma, R.K., Sharma, A., Sultana, S., Tripathi, R.P., Gadjeva, V. (2011) Radical scavenging and radiomodulatory effects of Psoralea corylifolia Linn. substantiated by in vitro assays and EPR spectroscopy. *Z. Naturforsch C.*, 66(1-2), 35-46.

[25] Karamalakova, Y. (2014) *Complex evaluation of antioxidant properties of natural and synthetic antioxidants such as potential protectors for anticancer drugs*, PhD Thesis, Trakia University, Stara Zagora, Bulgaria, pp.200.

[26] Nikolova, G. (2014) *Protected effect of synthetic and natural antioxidants from oxidative stress caused by Parkinson's disease and its therapy*, PhD Thesis, Trakia University, Stara Zagora, Bulgaria, pp.186.

[27] Kancheva, V.D. (2012) *Phenolic Antioxidants of Natural Origin – Structure Activity Relationship and their Beneficial Effect on Human Health. In: "Phytochemicals and Human Health: Pharmacological and Molecular Aspects"*, Nova Science Publishers Inc., USA, Ed. A.A.Farooqui, Chapter I, 1-45.

[28] Kancheva, V. (2010) *Antioxidants. Structure-activity relationship. In: "Antioxidants – Prevention and Healthy Aging"*, Ed. by F. Ribarova, SIMELPRESS Publ., Sofia, Bulgaria, Chapter 1, 56-72.

[29] Kancheva, V.D. (2009) Phenolic antioxidants – radical scavenging and chain breaking activities. Comparable study. *European Journal Lipid Science Technology*, 111 (11), 1072-1089.

[30] Roginsky, V. & Tikhonov, I. (2010) Natural polyphenols as chain-breaking antioxidants during lipid peroxidation, *Chem. Phys. Lipids*, 163, 127-133.

[31] Roginsky, V.A. & Lissi, E. A. (2005) Review of methods to determine chain - breaking antioxidant activity in food, *Food Chemistry,* 92, 235-254.

[32] Kancheva, V.D. & Kasaikina, O.T. (2012) *Lipid Oxidation in Homogeneous and Micro-heterogeneous Media in Presence of Prooxidants, Antioxidants and Surfactants.* In: Lipid peroxidation, ed. Angel Catala, In Tech Open Access Publ. Chapter 2, 31-62.

[33] Kasaikina, O.T., Kortenska, V.D., Yanishlieva, N.V. (1999) Effect of chain transfer and recombination/ dispropor-tionation of inhibitor radicals on inhibited oxidation of lipids, *Russ. Chem. Bull.* 48, 1891-1996.

[34] Naumov, V.V. & Vasil'ev, R. F. (2003) Antioxidant and prooxidant effect of tocopherol. *Kinet. Catal. 44*, 101-105.

[35] Burton, G.W., Doba, T., Gabe, E.J., Huges, L., Lee, F.L., Prasad, L., Ingold, K.U. (1985) Autoxidation of biological molecules. 4. Maximizing the antioxidant activity of phenols. *J. Am. Oil Chem. Soc.*, 107, 7053-7065.

[36] Small, R.D.Jr., Scaiano, J.C., Patterson, L.K. (1979) Radical process in lipids: A. Laser photolysis study of t-butoxy radical reactivity toward fatty acids. *Photochem. Photobiol.*29, 49-51.

[37] Frankel, E. N. (1998) Lipid oxidation, The Oily Press, Dundee (Scotland).

[38] Denisov, E.T. & Afanas'ev, I.F. (2005) *Oxidation and Antioxidants in Organic Chemistry and Biology*; CRC Press Taylor & Francis Group.,Boca Ration, F 33487-2742, pp.992.

[39] Kortenska-Kancheva, V.D. & V.A.Belyakov, V.D. (2005) Simulation of Lipid Oxidation Kinetics in Various Mechanisms of Hydroperoxides Decomposition, Riv. Ital. delle Sost. Grasse, 82, 177-185.

[40] Kortenska, V.D. & Vasil'ev, R.F. (2000) The Importance of Peroxyl Radical Cyclization into Peroxide C-Radical in the Mechanism of Linoleate Oxidation, *Oxidation Communications*, 23,161-171.

[41] Belyakov, V.A., Kortenska, V.D., Rafikova, V.S., Yanishlieva, N.V. (1992) Kinetics of the initiated oxidation of model lipid systems. Role of fatty alcohols, *Kinetics and Catalysis*, 33, 611-616.

[42] Kortenska, V.D., Yanishlieva, N.V., Kasaikina, O.T., Totzeva, I.R., Boneva, M.I., Rusina, I.F. (2002) Phenol antioxidant efficiency in presence of lipid hydroxy compounds in various lipid systems. *European J. Lipid Science and Technology*, 104 (8), 513-519.

[43] Kortenska, V.D., Yanishlieva, N.V., Roginskii, V.A. (1991) Kinetics of Inhibited Oxidation of Lipids in the Presence of 1-Octadecanol and 1-Palmitoylglycerol, *J Am Oil Chem Soc.* , 68, 888-890.

[44] Kortenska, V.D. & Yanishlieva, N.V. (1995) Effect of the phenol antioxidant type on the kinetics and mechanism of inhibited lipid oxidation in the presence of fatty alcohols, *J. Sci. Food Agric.*, 68, 117-126.

[45] Malhotra, Sh., Shakya, G., Kumar, A., Vankoeche, W.,... Saso, L., ...Prasad, A.K., Parmar, V.S. (2008) Antioxidant, anti-inflammatory and antiinvasive activities of biopolyphenols, *ARCIVOC*, (vi), 119-139.

[46] Kancheva, V.D.; Taskova, R.; Totseva, I.; Handjieva, N. (2007) Antioxidant activity of extracts, fractions and flavonoid constituents from *Carthamus lanatus* L., *Riv. Ital. delle Sost. Grasse*, 84, 77-86.

[47] Bors, W., Heller, W., Michel, C., Stettmaier, K. (1996) Flavonoids and polyphenols: chemistry and biology, in: *Handbook of Antioxidants*, Cadenas E. and Packer L. (eds), New York, Marcel Dekker, 409-66.

[48] Belyakov. V.A., Roginsky, V.A., Bors, W. (1995) Rate constants for the reaction of peroxyl free radical with flavonoids and related compounds as determined by the kinetic chemiluminiscence method, *J. Chem. Soc., Perkin Trans.*, 2, 2319-2326.

[49] Vasil'ev, R.F. & Trofimov, A.V. (2009) Dioxetane formation in the phenol inhibited oxidation of hydrocarbons. *Kinetics and Catalysis,* 50, 540-542.

[50] Vasil'ev, R.F., Kancheva, V.D., Fedorova, G.F., Batovska, D.I., Trofimov, A.V. (2010) Antioxidant activity of chalcones. The chemiluminescence determination of the reactivity and quantum – chemical calculation of the energies and structures of reagents and intermediates. *Kinetics and Catalysis*, 51, 507-515.

[51] Bors, W., Kazazic, S., Michel, C., Kortenska, V.D., Stettmaier, K., Klasinc, L. (2002) Methoxyphenols - Antioxidant Principles in Food Plants and Spices: Pulse Radiolysisd, EPR Spectroscopy and DFT Calculations, *International J. Quantum Chemistry,* 90 (2), 969-979.

[52] Nenadis, N., Zhang, H.-Yu., Tsimidou, M.Z. (2003) Structure-antioxidant activity relationship of ferulic acid derivatives. Effect of carbon side chain characteristic groups. *Journal of Agricultural and Food Chemistry* 51,1874-1879.

[53] Nenadis, N. & Tsimidou, M. (2002) Observations on the estimation of scavenging activity of phenolic compounds using rapid 1,1-diphenyl–2 picrylhydrazyl (DPPH) test. *J. Am. Oil Chem. Soc.*, 79, 1191-1195.

[54] V.D.Kortenska, M.P.Velikova, N.V.Yanishlieva, I.R.Totzeva, V.S.Bankova, M.C.Marcucci; *Kinetics of Lipid Oxidation in Presence of Cinnamic Acid Derivatives*, European J. Lipid Science and Technology, 104, 2002, 19-28.

[55] Yanishlieva – Maslarova, N. (2001) Inhibiting oxidation, in: *Antioxidants in Food. Practical Applications.* (Eds. Pokorny J., Yanishlieva N., Gordon M.), CRC Press, Boca Raton, Woodhead Publishing Ltd., Cambridge, UK, 22-70.

[56] Kancheva, V., Spasova, M., Totseva, I., Milkova, Ts. (2006) Study on the Antioxidant Activity of N-hydroxy-cinnamoyl-amino acid conjugates in bulk lipid autoxidation, *Riv. Ital. delle Sost. Grasse*, *83*, 162-169.

[57] Kasaikina, O.T., Kortenska, V.D., Marinova, E.M., Rusina, I.F., Yanishlieva, N.V. (1997) The inhibitory activity of natural phenolic antioxidants in the oxidation process of lipid substrates. *Russ. Chem. Bull.*, 46, 1070-1073.

[58] Rusina, I.F., Boneva, M.I., Kasaikina, O.T., Kortenska, V.D., Yanishlieva, N.V. (2004) Evaluation of the antiradical efficiency of cinnamic acid derivatives using a chemiluminescence method. *Oxidation Communications*, 27, 562-570.

[59] Kancheva, V.D., Saso, L., Boranova, P.V., Pandey, M.K. Malhorta, Sh., Nechev, J.T., Prasad, A.K., Georgieva, M.B., DePass, A.L., Parmar, V.S. (2010) Structure-activity relationship of some dihydroxy coumarins. Correlation вetween experimental and theoretical data and synergistic effect. *Biochimie*, 92 (9), 1089-1100.

[60] Kancheva, V.D.; Slavova-Kasakova, A.; Fabbri, D.; Angelova, S.; Dettori, M.A.; Nechev, J.; Delogu, G. (2012) Antiradical and antioxidant activities of new natural-like biphenyls of zingerone, dehydrozingerone and ferulic acid, *Comp. Rend. Acad. Bulg. Sci.*, 66 (3), 361-369.

[61] Kancheva, V.D., Slavova-Kazakova, A., Janek, M., Fabbri, D., Dettori, M.A., Delogu, G., Amarowicz, R.(2014) Protective effects of dehidrozingerone and its dimer in equimolar binary and triple mixtures with alpha-tocopherol and/or ascorbyl palmitate, *Food Chem.*, 157, 263-274.

Note: Assoc. Prof. Vessela D. Kancheva – former family names – Kortenska and Kortenska-Kancheva.

ISBN: 978-1-63321-886-4
© 2015 Nova Science Publishers, Inc.

Chapter 2

ASSESSMENT OF OXIDATIVE BALANCE IN THE LIPO- AND HYDRO-PHILIC CELLULAR ENVIRONMENT IN BIOLOGICAL SYSTEMS

G. Malanga, J. M. Ostera and S. Puntarulo[*]

Physical Chemistry-Institute of Biochemistry and Molecular Medicine (IBIMOL), School of Pharmacy and Biochemistry, University of Buenos Aires-CONICET, Buenos Aires, Argentina

ABSTRACT

Over the last decade, Electron Paramagnetic Resonance (EPR) technology has been successfully applied to detect free radicals in order to establish oxidative stress conditions. Since a variety of stable products are formed during the oxidation of lipids, several assays have been developed over the years in order to evaluate lipid peroxidation. EPR spectroscopy has shown the capacity to detect, in the presence of exogenous traps, the presence of lipid radicals (LR•) formed during peroxidation, by yielding unique and stable compounds. On the other hand, the one-electron oxidation of AH$^-$ produces ascorbyl radical (A•) which is easily detectable by EPR, even at room-temperature in aqueous solution. The A• free radical has a relatively long lifetime compared to other species, such as hydroxyl radical, peroxyl, alkoxyl, and LR• and has been proposed as a marker of oxidative stress, either *in vitro* or *in vivo*, in numerous systems, such as plasma. All biological systems contain many antioxidants, including both water-soluble compounds (such as AH$^-$ and glutathione), and lipid-soluble antioxidants, such as α-tocopherol (α-T). In this chapter, the most widely used indexes of oxidative balance in biological systems will be briefly summarized. Moreover, special mention will be made about the application of the A•/AH$^-$ and LR•/α-T ratios to situations of oxidative stress. The goal of this work is to discuss the possibility of detecting the actual state of lipid- and water-soluble fractions of a biological system, providing an early and simple diagnosis of stressing conditions.

[*] Corresponding author: Dr. Susana Puntarulo. Fisicoquímica-Instituto de Bioquímica y Medicina Molecular (IBIMOL), Facultad de Farmacia y Bioquímica, Junín 956 (C1113AAD), Buenos Aires, Argentina. Phone: 54-11-4964-8244, fax: 54-11-4508-3646, e-mail: susanap@ffyb.uba.ar.

Keywords: Oxidative indexes, lipophilic medium, hydrophilic medium, ascorbyl radical, lipid soluble radicals, antioxidants

1. INTRODUCTION

Facile detection of reactive oxygen (ROS) and nitrogen (RNS) species in biological systems is often problematic. The discovery by McCord and Fridovich [1] of the enzyme superoxide dismutase (SOD) defined an entirely new area of biomedical research [2]. This discovery suggested that reactive free radicals derived from O_2 could be produced *in vivo* in significant quantities, as it was previously shown by Gershman [3]. Until this landmark observation, chemists and biochemists believed that free radicals of any type were much too reactive and therefore much too toxic to be produced *in vivo*. With investigators more receptive to the idea that small molecular weight reactive radical species play important roles in normal physiology as well as pathophysiology, it was not surprising when Ignarro, Furchgott, and Murad identified the nitrogen-based free radical nitric oxide (NO) as the elusive endothelium-derived relaxing factor. In fact, NO has been shown to be important in the homeostatic regulation of the immune, cardiovascular, and nervous systems [4]. ROS and RNS are now known to play roles in mediating cytotoxicity through alterations in protein, lipid, and nucleic acid structure and function with resultant disruption of cellular homeostatic mechanisms. These noxious consequences are often due to markedly elevated (orders of magnitude) steady-state concentrations or rates of production of reactive species.

In addition, it has become apparent that more subtle changes in rates of production of reactive species may critically impact cellular homeostasis and may serve physiological roles in initiating signaling cascades. Thus, sensitive, specific, and reliable methods to detect changes in reactive species are essential to understanding the roles these substances play in both normal and diseased states [2].

Different approaches can be taken to analyze oxidative stress. These experimental strategies can be classified as follows: (1) General methods to identify oxidative stress *in vivo*, (2) Detection of individual reactive species, and (3) Detection of damage to biomolecules or cellular structures. Measurement of the *in situ* production of reactive species is difficult for several reasons. Low intracellular steady-state concentrations of these species occur as a result of the balance between the basal rates of generation, scavenging, and the extracellular release of small proportions of the intracellularly formed molecules. In addition, there is some formation of reactive molecules from plasma membrane-bound oxidases controlled by serum and extracellular fluid components, including low molecular weight oxidant scavengers and the heparin-binding extracellular-SOD [5].

Moreover, there is a complex network between ROS. The relatively short half-life (seconds or less) of reactive species and the efficient and redundant systems that have evolved to scavenge them, require that any detection technique must be sensitive enough to effectively compete with these intra- and extracellular antioxidant components for reaction with the substance in question. Additionally, methods for analysis of reactive species must have adequate intracellular access to faithfully reflect intracellular conditions. Finally, the often overlapping reactivities of reactive species with detection systems may hamper unequivocal identification and quantification of the responsible substance [2].

This review will focus on common approaches to detect oxidative stress in most research laboratories, as summarized in Figure 1. Particular attention will be given to those approaches that use methods for the *in vivo* assessment of global oxidative stress and their use in medicine and biology.

2. GENERAL INDEXES OF OXIDATIVE STRESS: INTACT ORGAN CHEMILUMINESCENCE (CL)

Many side reactions derived from the complex free radical sequence of lipid peroxidation could lead to light emission, which represents only about 10^{-4} of the utilization of peroxide [6]. Luminescence of organisms has fascinated scientists from long ago [7], and the phenomenon generally can be related to peroxide and free radical metabolism, a topic of current interest in disease processes [8]. The fact that luminescence might not be restricted to those forms of life having special organs containing enzyme systems such as luciferin/luciferase was underlined by the early findings of Tarusov et al. [9]. Those researchers used photon counting to identify a weak light emission from mouse liver *in situ*; but the observation was later extended to other tissue homogenates such as brain, muscle, or intestine, and lipid extracts [10]. The existence of such light emission, which was termed "low-level chemiluminescence" to differentiate it from the more effective photoemission of the luciferin/luciferase systems, was soon related to O_2-dependent chain reactions involving biological lipids [10]. These initial findings were long forgotten, however the reports by Nakano et al. [11] and Sugioka and Nakano [12] of light emission during lipid peroxidation and other oxidative reactions [13] in microsomes revived interest in the phenomenon, and suggested CL as a tool for the study of lipid peroxidation under physiological conditions.

The most important aspect of the organ CL is that it gives readily detectable, continuously monitorable, non-invasive signals of oxidative metabolism [6].

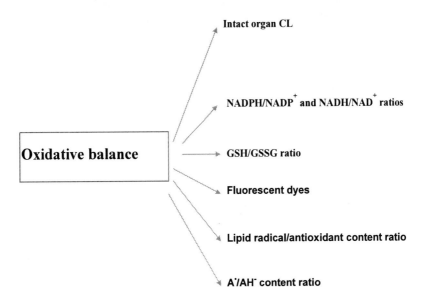

Figure 1. General scheme showing widely use indexes of oxidative stress in biological systems.

The CL of the perfused liver was O_2-dependent. Ethyl, t-butyl, and cumene hydroperoxides were almost equally effective in inducing light emission in the perfused liver. Glutathione release and CL showed a parallel increase upon hydroperoxide supply to the perfused liver. A partial spectral analysis of the CL of the perfused liver showed a predominance of red light emitting species, presumably arising from the singlet oxygen ($^1O_2$) dimol-emission peaks. The manuscript from Boveris et al. [6] explored the possibility of continuously monitoring the metabolism of *in vivo* exposed organs by the CL technique. The authors reported the spontaneous and hydroperoxide-induced CL of the *in situ* and perfused rat liver, as well as a partial spectral analysis of the CL of the perfused liver. Light emission seems to indicate the generation of short-lived free radicals and excited states derived from the side reactions of the free radical process of lipid peroxidation. From that pioneer work, studies were opened to many different organs and oxidative situations (Table 1).

In situ CL was also used to characterize oxidative stress in other biological systems, besides animal organs. Boveris et al. [14] reported that isolated soybean (*Glycine max* L. var Hood) embryonic axes have a spontaneous CL that increases showing two phases, upon water imbibition. From the sensitivity of the lipoxygenase reaction to inhibitors, the first burst was tentatively assigned to oxy-radicals mobilized upon water uptake by the embryonic axes, and the second phase was tentatively identified as due to lipoxygenase activity. CL may afford a noninvasive assay for lipoxygenase activity in intact plant tissues. However, the use of light emission to estimate *in vivo* lipoxygenase activity requires the consideration of the assay limitations. There are other sources of CL besides lipoxygenase, but the use of lipoxygenase inhibitors restricts the sources of error to other light emitters sensitive to the same inhibitors. There is also the possibility of an important difference between the *in vivo* and the *in vitro* counts to O_2 uptake ratio of the lipoxygenase reaction, and there is not enough information available on the effect that pH, ion composition, type of substrate, etc. might have on such ratio. But even if the activity of the enzyme could not be expressed in absolute units, the detection of changes in activity in relative terms may be very helpful [14].

Finally, it is also convenient to consider the absorption by the tissue of the emitted light. Preliminary work estimated that the measured light comes from the outer 50 to 100 nm of the tissue; consequently, the assay would have limited validity if considerable differences exist between the activity in the outermost cells and the rest of the tissue.

Table 1. Examples of intact CL measurements to study oxidative stress

Organ	Oxidative situation	References
Liver	mild Fe overload	[61]
	acute toxicity of Fe and Cu	[62]
	t-butyl, cumenehydroperoxides	[6]
	hydroperoxide infusion	[6]
	ischemia–reperfusion	[63]
	chronic alcohol intoxication	[64]
	acute alcohol intoxication	[65, 66]
Human biopsies		
Liver, heart, muscle	tert-butyl hydroperoxide exposure	[67]
Heart	ischemia-reperfusion	[67]
Eye	glaucoma	[68]

3. THE NADPH/NADP$^+$ AND NADH/NAD$^+$ RATIOS AS INDICATORS OF OXIDATIVE STRESS

In numerous biological hydrogen-transfer reactions, β-nicotinamide adenine dinucleotide (NAD$^+$) functions as a coenzyme by accepting two electrons and a proton from a substrate (SH) in the presence of a suitable enzyme to form 1,4-dihydronicotinamide adenine dinucleotide (NADH), the oxidized form of the substrate (S) and a proton. The nicotinamide ring is the site of the reversible redox process. In particular, NAD$^+$ serves as a coenzyme for pyridinoproteins (dehydrogenases) in the electron transport chain [15]. The ratio of NADPH/NADP$^+$ was widely regarded as an indicator of oxidative stress [16]. A few decades ago, assessment of this ratio by measuring the concentrations of NADP$^+$/NADPH and NAD$^+$/NADH by the spectrophotometric recycling method [17] was often used. As an example, it could be mentioned the aging studies by Sohal et al. [16, 18] in *Drosophila melanogaster*. However, a complex crosslink with glutathione metabolism in the cells made it difficult to have a clear idea of the oxidative scenario in many situations. Sohal et al. [16] suggested that the accumulation of oxidized glutathione (GSSG) and decrease in reduced glutathione (GSH) concentration in the old flies is the result of an interrelated process whereby the decrease in catalase activity leads to an increased oxidation of GSH, and the concomitant decline in glutathione reductase activity results in the decrease of GSH concentration and accumulation of GSSG. The decrease in NADPH/NADP$^+$ ratio may contribute to GSSG accumulation since NADPH is the electron donor in the conversion of GSSG to GSH; however, the significance of the reported increase in NADH/NAD$^+$ in the latter part of life is unclear.

Besides its limitations, the index is frequently used, and recently Shetty et al. [19] reported that after severe, prolonged hypoxia in hippocampal slices (maintained for 3 min after spreading depression) there was hyperoxidation of NADH following reoxygenation, an increased soluble NAD$^+$/NADH ratio, loss of neuronal field excitatory post-synaptic potential and decreased ATP content.

4. GSH/GSSG RATIO AND CELL REDOX STATUS

The tripeptide GSH is the major antioxidant and redox regulator in cells that is important in combating oxidation of cellular constituents. Cells spend a great deal of energy to maintain high levels of GSH, which in turn, helps to keep proteins in a reduced state. Drugs, infections, and inflammation in the liver can increase ROS generation and/or decrease GSH levels, and cause a shift in the cellular redox status of hepatocytes to become more oxidized [20]. An alteration of the normal redox balance can alter cell signaling pathways in hepatocytes and may thus be an important mechanism in mediating the pathogenesis of many liver diseases. Redox status has historically been used to describe the ratio of interconvertible reduced/oxidized forms of a molecule. The thiol group in the cysteine residue of GSH can become oxidized to form a disulfide. To define a cellular redox state, the ratios of important and abundant redox molecules such as GSH/GSSG can be measured. GSH/GSSG is the most important and commonly measured redox couple used to obtain an estimate of cellular redox state because: i) it is found at high levels in cells, far higher (100–10,000 greater) than most redox active compounds; and ii) the GSH/GSSG ratio is important in determining the redox status of proteins, thus influencing protein function and activity [20].

GSH is synthesized by two enzymes: glutamate-cysteine ligase and GSH synthetase, with the former catalyzing the rate-limiting step and being a point of feedback for GSH regulation. A specific distribution of GSH occurs in cells, with mitochondria, the endoplasmic reticulum, and possibly the nucleus containing separate GSH pools. Mitochondrial GSH, which comprises about 10% of hepatic GSH, is generally considered more important than cytoplasmic GSH levels for cell survival. It is generally accepted that the GSH/GSSG ratio in cells is 100:1 under normal circumstances, but the redox ratio can shift to 4:1 during times of severe oxidative stress [20]. The GSH/GSSG ratio is maintained by the activity of the enzyme GSSG reductase, which uses the reducing power of NADPH to convert GSSG to GSH. The GSH/GSSG ratio is, thus, ultimately tied to NADPH levels, which are determined by the energy status of the cell. Hepatocytes also export GSH through sinusoidal transport into plasma or into bile through canalicular transport. The maintenance of hepatic GSH is a dynamic process achieved by a balance between rates of GSH synthesis, GSH and GSSG efflux, GSH reactions with ROS and RNS, and utilization by GSH peroxidase. To assess the redox potential (E_h) in biological samples equation 1 must be applied:

$$\text{Redox potential } (E_h) = E_0 + 30 \log ([GSSG]/[GSH]^2) \tag{1}$$

being $E_0 = -264$ mV at pH = 7.4 and [GSSG] and [GSH] the molar concentrations of the species that could be determined by HPLC or biochemically [21]. To avoid artifacts in the assessment of E_h in plasma, care should be taken in preventing hemolysis, and oxidation processes, basically isolating the tissues fast enough to limit disruption; moreover, GSH degrading enzyme α-glutamyltranspeptidase activity should be inhibited.

The GSH/GSSG ratio was also extensively used to study oxidative balance in invertebrates [22] and fish [23]. In plants, a decrease in the GSH/GSSG ratio was found in leaves of *Arabidopsis thaliana* under Cd and Cu stress [24].

5. FLUORESCENT DYES

Dichlorodihydrofluorescein diacetate (DCFH-DA) is commonly used for detecting intracellular H_2O_2 [25]. The oxidation of 2',7'-dichlorodihydrofluorescein (DCFH) generates 2',7'-dichlorofluorescein (DCF), a fluorescent compound (λ exc=498 nm; λ em=522 nm) initially thought to be useful as a specific indicator for H_2O_2 [26]. However, it was already demonstrated that DCFH is oxidized by other ROS, such as hydroxyl radical ($^{\bullet}$OH) and peroxyl (ROO•), and also by RNS (nitric oxide, NO and peroxinitrite, ONOO⁻) [27]. DCFH-DA is a cell-permeable ester and is hydrolyzed inside the cell to dihydroxy-DCFH, which is retained intracellularly. Despite the popularity of this assay, it cannot be reliably used to measure intracellular H_2O_2 [28]. Some of the reasons that justify this statement are: (i) DCFH does not directly react with H_2O_2; (ii) several one-electron oxidizing species will oxidize DCFH to DCF; (iii) DCF can actually produce O_2^- and H_2O_2 via reaction of DCF radical with O_2, artificially elevating the ROS content that it is attempting to quantify; (iv) transition metals, cytochrome c, and heme peroxidases can catalyze DCFH oxidation [29].

Dihydrorhodamine (DHR) is commonly used for the detection of ONOO⁻ [30]. This assay is based on the oxidative conversion of DHR to its corresponding two-electron-oxidized fluorescent product, rhodamine (R). However, DHR oxidation to R is not only caused by the reaction with ONOO⁻. The oxidative conversion of DHR to R is mediated by an intermediate DHR radical that can be reduced by thiols and ascorbic acid, leading to false-negative data. It is, therefore concluded that DHR can only be used as a nonspecific indicator of intracellular ONOO⁻ and HOCl or other one-electron oxidants [31]. DHR is a non-fluorescent molecule that, by oxidation, yields R123, a fluorescent cationic and lipophilic probe (λexc=505 nm; λem = 529nm) [32]. The lipophilicity of DHR facilitates its diffusion across cell membranes. Upon oxidation of DHR to the fluorescent R123, one of the two equivalent amino groups tautomerizes into an imino, effectively trapping R123 within cells [27]. H_2O_2 oxidizes DHR in the presence of peroxidases, although this probe has low specificity for this ROS since it can also be oxidized by other reactive oxidants, namely ONOO⁻, Fe(II), Fe(III)/ascorbate, Fe(III)/EDTA, cytochrome c, or HOCl [33, 34]. On the other hand, DHR is not directly oxidizable by H_2O_2 alone, by O_2^-, or by xanthine/xanthine oxidase [34].

HE, or dihydroethidium, is another widely used probe for detecting intracellular O_2^-. The red fluorescence formed from the two-electron oxidation product, ethidium (E^+), is usually employed to assess intracellular O_2^- formation. Previous research suggests that E^+ is not formed from the direct oxidation of HE by O_2^-. Instead, another product, 2-hydroxyethidium (2-OH-E^+), with similar fluorescence characteristics, is formed from the HE/O_2^- reaction [35].

On the other hand, mitochondrial-targeted HE (Mito-HE) or Mito-SOX, a triphenylphosphonium cation conjugated to HE via a linker carbon-carbon alkyl chain, has been used to measure mitochondrial O_2^-. Mito-SOX reacts faster with O_2^- as compared to HE [29]. Mito-SOX reacts with O_2^- and forms a red-fluorescent product, 2-hydroxymitoethidium (2-OH-Mito-E^+), and not Mito-E^+. However, 2-OH-Mito-E^+ and Mito-E^+ (nonspecific oxidation product of Mito-SOX) have overlapping fluorescence spectra; thus, the red fluorescence formed from Mito-SOX localized in mitochondria is not a reliable indicator of mitochondrial O_2^- formation [29]. Moreover, it was shown recently that aromatic boronates are oxidized by ONOO⁻ yielding the corresponding phenols as a major product (85% yield). Boronate-containing fluorophores (such as coumarin boronate) react in a similar fashion with ONOO⁻ giving rise to fluorescent products. Since some of these boronate-based fluorophores are cell-permeable, they were suggested to be employed to measure intracellular ONOO⁻ [29]. Another probe that can be used to measure H_2O_2 is Amplex red. Amplex red is oxidized by horseradish peroxidase (HRP) and H_2O_2 to a fluorescent product, resorufin.

The oxidation catalyzed by HRP in the presence of H_2O_2 is highly efficient and vastly increases the yield of resorufin. Information summarized in Table 2 lists the challenges and limitations of the use of fluorescent probes for measuring ROS and RNS.

However, the oxidation of DCFH-DA was successfully used as a general index of ROS generation in algae exposed to UV-B radiation [36], and in soybean roots *in vivo* exposed to Fe overload, and also as an *in vitro* assay to study the ability of isolated microsomal membranes to generate oxygen radical species in the presence of NADPH [37].

More recently, Patetsini et al. [38] examined, employing flow cytometry, the influence of environmentally relevant concentrations of two pesticides (chlorpyrifos and penoxsulam) on mussel physiological status. These works established this methodology as a reliable biomarker for the evaluation of pollution or other environmental stressors.

Table 2. Advantages and disadvantages of fluorescent probes used to determine the oxidative state in biological systems

Fluorescent probe	Advantages	Disadvantages
HE	Intermediate HE-derived radical is not able to react with molecular O_2 to form O_2^- and H_2O_2.	2-OH-E^+ and E^+ have similar fluorescence spectral features.
Mito-SOX and Mito-HEONOO$^-$	Reacts with other oxidants to form Mito-E^+ and dimers. Intermediate Mito-HE-derived radical does not react with O_2 to form O_2^- and H_2O_2.	2-OH-Mito-E^+ and Mito-E^+ have similar fluorescence spectral features.
DCFH-DA	Cell-permeable. Easy to use. Responds to changes in cellular Fe signaling or enhanced peroxidase activity.	Artifactual amplification of fluorescence intensity via redox-cycling mechanism by the intermediate radical DCF$^-$.
DHR	Cell-permeable. Easy to use. Responds to generation of NO and O_2^- via a predictable radical chemistry.	Artifactual amplification of fluorescence intensity via redox-cycling mechanism by the intermediate radical DHR$^-$.
Coumarin boronate	Reacts very rapidly and nearly stoichiometrically with ONOO$^-$ to form a fluorescent product.	Further metabolism of the product(7-hydroxycoumarin) and possible excretion out of the cell.
Amplex red	Resorufin formation will be inhibited by reducing agents, peroxidases substrates and the reaction of intermediate Amplex red-derived radical with O_2^-.	Room light-mediated photochemical oxidation of resorufin in the presence of GSH, NAD(P)H, or ascorbate will generate H_2O_2. Amplex red-derived radical can react with O_2^- and inhibit product formation.

Taken and modified from Kalyanaraman et al. [29].

Also with an ecological aim, a study was performed by Gusta el al. [39] showing the immunotoxic effects of surface waters contaminated by a municipal effluent dispersion plume employing the snail *Lymnaea stagnalis*. On the other hand, Fu et al. [40] reported that valproic acid, a widely used anti-epilepsy drug, induces autophagy in glioma cells. Moreover, the authors confirmed oxidative stress induction in these cells upstream of autophagy.

DHR123 conversion to R123 was used as a sensitive method for the detection of peroxide (presumably hydrogen peroxide) formation in isolated chloroplasts in *Chlorella vulgaris* [41]. The following mechanism was proposed for the accumulation of the dye [42]: i) the peroxides, or H_2O_2 formed inside the cell diffuse out through the cell membrane; ii) the diffused peroxides or H_2O_2 oxidize DHR to R123, and the R123 formed is accumulated in cells. The driving force for the R123 accumulation in cells may be the interior-negative membrane potential, because R123 is a lipophilic cation and is used as a probe for measuring membrane potential of cells or mitochondria [43, 44]. However, since DHR can permeate membranes, it could not be discarded that oxidation occurred inside the chloroplast and the formed R123 was attracted by the negative membrane potential of the chloroplast.

The accumulation of R123 in the chloroplasts from algae exposed to UV-B was higher than in chloroplasts from control algae.

6. Oxidative Index in the Lipophilic Cellular Environment. Lipid Radical/Antioxidant Content Ratio

EPR, also known as Electron Paramagnetic Resonance, is presently the only analytical approach that allows direct detection of free radicals. This technique reports on the magnetic properties of unpaired electrons and their molecular environment [2].

Biologically important paramagnetic species include free radicals and many transition elements. In addition, there is a substantial and rapidly growing use of synthetic stable free radicals (spin labels) to obtain information on a wide variety of complex biochemical environments, such as macromolecules and membranes [45].

Therefore, EPR techniques have become increasingly used in biochemical and biophysical investigations, and most likely their use will increase further as more biologically oriented scientists become aware of the capabilities of these techniques.

Moreover, EPR spectroscopy has developed into a multifaceted field that employs different techniques that have a common basis of resonant absorption of microwaves by paramagnetic substances.

In spite of the fact that probe instability, tissue metabolism, and lack of spin specificity are drawback factors for employing EPR for *in vivo* determination of free radicals, the dependability of this technique, mostly by combining it with other biochemical strategies, enhances the value of these procedures as contributors to the knowledge of oxidative condition [45].

In the presence of exogenous traps, EPR spectroscopy has shown the capacity to detect lipid radicals (LR•) formed during peroxidation, by yielding unique and stable products. Thus, even though EPR detection of LR• could be considered a fingerprint of radical presence, spin-trapping studies cannot really distinguish among ROO•, alcohoxyl (RO•) and alkyl (R•) adducts owing to the similarity of the corresponding coupling constants.

Values for the LR•/α-T index were calculated in several biological systems, such as in digestive glands and gills from limpets [46], digestive glands from bivalves [47] and fish [23]. In other situations, values of both, the LR• and α-T content were reported independently and the LR•/α-T index could be calculated as shown in Table 3. Among stress situations, lipid peroxidation was evaluated by EPR in wheat leaves subjected to drought and watering, soybean cotyledons during natural senescence, and sorghum embryonic axes during imbibition [48].

Also, the effect of NO donors on LR• content in sorghum embryonic axes, and in soybean chloroplast membranes was assessed.

Thus, this reliable method can be successfully adapted to study biological implications of oxidative damage to lipids in different types of biological materials, and especially in photosynthetic tissues, such as green algae undergoing oxidative stress conditions [48].

Table 3. Values of the LR•/α-T index in biological systems

Biological system	LR•content	α-T content	LR•/α-T ratio	References
Algae				
Chlorella vulgaris	6 ± 2^a	3.4 ± 0.6^d	$(3.8\pm0.3)\ 10^{-3}$	[36]
Plants				
Sorghum axes	0.41 ± 0.02^b	44 ± 12^e	$(9.3\pm0.5)\ 10^{-5}$	[69]
Soybean chloroplasts	9 ± 1^c	8 ± 1^f	$(1.2\pm0.8)\ 10^{-3}$	[70]
Invertebrates digestive glands				
Mya arenaria	114 ± 21^b	2.7 ± 0.8^f	1.3 ± 0.2	[71]
Nacella magellanica	122 ± 29^b	2.7 ± 0.4^f	1.3 ± 0.3	[71]
Vertebrates digestive glands				
Odontesthes nigricans	1.2 ± 0.3^b	1135 ± 28^f	$(1.4\pm0.7)\ 10^{-6}$	[23]

Units for LR•/α-T content are as follows: [a](pmol/10^7 cell) for algae cells; [b](pmol/mg FW) for sorghum embryonic axes, invertebrates and vertebrates and [c](pmol/mg FW) for soybean chloroplasts.

Units for α-T content are as follows: [d](nmol/10^7 cell) for algae cells; [e](nmol/axes) for sorghum embryonic axes and [f](nmol/mg prot) for soybean chloroplast, invertebrates and vertebrates.

Experimental data were taken from the indicated references and the LR•/α-T ratio was calculated.

7. Oxidative Index in the Hydrophilic Cellular Environment. Ascorbyl Radical (A•)/Ascorbate(AH⁻) Content Ratio

Certain free radicals, such as A• show a stable spectrum, and can be directly detected by EPR at room temperature [49]. A• may be considered as a terminal free radical product of free radical transformations in the biological antioxidant defense system. Thus, the rate of A• generation may be taken to be equal to the total rate of AH⁻ oxidative transformations, which includes the sum of the rate of AH⁻ oxidation and that of reactions of AH⁻ with free radicals. A• can be reconverted, in photosynthetic organisms, to AH⁻ by means of ascorbate radical reductase or can undergo spontaneous disproportionation [50].

Thus, the use of A• as an index of oxidative stress seems reasonable under conditions where total content of AH⁻ was not affected under the experimental conditions tested [51]. A• exhibited a prolonged life span and a strong EPR doublet with the spectral features (a_H=1.88 G, g=2.005), while both AH⁻ and dehydroascorbate (DHA) are EPR-silent species.

Exposure of plasma to aqueous ROO• generated at a constant rate leads immediately to oxidation of endogenous AH⁻ and sulfhydryl groups, followed by sequential depletion of bilirubin, urate, and α-T. Stimulating polymorphonuclear leukocytes in plasma initiates very rapid oxidation of AH⁻, followed by partial depletion of urate. Once AH⁻ is consumed completely, micromolar concentrations of hydroperoxides of plasma phospholipids, triglycerides, and cholesterol esters appear simultaneously, even though sulfhydryl groups, bilirubin, urate, and α-T are still present at high concentrations. Non-esterified fatty acids, the only lipid class in plasma not transported in lipoproteins but bound to albumin, are preserved from peroxidative damage even after complete oxidation of AH⁻, most likely due to site-specific antioxidant protection by albumin-bound bilirubin and possibly by albumin itself.

Hydroperoxides of linoleic acid, phosphatidylcholine, and cholesterol added to plasma in the absence of added reducing substrates are degraded, in contrast to hydroperoxides of trilinolein and cholesterol linoleate [52]. The A•/AH⁻ ratio was recommended to be used to characterize oxidative stress in plasma under physiological [53] and Fe overload [54] conditions. Oxidative stress has been developed using dietary carbonyl-Fe and Fe-dextran parenteral administration as models of *in vivo* Fe overload in rats. However, a different profile of response was observed by Galleano et al. [54]. Carbonyl-Fe led to a significant decrease in AH⁻ content with non-significant changes in plasma A• radical content, while in Fe-dextran treatment, the A• radical content increased significantly but AH⁻ level was not affected. The A•/AH⁻ ratio was significantly higher in both Fe treated groups, as compared with the control group suggesting that evaluation of this ratio is an appropriate *in vivo* indicator of oxidative stress under both conditions of Fe overload. The overall mechanism that describes the AH⁻ status in plasma seems to be strongly dependent on the way the Fe excess is stored and thus, to the availability of the catalytically active Fe to interact with the plasma components. On this regard, evaluation of A•/AH⁻ ratio did not help to discriminate between the possible involved mechanisms. It could be hypothesized that the excess of catalytically active Fe could increase AH⁻ oxidation rate leading to an increased concentration of A• in plasma and oxidative stress. In carbonyl-Fe treated animals, the ratio A•/AH⁻ increased presumably due to not only a slightly higher oxidation rate of AH⁻ (since a gradual Fe intake favored its 'safe' storage conditions), but to a significant decrease in the content of AH⁻ in plasma as well [54].

The A•/AH⁻ ratio could be successfully used to estimate mild oxidative transformations, and provides a simple diagnosis of stress due to the interaction of UV-B radiation with photosynthetic organisms. Kozak et al. [55] reported data obtained with algae cultures indicating that even when total AH⁻ content was changed by oxidative conditions, the A•/AH⁻ ratio could be successfully used to estimate early oxidative transformations by UV-B irradiation in algae cultures and soybean leaves. Later, Giordano et al. [56] showed that biologically effective UV-B doses that overlap with the range of doses that *Gunnera magellanica* plants experienced in their natural environment, induced a transient oxidative stress situation as evaluated using the A•/AH⁻ ratio. This transient oxidative stress situation was rapidly controlled by an increase in the AH⁻ pool.

Even more, Galatro et al. [49] reported a kinetic analysis that was performed applying a simple physical chemistry mechanism, which allowed the estimation of A• steady state concentrations that properly parallel experimental values obtained by EPR.

The A•/AH⁻ ratio was applied to a wide range of aquatic systems including sea urchin, limpets, bivalves and fish, under physiological and oxidative stress conditions as well, reflecting the state of one part of the oxidative defense system and providing the diagnosis of environmental stressing conditions [57-60].

The application of a kinetic analysis also allowed the estimation of the generation rate of A• in a marine invertebrate, opening the possibility of a mechanistic understanding of the complexity of free radical interactions in a metabolically slow, cold water bivalve *Mya arenaria* under unstressed conditions, that could be further compared to cells of higher organisms [60].

Figure 2 shows typical EPR spectra of A• and the values of the A•/AH⁻ ratio in different biological systems. The enclosed data suggest that the A•/AH⁻ ratio takes similar values (at least in the same range) in photosynthetic organisms such as algae and soybean seedlings, and it increases with the complexity of organisms.

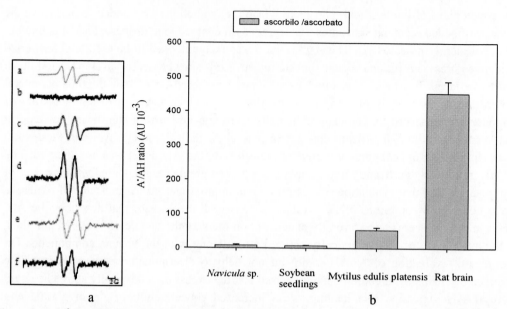

Figure 2. A: A$^\bullet$ detection by EPR. Spectra from: a) computer-simulated spectrum employing the following spectral parameters, g = 2.005 and a$_H$ = 1.88 G, b) DMSO, c) rat brain d) isolated digestive glands from *M. edulis platensis*, e) soybean seedlings and f) *Navicula sp.* cells. B: A$^\bullet$/AH$^-$ ratio in different organisms under physiological conditions.
Data, expressed as arbitrary units (AU), were taken from Galatro et al. [49], Gonzalez et al. [57]; and Piloni et al. [72].

CONCLUSION

The importance of free radical reactions in the physiological processes and in the mechanisms of toxicity by stressors, such as an alteration in the antioxidant system and/or oxidative damage has been of great interest. Adaptation to the increase in the steady state concentration of ROS and/or RNS involves extended periods of metabolic reduction which may reduce the overall rate of metabolically produced radicals as compared to basal conditions. Antioxidant defenses are ubiquitous in aerobic species and vary in different tissue-types. Thus, environmental and metabolic requirements of different tissues should result in different profiles in the oxidative cellular status. Oxidative stress ratios (damage/ protection) successfully reflect the actual state of one part of the oxidative defense system and provide an adequate tool for the diagnosis of stress. These indexes could be considered as a powerful method for the detection of initial stages of oxidative stress in the cellular lipophilic and hydrophilic media. The dependability of these parameters, mostly by combining it with other biochemical strategies, drastically improves the value of these procedures. The complex cellular scenario, including ROS and RNS production, should be taken into account when evaluating oxidative stress.

As it is shown in Figure 3, simultaneous increases in ROS and RNS may drastically enhance potential cellular damage by affecting cellular redox status. It is also important to point out that NO could exert a dual effect avoiding lipid oxidation by chelating Fe catalytically active and limiting the chain reaction, besides reacting with O_2^-.

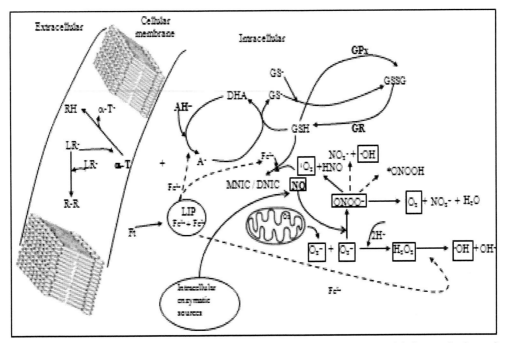

Figure 3. Schematic diagram proposing an interaction network between oxidative and nitrosative metabolism, and cellular antioxidants including enzymatic and non-enzymatic compounds.

MNIC: mononytrosyl-Fe complexes, DNIC: dinytrosyl-Fe complexes. RH, membrane fatty acids; LR$^\bullet$, lipid radicals; α-T$^\bullet$, tocopheryl radical; A$^\bullet$, ascorbyl radical; DHA, dehydroascorbate; GS$^\bullet$, glutathione radicals.

The generation of ONOO$^-$ could act to suppress possible signaling effects of O$_2^-$ and NO, as it was suggested in several biological systems. Many biochemical reactions take place linking the consumption and regeneration of antioxidants in the cell, such as re-oxidation of α-T by AH$^-$. Further, deeper studies are urgently required to fully understand the global chain of responses that takes place in cell exposed to hostile conditions.

These studies should include not only assessing oxidative indexes, as described here, but measuring both the steady concentration of oxidative species and antioxidants contents. The integrative view of all these parameters, would lead to fulfill the goal.

ACKNOWLEDGMENTS

This study was supported by grants from the University of Buenos Aires, ANPCyT and CONICET to S.P. S.P. and G.M. are career investigators from CONICET.

REFERENCES

[1] McCord, J. M., Fridovich, I. The reduction of cytochrome c by milk xanthine oxidase. *J. Biol. Chem.* 1968, 243, 5753-5760.

[2] Tarpey, M. M., Wink, D. A., Grisham, M. B. Methods for detection of reactive metabolites of oxygen and nitrogen: in vitro and in vivo considerations. *Am. J. Physiol. Regul. Integr. Comp. Physiol.* 2004, 286, R431-R444.

[3] Gershman, R., Gilbert, D. L., Nye, S. W., Dwyer, P., Fenn, W. O. Oxygen poisoning and x-irradiation: a mechanism in common. *Science* 1954, 119, 623-626.

[4] Ignarro, L. J. Nitric oxide as a unique signaling molecule in the vascular system: a historical overview. *J. Physiol. Pharmacol.* 2002, 53, 503-514.

[5] Abrahamsson, T., Brandt, U., Marklund, S. L., and Sjoqvist, P. O. Vascular bound recombinant extracellular superoxide dismutase type C protects against the detrimental effects of superoxide radicals on endothelium-dependent arterial relaxation. *Circ. Res.* 1992, 70, 264-271.

[6] Boveris, A., Cadenas, E., Reiter, R., Filipkowski, M., Nakase, Y., Chance, B. Organ chemiluminescence: Noninvasive assay for oxidative radical reactions. *Proc. Natl. Acad. Sci. US,* 1980, 77, 347-351.

[7] Harvey, E. N. *Living Light.* 1st Edition. Princeton: Princeton University Press; 1940.

[8] Chance, B., Sies, H., Boveris, A. Hydroperoxide metabolism in mammalian organs. *Physiol. Rev.* 1979, 59, 527-605.

[9] Tarusov, B. N., Polivoda, A. I., Zhuravlev, A. I. *Radiobiologiya 1 (Radiobiology 1):* 1961.

[10] Barenboim, G. M., Domanskij, A. N., Turoverov, K. K. *Luminescence of Biopolymers and Cells.* 1st Edition. New York: Plenum Press; 1969.

[11] Nakano, M., Noguchi, T., Sugioka, K., Fukuyama, H., Sato, M., Shimizu, Y., Tsuji, Y., Inaba, H. Spectroscopic evidence for the generation of singlet oxygen in the reduced nicotinamide adenine dinucleotide phosphate – dependent microsomal lipid peroxidation system. *J. Biol. Chem.* 1975, 250, 2404-2406.

[12] Sugioka, K., Nakano, M. A possible mechanism of the generation of singlet molecular oxygen in NADPH-dependent microsomal lipid peroxidation. *Biochim. Biophys. Acta* 1976, 423, 203-216.

[13] Hamman, J. P., Gorby, D. R., Seliger, H. H. A new type of biological chemiluminescence: The microsomal chemiluminescence of benzo[a]pyrene arises from the diol epoxide product of the 7, 8-dihydrodiol. *Biochem. Biophys. Res. Commun.* 1977, 75, 793-798.

[14] Boveris, A., Puntarulo, S., Roy, A. H., Sanchez, R. A. Spontaneous Chemiluminescence of Soybean Embryonic Axes during Imbibition. *Plant Physiol.* 1984, 76, 447-451.

[15] Elving, P. J., Bresnahan, W. T., Moiroux, J., Samec, Z. NAD/NADH as a model redox system: Mechanism, mediation, modification by the environment. *Bioelectrochem. Bioenerg.* 1982, 9, 365-318.

[16] Sohal, R. S., Arnold, L., Orr, W. C. Effect of age on superoxide dismutase, catalase, glutathione reductase, inorganic peroxides, TBA – reactive material, GSH/GSSG,

NADPH/NADP and NADH/NAD in *Drosophila melanogaster. Mech. Ageing Dev.* 1990, 56, 223-235.

[17] Pinder, S., Clark, J. B., Greenbaum, A. L. Estimation of nicotinic acid mononucleotide, nicotinamide mononucleotide, and diamide-NAD formed from radioactive precursors. *Meth. Enzymol.*, 1977 58, 24-27.

[18] Sohal, R. S., Toy, P. L., Farmer, K. J. Age-related changes in the redox status of the housefly, *Musca domestica. Arch. Gerontol. Geriatr.* 1987, 6, 95-100.

[19] Shetty, P. K., Galeffi, F., Turner, D. A. Nicotinamide pre-treatment ameliorates NAD(H) hyperoxidation and improves neuronal function after severe hypoxia. *Neurobiol. Dis.* 2014, 62, 469-478.

[20] Han, D., Hanawa, N., Saberi, B., Kaplowitz, N. Mechanisms of Liver Injury. III. Role of glutathione redox status in liver injury. *Am. J. Physiol. Gastrointest. Liver Physiol.* 2006, 291, G1-G7.

[21] Jones, D. P. Redox potential of GSH/GSSG couple: assay and biological significance. *Meth. Enzymol.* 2002, 348, 93-112.

[22] González, P. M., Abele, D., Puntarulo, S. Exposure to excess dissolved iron in vivo affects oxidative status in the bivalve *Mya arenaria. Comp. Biochem. Physiol. C Toxicol. Pharmacol.* 2010, 152, 167-174.

[23] Lattuca, M. E., Malanga, G., Aguilar Hurtado, C., Pérez, A. F., Calvo, J., Puntarulo, S. Main features of the oxidative metabolism in gills and liver of de *Odontesthes nigricans* Richardson (Pisces, Atherinopsidae). *Comp. Biochem. Physiol. B* 2009, 154, 406-411.

[24] Drążkiewicz, M., Skórzyńska-Polit, E., Krupa, Z. The redox state and activity of superoxide dismutase classes in *Arabidopsis thaliana* under cadmium or copper stress. *Chemosphere* 2007, 67, 188-193.

[25] Hempel, S. L., Buettner, G. R., O'Malley, Y. Q., Wessels, D. A., Flaherty, D. M. Dihydrofluorescein diacetate is superior for detecting intracellular oxidants: comparison with 2,7-dichlorodihydrofluorescein diacetate, 5(and 6)-carboxy-2, 7 – dichlorodihydrofluorescein diacetate, and dihydrorhodamine 123. *Free Radic. Biol. Med.* 1999, 27, 146-159.

[26] Keston, A. S., Brandt, R. The fluorometric analysis of ultramicro quantities of hydrogen peroxide. *Anal. Biochem.* 1995, 1, 1-5.

[27] Crow, J. P. Dichlorodihydrofluorescein and dihydrorhodamine 123 are sensitive indicators of peroxynitrite in vitro: implications for intracellular measurement of reactive nitrogen and oxygen species. *Nitric Oxide* 1997, 1, 145-57.

[28] Dikalov, S. I., Harrison, D. G. Methods for Detection of Mitochondrial and Cellular Reactive Oxygen Species. *Antioxid. Redox Signal.* 2012, 1-11. DOI: 10.1089/ars.2012. 4886.

[29] Kalyanaraman, B., Darley-Usmar, V., Davies, K. J., Dennery, P. A., Forman, H. J., Grisham, M. B., Mann, G. E., Moore, K., Roberts, L. J., Ischiropoulos, H. Measuring reactive oxygen and nitrogen species with fluorescent probes: challenges and limitations. *Free Radic. Biol. Med.* 2012, 52; 1-6.

[30] Papapostolou, I., Patsoukis, N., Georgiou, C. D. The fluorescence detection of superoxide radical using hydroethidine could be complicated by the presence of heme proteins. *Anal. Biochem.* 2004, 332, 290-298.

[31] Silveira, L. R., Pereira-da-Silva, L., Juel, C., Hellstein, Y. Formation of hydrogen peroxide and nitric oxide in rat skeletal muscle cells during contractions. *Free Radic. Biol. Med.* 2003, 35, 455-64.

[32] Kooy, N. W., Royall, J. A., Ischiropoulos, H., Beckman, J. S. Peroxynitrite-mediated oxidation of dihydrorhodamine 123. *Free Radic. Biol. Med.* 1994, 16, 149-56.

[33] Royall, J. A., Ischiropoulos, H. Evaluation of 2′,7′-dichlorofluorescin and dihydrorhodamine 123 as fluorescent probes for intracellular H_2O_2 in cultured endothelial cells. *Arch. Biochem. Biophys.* 1993, 302, 348-55.

[34] Henderson, L. M., Chappell, J. B. Dihydrorhodamine 123: a fluorescent probe for superoxide generation? *Eur. J. Biochem.* 1993, 217, 973-980.

[35] Zielonka, J., Kalyanaraman, B. Hydroethidine- and MitoSOX-derived red fluorescenceis not a reliable indicator of intracellular superoxide formation: another inconvenient truth. *Free Radic. Biol. Med.* 2010, 48, 983-1001.

[36] Malanga, G., Puntarulo, S. Oxidative stress and antioxidant content in *Chlorella vulgaris* after exposure to ultraviolet-B radiation. *Physiol. Plant* 1995, 94; 672-679.

[37] Caro, A., Puntarulo, S. Effect of in vivo iron supplementation on oxygen radical production by soybean roots. *Biochim. Biophys. Acta* 1996, 1291, 245-251.

[38] Patetsini, E., Dimitriadis, V. K., Kaloyianni, M. Biomarkers in marine mussels, *Mytilus galloprovincialis*, exposed to environmentally relevant levels of the pesticides, chlorpyrifos and penoxsulam. *Aquatic. Toxicol.* 2013, 126, 338-345.

[39] Gusta, M., Fortier, M., Garric, J., Fournier, M., Gagné, F. Immunotoxicity of surface waters contaminated by municipal effluents to the snail *Lymnaea stagnalis*. *Aquatic Toxicol.* 2013, 126, 393-403.

[40] Fu, J., Shao, C.-J., Chen, F.-R., Ng, H.-K., Chen, Z.-P. Autophagy induced by valproic acid is associated with oxidative stress in glioma cell lines. *Neuro-Oncology* 2010, 12 (4), 328-340.

[41] Malanga, G., Calmanovici, G., Puntarulo, S. Oxidative damage to chloroplasts from Chlorella vuigaris exposed to ultraviolet-B radiation. *Physiol. Plant.* 1997, 101, 455-462.

[42] Ichiki, H., Sakurada, H., Kamo, N., Takahashi, T. A., Sekiguchi, S. Generation of active oxygens, cell deformation and membrane potential changes upon UV-B irradiation in human blood cells. *Biol. Pharm. Bull.* 1994, 17, 1065-1069.

[43] Emaus, R. K., Grunwald, R., Lemasters, J. J. Rhodamine 123 as a probe of transmembrane potential in isolated rat-liver mitochondria: Spectral and metabolic properties. *Biochim. Biophys. Acta* 1986, 850, 436-448.

[44] Sobreira, C., Davidson, M., King, M. P., Miranda, A. F. Dihydrorhodamine 123 identifies impaired mitochondrial respiratory chain function in cultured cells harboring mitochondrial DNA mutations. *J. Histochem. Cytochem.* 1996, 44, 571-579.

[45] Malanga, G., Aguiar, M. B., Puntarulo, S. *The Ascorbyl Radical/Ascorbate Ratio as Index of Oxidative Stress in Aquatic Organisms*. In: Zenteno-Savin, T., Vasquez Medina, J. P., Abele, D., editors. Oxidative Stress in Aquatic Ecosystems. Wiley-Blackwell Publishing Ltd, Oxford, 2012, 458-464.

[46] Malanga, G., Estevez, M. S., Calvo, J., Abele, D., Puntarulo, S. Oxidative stress in gills of limpets from the Beagle Channel: comparison with limpets from the Antarctic. *Sci. Mar.* 2005, 69, 297-304.

[47] Gonzalez, P. M., Puntarulo, S. Iron and nitrosative metabolism in the Antarctic mollusc *Laternula elliptica*. *Comp. Biochem. Physiol. C Toxicol. Pharmacol.* 2011, 153, 243-250.

[48] Simontacchi, M., Buet, A., Puntarulo, S. The Use of Electron Paramagnetic Resonance (EPR) in the Study of Oxidative Damage to Lipids in Plants. In: Catalá, A., editor. *Lipid Peroxidation: Biological Implications. Res. Signpost Transworld Res.* Network, Kerala, India, 2011, 141-160.

[49] Galatro, A., Rousseau, I., Puntarulo, S. Concentration Analysis in Steady State of Ascorbate Radical in Soybean Seedlings Determined by Electronic Paramagnetic Resonance. *Phyton. Internat. J. Exp. Bot.* 2006, 75, 7-20.

[50] Arrigoni, O. Ascorbate system in plant development. *J. Bioenerg. Biomemb.* 1994, 26, 407-419.

[51] Roginsky, V. A., Stegmann, H. B. Ascorbyl radical as natural indicator of oxidative stress: quantitative regularities. *Free Radic. Biol. Med.* 1994, 17, 93-103.

[52] Frei, B., Stocker, R., Ames, B. N. Antioxidant defenses and lipid peroxidation in human blood plasma. *Proc. Natl. Acad. Sci. US* 1988 85, 9748-9752.

[53] Courderot-Masuyer, C., Lahet, J. J., Verges, B., Brun, J. M., Rochette, L. Ascorbyl free radical release in diabetic patients. *Cell Mol. Biol.* 2000, 46(8), 1397-1401.

[54] Galleano, M., Aimo, L., Puntarulo, S. Ascorbyl radical/ascorbate ratio in plasma from iron overloaded rats as oxidative stress indicator. *Toxicol. Lett.* 2002, 133, 193-201.

[55] Kozak, R. G., Malanga, G., Caro, A., Puntarulo, S. Ascorbate Free Radical Content in Photosynthetic Organisms after Exposure to Ultraviolet-B. *Recent Res. Devel. in Plant Physiol.* 1997, 1, 233-239.

[56] Giordano, C. V., Galatro, A., Puntarulo, S., Ballaré, C. L. The inhibitory effects of UV-B radiation (280–315 nm) on *Gunnera magellanica* growth correlate with increased DNA damage but not with oxidative damage to lipids. *Plant, Cell and Environm.* 2004 27, 1415-1423.

[57] Gonzalez, P. M., Aguiar, M. B., Malanga, G., Puntarulo, S. Electronic Paramagnetic Resonance (EPR) for the Study of Ascorbyl Radical and Lipid Radicals in Marine Organisms. *Comp. Biochem. Physiol. Part A Mol. Integr. Physiol.* 2013, 165(4), 439-447.

[58] Malanga, G., Calvo, J., Puntarulo, S. Ascorbyl/Ascorbate Ratio as an Index of Oxidative Stress in Gills of Limpets. In: Puntarulo, S., Boveris, A., editors. *Proceedings of the XII Biennial Meeting of the Society for Free Radical Research Society*, Medimond srl, Bologna, Italia, 2004, 391-394.

[59] Malanga, G., Pérez, A., Calvo, J., Puntarulo, S. The effect of seasonality on oxidative metabolism in the sea urchin *Loxechinus albus. Mar. Biol.* 2009, 156, 763-770.

[60] Gonzalez, P. M., Abele, D., Puntarulo, S. A Kinetic Approach to Assess Oxidative Metabolism Related Features in the Bivalve *Mya arenaria. Theory in Biosci.*, 2012, 131, 253-264.

[61] Galleano, M., Puntarulo, S. Hepatic chemiluminescence and lipid peroxidation in mild iron overload. *Toxicology* 1992, 76, 27-38.

[62] Boveris, A., Musacco-Sebio, R., Ferrarotti, N., Saporito-Magriñá, C., Torti, H., Massot, F., Repetto, M. G. The acute toxicity of iron and copper: Biomolecule oxidation and oxidative damage in rat liver. *J. Inorg. Biochem.* 2012, 116, 63-69.

[63] Cutrin, J. C., Boveris, A., Zingaro, B., Corvetti, G., Poli, G. *In situ* determination by surface chemiluminescence of temporal relationships between evolving warm ischemia-reperfusion injury in rat liver and phagocyte activation and recruitment. *Hepatology* 2000, 31, 622-632.

[64] Boveris, A., Fraga, C., Varsavsky, A., Koch, O. Increased chemiluminescence and superoxide production in the liver of chronically ethanol-treated rats. *Arch. Biochem. Biophys.* 1983, 227, 534-541.

[65] Boveris, A., Llesuy, S., Azzalis, L., Giavarotti, L., Simon, K., Junqueira, V., Porta, E., Videla, L., Lissi, E. *In situ* rat brain and liver spontaneous chemiluminescence after acute ethanol intake. *Toxicol. Lett.* 1997, 93, 23-28.

[66] Videla, L., Fraga, C., Koch, O., Boveris, A. Chemiluminescence of the *in situ* rat liver after acute ethanol intoxication-effect of (+)-cyanidanol-3. *Biochem. Pharmacol.* 1983, 32, 2822-2825.

[67] Gonzalez Flecha, B., Llesuy, S., Boveris, A. Hydroperoxide initiated chemiluminescence: an assay for oxidative stress in biopsies of heart, liver, and muscle. *Free Radic. Biol. Med.* 1991, 10, 93-100.

[68] Ferreira, S. M., Lerner, S. F., Brunzini, R., Reides, C. G., Evelson, P. A., Llesuy, S. F. Time Course Changes of Oxidative Stress Markers in a Rat Experimental Glaucoma Model. *Inves. Ophthalmol. Vis. Sci.* 2010, 51 (9), 4635-4640.

[69] Simontacchi, M., Jasid, S., Puntarulo, S. Nitric oxide generation during early germination of sorghum seeds. *Plant Sci.* 2004, 167, 839-847.

[70] Galatro, A., Simontacchi, M., Puntarulo, S. Free radical generation and antioxidant content in chloroplasts from soybean leaves exposed to ultraviolet-B. *Physiol. Plant* 2001, 113, 564-570.

[71] Puntarulo, S., Boveris, A. D., Estevez, M. S. Oxidative Stress and Iron in MolluscsAdapted to Different Environments. In: Puntarulo, S., Boveris, A., editors. *Proceedings of the XII Biennial Meeting of the Society for Free Radical Research Society*, Medimond srl, Bologna, Italia, 2004, 378-382.

[72] Piloni, N. E., Fermandez, V., Videla, L. A., Puntarulo, S. Acute iron overload and oxidative stress in brain. *Toxicology* 2013, 314, 174-182.

Chapter 3

MASS SPECTROMETRY DETECTION OF PROTEIN MODIFICATION BY CROSS-REACTION WITH LIPID PEROXIDATION PRODUCTS

M. Rosário Domingues[1,*], Maria Fedorova[2] and Pedro Domingues[1]

[1] Mass Spectrometry Centre, QOPNA, Department of Chemistry,
University of Aveiro, Aveiro, Portugal
[2] Institute of Bioanalytical Chemistry, Faculty of Chemistry and Mineralogy,
Center for Biotechnology and Biomedicine, Universität Leipzig, Germany

ABSTRACT

Lipid oxidation, which occurs during oxidative stress, leads to the formation of a wide array of lipid peroxidation products (LPPs). Among them are several highly reactive products with terminal electrophilic carbonyl groups (oxoLPPs), which can covalently react with different nucleophilic molecules, including proteins. Lysine, histidine, arginine and cysteine residues within the protein backbone are most susceptible to modifications by oxoLPPs via formation of Michael and Schiff base adducts. These reactions are considered to be one of the major pathways of protein carbonyl formation. The protein-oxoLPPs adducts, commonly referred as advanced lipoxidation end products (ALEs), can have negative health effects, being responsible for the loss of protein function. Several studies indicated a role of ALEs in different pathologies, however an exact mechanism of their action is yet to be fully understood. Identification and characterization of ALEs is an essential step in understanding the biological effects of these protein modifications. However, this task requires an extensive chemical characterization of a myriad of aldehyde/keto compounds adducted to peptides and proteins, as well as type of the linkage and adduction sites. High dynamic range of oxoLPP molecular weights, ranging from small aldehydes to truncated phospholipids (PLs) with shortened fatty acyl chains, further complicate this task. Nowadays, mass spectrometry (MS) utilizing soft ionization

* Corresponding Author: M. Rosário Domingues; Mass Spectrometry Centre, QOPNA, Department of Chemistry, University of Aveiro, 3810-193 Aveiro, Portugal; e-mail: mrd@ua.pt; Phone: +351 234 370 698; Fax:+ 351 234 370 084.

techniques, such as electrospray ionization (ESI) and matrix-assisted laser desorption/ionization (MALDI), coupled to liquid chromatography (LC), is one of the commonly used techniques for characterization of protein-oxoLPP adducts. Such MS-based approaches have proven successful in identification of modified peptides and proteins both *in vitro* and *in vivo*. The detailed structural assignment of protein-oxoLPP adducts is usually based on a tandem MS experiments. Presence of specific product ions in MS/MS spectra depends on the chemical structure of oxoLPP as well as on the type of protein-oxoLPP linkage. To improve the sensitivity of MS analysis, specific derivatization and/or enrichment strategies can be used in combination with different MS approaches. This chapter aims to cover the main MS based methodologies currently used to identify lipid-peptide/protein adducts.

1. INTRODUCTION

Lipid peroxidation is an oxidative lipid modification caused by reactive oxygen species (ROS) in response to changes in redox homeostasis. Both enzymatic and non-enzymatic (radical mediated) oxidation reactions are responsible for the *in vivo* lipid oxidation. An increased amount of ROS and reactive nitrogen species (RNS) mediate the formation of a wide array of oxidized lipids, including a highly-diversified class of oxidized lipids carrying reactive carbonyl groups. Many of the lipid peroxidation products (LPP) formed by β-scission of alkoxyl radicals are transformed into strong electrophiles, by gaining a terminal carbonyl functional group (terminal aldehyde). These compounds are capable of reacting with multiple nucleophilic substrates such as amino acid residues in proteins (cysteine, lysine, histidine, and arginine), amino groups in aminophospholipids (phosphatidylethanolamines and phosphatidylserines) and as well as nucleic acids. Such high reactivity of carbonylated LPP (oxoLPP) determines the *in vivo* toxicity of these compounds. The increased production of oxoLPP was demonstrated in several pathological conditions, both in human patients as well as in different animal models. [1–4]

Protein-lipid adducts are generated by the reaction of oxoLPP with proteins, and considered as one of the major routes of protein carbonylation, along with direct oxidation of amino acid residues and reactions with products of glycoxidation. Carbonylation is a non-enzymatic irreversible post-translational modification (PTM) and protein carbonylation via oxoLPP adduction is considered to be pathophysiologically relevant, leading to a loss of target protein function. [5] Additionally, protein-lipid adducts can alter membrane properties including fluidity, permeability, protein assembly and ion transport. [6,7] Elevated levels of protein-oxoLPP adducts have been identified in cardiovascular [8] and neurodegenerative diseases (Parkinson and Alzheimer disease), [1,9–12] associated with inflammatory, immunogenic responses, [13] aging, [14] atherosclerosis, diabetic complications, lupus and multiple sclerosis. [2,4,15] Although protein carbonylation and oxoLPP-protein adducts are usually associated with activation of pro-inflammatory signaling pathways [16–18], recently several authors proposed that these compounds could possibly effect cell signaling pathways responsible for anti-inflammatory activity. [19,20]

Nucleophilic amino acid residues in proteins and peptides can be modified either by low molecular weight electrophilic lipid species that are formed by decomposition of free and phospholipid (PL)-bound polyunsaturated fatty acids (PUFA), or by oxidized electrophilic PL themselves. These electrophilic PL include both saturated and as well as α,β-unsaturated carbonyl compounds formed by oxidative truncation of PUFA in the PL structure. [21–24] Reactions with nucleophilic substrates occur either via reversible Schiff base formation and/or Michael addition, depending on the oxoLPP structure. Such dual mechanism of adduct formation further increases the diversity of products formed. Michael addition leads to the formation of carbonylated proteins, while Schiff base adducts do not carry carbonyl function. Protein-oxoLPP adducts are often referred as lipoxidation adducts and/or advanced lipid peroxidation end products (ALEs) by similarity with advanced glycation end products (AGEs) formed by oxidation of glycated proteins.

Numerous analytical methods were developed for detection, identification and quantification of various ALEs in complex biological samples. Originally, untargeted colorimetric methods have been used to quantify the extent of protein carbonylation. [25,26] More recently, advanced approaches such as antibody-based immunoassays or sensitive mass spectrometry (MS)-based techniques have been introduced. Immunochemistry based detection (Western blot, ELISA, immunoprecipitation, antibody based affinity enrichment) utilizes specific antibodies raised against ALEs or ALEs specific chemical tags. Despite a high sensitivity in detection (usually in a picomole range) [27], the lack of specificity for some antibodies might complicate data interpretation. Moreover, immunochemical detection does not allow structural characterization of the oxoLPP involved in protein adduction, as well as localization of modification sites. Nevertheless, more complete information can be obtained by combining immunochemical approaches with MS analysis. [28]

MS-based analytical protocols play an essential role in the identification of various oxoLPP and oxoLPP-protein adducts (ALEs). Over the last two decades, a highly sensitive and accurate MS technology has emerged, offering additional capabilities for structural characterization of modified biomolecules. However, oxoLPPs and oxoLPP-peptide adducts have relatively low ionization efficiencies in ESI and MALDI-MS due to the presence of the carbonyl group, and can be difficult to detect. Thus, many of the available detection methods rely on specific derivatization of carbonyls prior analytical separation and MS detection in order to increase the sensitivity. [26] MS-based studies of ALEs focused mainly on the detection of protein adducts with selected α, β-unsaturated aldehydes such as 4-hydroxy-nonenal (HNE), malonaldehyde (MDA) and acrolein (ACR), which are known for their high reactivity. [10,28–32] Using these approaches, ALEs formed by low molecular weight oxoLPP have been fairly studied, but little is known about PL-bound oxoLPP-protein adducts.

Despite the increasing interest, chemical diversity of ALEs as well as the mechanisms involved in their formation are far from being fully elucidated. High diversity of potentially reactive oxoLPP, low abundance of ALEs *in vivo*, as well as reversibility of Schiff base and Michael adducts significantly challenge their identification and characterization. This chapter will describe the chemical pathways of oxoLPP-protein adduct formation as well as modern analytical techniques used for their detection. We will discuss the main analytical approaches, with a focus on liquid chromatography (LC) coupled with mass spectrometry (MS) and tandem mass spectrometry (MS/MS), to detect and characterize reactive carbonylated species formed during lipid oxidation and the corresponding lipid-protein adducts.

2. ELECTROPHILIC SPECIES GENERATED BY LIPID PEROXIDATION

Polyunsaturated fatty acids (PUFA), either free or esterified to lipids, can undergo oxidative modifications by selective enzymatic reactions or random radical mediated oxidation. Enzymatic oxidation is more selective in terms of the oxidation products that are generated. For instance, different isoforms of lipoxygenase (LOX), classified originally by the position of selective oxidation (e.g., 5-, 8-, 12- and 15-LOX), produce different oxygenated PUFA. Non-enzymatic oxidations may occur via reaction with reactive oxygen species (ROS), such as hydroxyl radical (generated by Fenton reaction) or singlet oxygen (produced by photo-oxidation). ROS induced lipid oxidation is usually associated with the formation of a large number of diverse LPP species. [7,33,34] This process involves a free radical initiated chain-reaction characterized by three consecutive steps: initiation, propagation, and termination. [7] In the initiation phase, ROS, namely the hydroxyl radical ($^{\cdot}$OH), initiate the chain reaction by radical-mediated abstraction of the bis-allylic hydrogen atom from the PUFA methylene group, to produce a lipid radical (L$^{\cdot}$). The presence of a double bond in PUFA weakens the C–H bonds on the allylic carbon atom and thus facilitates the hydrogen abstraction. The lipid radical (L$^{\cdot}$) react further with molecular oxygen to form a lipid peroxyl radical (LOO$^{\cdot}$), which in turn can abstract another hydrogen atom from an adjacent PUFA to produce a lipid hydroperoxide (LOOH) and a second lipid radical, thus propagating the chain reaction. [7,34,35] Further oxidation of LOOH either by ROS or enzymatic oxidation, can lead to the formation of LPP carrying different functional moieties (e.g., hydroxy, epoxy, carbonyl) introduced into a lipid structure (long chain products) or result in oxidative cleavage with a formation of truncated species. Such oxidative cleavage can occur on both sides of the peroxy group resulting in low molecular weight aldehydes (oxoLPP) or phospholipids with a truncated *sn-2* residue (short chain products) (Figure 1). Moreover, enzymatic and non-enzymatic PUFA oxidation can result in formation of electrophilic eicosanoids bearing cyclopentenone rings [36], while nitrative/nitroxidative stress conditions can induce formation of nitro fatty acids [37] that are reactive towards proteins (Figure 1, Table 1).

The structures and activity of oxidatively modified phospholipids were recently reviewed. [7,23] In general, the LPP produced depends on PUFA composition of lipid mixture as well as oxidative conditions applied. So far, most of the studies addressed low molecular weight LPP formed by oxidation of free PUFA or after PUFA de-esterification from the original lipid. These low molecular weight electrophilic species can be classified according to their structures into alkanals, 2-alkenals and 4-hydroxy-2-alkenal (also named α,β-unsaturated aldehydes), keto-alkenals, and alkanedial (dialdehydes) (Figure 1). The most widely studied oxoLPP are listed in Table 1. Of these, α,β-unsaturated aldehydes (2-alkenals) are more reactive towards proteins and 4-hydroxynonenal (4-HNE) is by far the most investigated electrophilic aldehyde which readily react with peptides and proteins. [3,29,39]

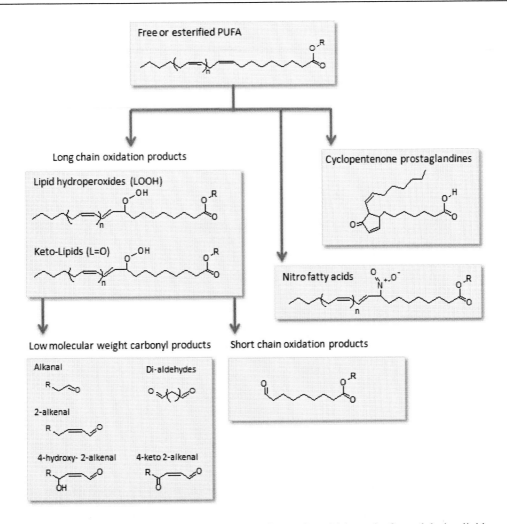

Figure 1. Exemplified structures of reactive electrophilic species which can be formed during lipid oxidation and nitration.

Most of the proteomics approaches dealing with identification of oxoLPP-protein adducts rely on a known set oxoLPP, which potentially are capable of modifying nucleophilic amino acid residues. Thus it is extremely important to identify which carbonylated compounds are formed during *in vivo* lipid peroxidation. HPLC and HPLC-MS or GC-MS have been used to detect, identify and quantify carbonylated oxoLPP in tissues and cells exposed to various pro-oxidative stimuli. As mentioned above, carbonylated LPP have relatively low ionization efficiencies in ESI-MS, and thus difficult to detect. Additionally, many of the low molecular weight oxoLPP are very volatile and can be easily lost during sample preparation. Thus, most of the strategies to study oxoLPP rely on a derivatization step prior analytical separation and mass spectrometry detection. Derivatization of oxoLPP with 2,4-dinitrophenylhydrazine (DNPH) is a popular approach. Classical works by Esterbauer (39,40) demonstrated the applicability of DNPH derivatization followed by HPLC separation and MS detection for identification of different classes of oxoLPP in *in vitro* and *in vivo* samples. DNPH derivatized aldehydes were also analyzed by MS using atmospheric pressure chemical ionization [41] and MALDI-MS as well. [25]

Table 1. Main electrophilic lipid peroxidation products (oxoLPP) known to form protein adduct. OxoLPP class, protein adduct type (Schiff base and Michael adducts), and corresponding mass increments are listed for each oxoLPP. MA- Michael adduct, SB- Schiff base adduct, PC - phosphatidylcholine

	Adduct type	Selected Examples	MA mass increment	SB mass increment
Low molecular weight carbonyl species				
Alkanals	SB	Pentanal	86	68
		Hexanal	100	82
Alkenals	SB, MA and cross links	Acrolein	56	38
		Crotonaldehyde	70	52
		2-pentenal	84	66
		2 –hexenal	98	80
		2-octenal	126	108
		2,4-heptadienal	110	92
		2,4-decadienal	152	134
4-hydroxy – - 2-alkenals	SB, MA and cross links	4-hydroxy-2-nonenal 4-hydroxy-2-hexenal 4-hydroxy-2,6-nonadienal 4-hydroxy-2,6-dodecadienal 4-hydroxy-2,6,9-dodecatrienal	156 114 154 196 194	138 96 136 178 176
Keto-alkenals	SB, MA and cross links	4-oxo-2-nonenal	154	136
Alkanedial(dialdehydes)	SB and cross links	Glyoxal	58	40
		Malonaldehyde	72	54
Modified fatty acids				
Nitro fatty acids	MA	Nitro-oleic acid	327	
		Nitro-linoleic acid	325	
		Nitro-arachidonic acid	349	
Cyclopentenone-containing compounds with α,β-unsaturated carbonyl moieties				
Prostanglandins	MA	Prostaglandin A1	336	
Isoprostanes	MA	15-Deoxy-Delta-12,14-prostaglandin J2	316	
Levuglandins	MA	Levuglandin E_2	352	
Phospholipids with reactive carbonyl moieties				
PC with truncated fatty acyl chains	SB and MA	1-Palmitoyl-2 (5 –oxo-valeroyl) PC	594	576
		1-Palmitoyl -2- **oxo-nonanoyl**- PC	650	632

OxoLPP has also been analyzed by gas chromatography (GC)–MS after derivatization with O-(2,3,4,5,6-pentafluoro-benzyl)hydroxylamine (PFBOA). [42–44] In a targeted approach using isotopically labeled standards, acrolein, hydroxy-nonenanal and hydroxy-hexenal were detected and quantified in brain tissue biopsy of patients with preclinical Alzheimer's disease. [9,45] Recently, we reported a new derivatization method for simultaneous detection of low and high (phospholipid-esterified) molecular weight oxoLPP based on the reaction with 7-(diethylamino)coumarin-3-carbohydrazide (CHH). [46] Using this approach coupled with direct infusion MS and MS/MS detection, we were able to identify 122 different oxoLPP using *in vitro* oxidized mixtures of phosphatidylcholine vesicles containing four different polyunsaturated fatty acids - oleic, linoleic, arachidonic and docosahexaenoic. [46] Several other regents were also proposed for oxoLPP labeling followed by LC-MS analysis, including dimedone, [47,48] cyclohexanedione, [49] modified Girard's reagent, [50] and several others. For a comprehensive review on this subject, readers are referred to Berdyshev et al. [51]

Complimentary to low molecular weight reactive carbonyls, several studies were focused on detection and characterization of PL-bound oxoLPP (Table 1). The majority of these species were observed in different *in vitro* model systems of PL oxidation, but some were also detected in biological samples. [4,34,35,52,53] PL-bound oxoLPP were identified in oxidized phosphatidylcholines (PC), [56,57] phosphatidylethanolamines (PE), [55] phosphatidylserines (PS) [58,59] and cardiolipin (CL) [21,60,61] samples.

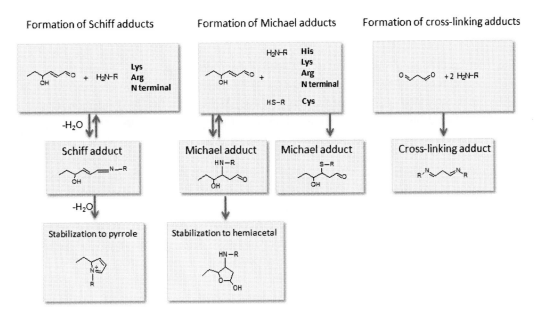

Figure 2. Mechanisms of Schiff base, Michael adducts and cross-link formation between oxoLPP (HNE and malondialdehyde) and nucleophilic amino acids residues (Lys, His, Cys and Arg).

Despite the increasing number of available analytical tools, there are no evidences on how the measured levels of oxoLPP reflect the biological amounts of reactive electrophilic compounds produced *in vivo*. Due to the high reactivity of oxoLPP towards multiple nucleophilic substrates as well as quick biological detoxification by phase I and II enzymes, a cumulative measure of free and adducted oxoLPP should be considered to estimate the amount of oxoLPP produced in biological systems.

As previously mentioned, protein-oxoLPP adducts are formed in a reaction between oxoLPP carbonyl group (especially the terminal carbonyl aldehydes) and nucleophilic amino acid residues via Schiff base or Michael addition mechanisms. Schiff bases are reversible covalent adducts formed between the amine group of Lys or Arg residues and electrophilic lipid species (Figure 2). Thus alkanals can only be linked to amines via Schiff base adducts. Michael addition reaction occur between nucleophilic functional groups of His, Lys, Cys residues and α,β-unsaturated carbonyls (Figure 2). α,β-Unsaturated aldehydes comprise both 2-alkenal, 4-hydroxy-2-alkenal and keto-alkenals. These compounds are the most reactive oxoLPP and can form both Michael and Schiff base adducts (Table 1). Although both Schiff base and Michael adducts are reversible, the latter are usually more stable. Michael adducts with 4-hydroxy-alkenals are usually stabilized via intramolecular cyclization, with the formation of hemiacetals (Figure 2), while Schiff base adducts with histidine can be stabilized by the formation of a pyrrole ring with a loss of water molecule.

3. APPLICATION OF MASS SPECTROMETRY TO STUDY LOW MOLECULAR WEIGHT LPP –PEPTIDE/PROTEIN ADDUCTS (ALEs)

Bottom-up proteomics is a common method to study protein-oxoLPP adducts by MS (Figure 3). In a classical bottom-up approach, the protein mixture containing protein-oxoLPP adducts (ALEs) is subjected to enzymatic hydrolysis, for example by trypsin, and resulting peptides are subsequently analyzed by LC-MS. Modification specific derivatization and enrichment methods can be introduced prior LC-MS analysis to improve the sensitivity in detection and structural characterization of ALEs. ALEs specific derivatization can be performed either before or after enzymatic digestion of the protein mixture [28,65–67]. Most of the available protocols rely on chemical labeling of reactive carbonyl groups retained on peptide after oxoLPP Michael addition reaction. Thus, hydrazine/hydrazide or hydroxylamine based probes are widely used for carbonyl derivatization. Derivatization with carbonyl reactive biotinylated probes, [27] Girards P reagent, [62] or click chemistry probes [63,64] offers the possibility to enrich derivatized oxoLPP-peptide adducts. Such enrichment strategies prior to LC-MS analysis allows increased sensitivity and specificity in identification of oxoLPP-peptide adducts. [8] For instance, using biotin-conjugated carbonyl specific probes (e.g., biotin hydrazide or aldehyde reactive probe) modified peptides can be enriched by avidin-biotin affinity chromatography prior to LC-MS analysis. [64,65] It is important to note that protein-oxoLPP Schiff base adducts cannot be derivatized using carbonyl reactive probes due to the absence of available carbonyl function. As an exception, Schiff base adducts formed with di-carbonyl compounds such as malodialdehyde can still be derivatized using the second carbonyl function. Thus usually, peptide-oxoLPP Schiff base adducts has to be assessed by LC-MS directly without derivatization and enrichment. However, due to the instability of the Schiff base, it might be of helpful to reduce them to the corresponding amines, prior to enzymatic digestion and LC-MS analysis. [28,68,69]

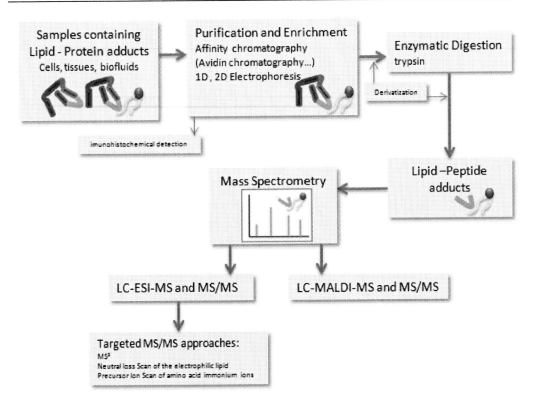

Figure 3. Schematic representation of bottom-up MS-based proteomics workflow used to study of oxoLPP-protein adducts.

LC-MS based techniques addressed so far were widely applied for *in vivo* and *in vitro* identification of protein/peptide adducts with small electrophilic LPP formed by degradation of lipid peroxides. Till date, most of the published studies focused on the identification of protein/peptide adducts with highly reactive α,β-unsaturated aldehydes. For instance, 4-hydroxy-nonenal (4-HNE) is one of the most reactive aldehydes generated by oxidation of n-6 PUFA such as linoleic and arachidonic acids, which are present at high content in membrane phospholipids, triglycerides and low density lipoproteins. Thus, protein-HNE adducts were addressed in multiple studies. [3,29,30,39]

Originally, *in vitro* studies, based on a co-incubation of pure peptides and proteins with selected oxoLPP, have been used to identify the chemical nature of the ALEs. The majority of these studies utilized MS and tandem MS (MS/MS) analysis to characterize structural features of new adducts. These experiments were mostly performed using soft ionization techniques such as matrix-assisted laser desorption/ionization (MALDI) [70,71] and/or electrospray ionization (ESI), which allowed to avoid in-source fragmentation of adducts. Both MALDI and ESI can be coupled off- and on-line to LC prior to MS detection. [29,68,72–76] ALEs are generally analyzed in positive ion mode as singly ($[M+H]^+$) or multiple ($[M+nH]^{n+}$) protonated species. MALDI ionization usually results in singly protonated quasimolecular ions, whereas ESI more often generates multiply protonated species. Using MS, the peptide-oxoLPP adducts can be detected as a new ions with a particular mass increment in regard to the corresponding ion of a non-modified peptide. Based on the calculated mass increment between non-modified peptide ion and new ion formed after oxoLPP co-incubation, the nature of oxoLPP as well as addition chemistry can be deduced. Thus, the mass increment for peptide-oxoLPP Michael adducts will be equal to the molecular weight of reactive oxoLPP, whereas mass increment of Schiff base adduct will be 18 mass units (u) less than oxoLPP molecular weight, due to the loss of water molecule during Schiff base formation.

Mass increments which correspond to the most common low molecular weight oxoLPP-peptide Michael and Schiff base adducts are listed in Table 1. To retrieve the mass increment from recorded MS data, it is important to take into account the charge state of detected ion that belongs to the oxoLPP-peptide adduct. Thus, for HNE Michael adducts the mass increment correspond to 156 u (HNE molecular weight) and can be retrieved directly when singly charged ions were detected. In a case of doubly or triply charged ions, the observed mass-to-charge (m/z) increments would be 84 and 52 u, respectively. To obtain the mass increment, these values should be multiplied by the charge of corresponding ion.

Identification of ALEs in biological samples requires not only to specify the oxoLPP compound which reacted with a peptide, but also to retrieve a peptide sequence which will allow to identify corresponding protein as well as to localize the addition site. This information can be obtained by performing gas phase fragmentation reactions of oxoLPP-peptide ions and assignment of obtained fragments using tandem mass spectrometry. Usually, such fragmentation is induced by collision induced dissociation (CID), promoted by collisions of isolated oxoLPP-peptide ions (precursor ion) with inert gas molecules (e.g., He, Ar or N_2). Obtained product ions can be used to elucidate the peptide sequence and position of oxoLPP addition. CID fragment spectra (MS/MS spectra) of ALEs formed by low molecular weight aldehydes typically show three main types of product ions: *(i)* product ions arising from the peptide backbone cleavage, usually named as *b* and *y* ions, which allow identification of peptide sequence and oxoLPP addition site (Figure 4); *(ii)* immonium ions of modified amino acids (mainly observed when addition occur on histidine), which allow identification of modified amino acid residue but not the position within the peptide sequence; *(iii)* product ions formed by the loss of oxoLPP from corresponding amino acid residue, which can confirm mass increment of reactive oxoLPP and peptide sequence, but would not allow to localize the modification site. However, the relative abundance of each of these ion types in certain MS/MS spectrum will depend on the peptide sequence, oxoLPP and adduct type as well as instrumental conditions used. [28,69]

Instrumental conditions have an important influence on the quality of the information which can be retrieved from the MS/MS spectrum. ESI-CID-MS/MS spectra usually show informative product ions which correspond to the cleavage of peptide backbone, yielding predominantly *y* and *b* type ions. However, major neutral losses can be observed from Schiff base modified amino acid residues (Figure 4). On the other hand, MALDI-MS/MS spectra of ALEs show predominantly ions corresponding to oxoLPP neutral losses both for Schiff base and Michael adducts. [71] As a consequence, the modified peptide backbone fragment ions are low abundant, which makes difficult or even impossible to retrieve information about the site of modification. [30,71] Thus, dominant neutral losses of oxoLPP moiety, specially in the case of Schiff base adducts, significantly challenge the MS/MS spectral analysis of ALEs. One of the ways to avoid this limitation is to increase the stability of oxoLPP-peptide adduct by reducing imine bond of Schiff base. For instance, in several studies the imine group was reduced to the corresponding amine by sodium borohydride ($NaBH_4$) or sodium cyanoborohydride ($NaCNBH_4$). [77,78] The newly formed amine bond stabilizes the linkage, thus allowing generation of peptide backbone product ions with intact modification.

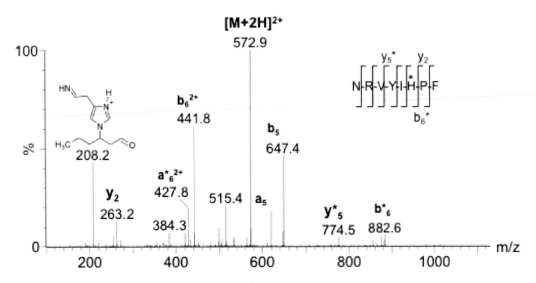

Figure 4. ESI-CID-MS/MS spectrum of $[M+2H]^{2+}$ ion at m/z 572.9 corresponding to the Michael adduct of the 2-hexenal with angiotensin II (NH_2-Asp-Arg-Val-Tyr-Ile-His-Pro-Phe-COOH). (* - modified amino acid residue). The ion at *m/z* 208 corresponds to the immonium ion of hexenal-His Michael adduct.

By defining specific fragmentation pathways of oxoLPP-peptide adducts it is possible to design targeted MS-based strategies, such as precursor ion scanning (PIS), neutral loss scanning (NLS) and multiple reaction monitoring (MRM). Thus, some specific PIS methods rely on formation of immonium ions of modified amino acid residues. For instance, by monitoring immonium ion of reduced Schiff base HNE adduct of histidine (*m/z* 266) all precursor ions carrying this modifications can be identified by PIS. [29,72,79] Alternatively, NLS experiments, based on a specific oxoLPP neutral loss, can be used to identify all precursor ions corresponding to modified peptides in complex protein samples.(80,81) Neutral losses specific for oxoLPP have been used for identification of ALEs in complex protein samples using data-dependent acquisition and neutral loss-driven MS^3 tandem experiments. [81–85]

Despite the advantages of oxoLPP neutral losses for targeted MS approaches, they complicate spectral analysis and thus CID fragmentation of oxoLPP-peptide adducts often do not provide enough information to localize the modification site. When the peptide sequence has only one potentially modifiable amino acid residue, identification of modification site can be rather straightforward. However, in the case when multiple nucleophilic sites are available within the peptide sequence, such assignment is no longer possible. In such cases electron capture dissociation (ECD) or electron transfer dissociation (ETD) can be used as an alternative fragmentation techniques. Due to the more efficient energy transfer, retro-Michael addition is prevented and the oxoLPP-peptide bond remains intact during ECD and ETD fragmentation. At the same time, most of the cleavages occur on the peptide backbone yielding *c*- and *z*-fragment ions, which are useful for the assignment of peptide sequence and localization of modification site. [84,86]

Over the last decades MS have been extensively used to study oxoLPP-peptide adducts *in vitro* and *in vivo*. These studies significantly improved our understanding of oxoLPP reactivity towards proteins and chemical properties of ALEs, thus helping to evaluate the possible biological and pathophysiological role of oxoLPP-proteins adducts. Below we briefly describe some of the MS studies directed towards identification of low molecular weight oxoLPP-protein/peptide adducts.

In vitro studies using biomimetic model systems were performed to investigate the reactivity of selected oxoLPP standards and their mixtures towards peptides and proteins. Thus using LC-ESI-MS/MS and MALDI-MS, Lee et al., identified that co-incubation of angiotensin II (Ang II) with 4-HNE and 4-oxo-nonenal (ONE) result in the formation of corresponding Michael adducts on N-terminal amino group, Arg, and His amino acid residues.[87] These authors also demonstrated time-dependent adduct formation by showing that His-HNE Michael adduct was more abundant at the beginning of the experiment, whereas intensity of Schiff base adduct on the same residue tend to increase in the later stages. Further on, the same authors, using endogenous bioactive peptides, demonstrated that chemistry of ONE and HNE modifications depends on peptide microenvironment and conformation. [87] Silva et al., studied the reactivity of oxoLPP (formed by oxidation of arachidonic acid containing PL) towards Ang II. [71] In this study, Ang II was incubated with oxidized 1-palmitoyl-2-arachidonoyl-glycerophosphatidylcholine (PAPC) and generated adducts were separated by LC and analyzed by MALDI-MS/MS. 26 different low molecular weight oxoLPP, formed by fatty acyl chain oxidative cleavage, reacted with Ang II via Michael and Schiff base addition, leading to 37 distinct ALEs. OxoLPP adduction prevalently took place at the peptide N-terminus or at arginine residue. Histidine was modified via Michael addition by HNE and 2-octenal, while ONE reacted preferentially with arginine side chain, and malondialdehyde addition was confirmed at the N-terminus.

Bottom up proteomics approach was used to identify oxoLPP adducts with model proteins using standard oxoLPP compounds as well as mixtures resulted from PUFA oxidation. [29,30,88–92] Myoglobin-HNE and -ONE adducts were analyzed by LC-MS/MS after tryptic digestion. Several oxoLPP-peptide adducts were identified mainly on His and Lys residues. [93,94] Similarly His-, Cys- and Lys-HNE adducts on glyceraldehyde-3-phosphate dehydrogenase (GAPDH) were detected. [95] Furthermore, the loss of GAPDH activity after co-incubation with HNE was connected with the modification of amino acid residues primarily located on the surface of the protein. [95] Michael adducts of β-lactoglobulin with oxoLPP formed by linoleic acid (LA) oxidation were detected by MALDI-TOF-MS and LC-ESI-MS/MS. Among adducted oxoLPP, keto-octadecenoic acid, a product of LA oxidation, and HNE, ONE and 2-octenal, products of LA oxidative cleavage, were identified. [68,96] Schiff base and Michael adducts of 2,4-decadienal with cytochrome c and ribonuclease A were detected by MALDI-TOF-MS and LC-ESI-MS in another study. [96] Overall, there are a large number of well-designed MS studies dealing with identification of ALEs and several recent reviews were published on this topic. [3,29,69,90,91]

However, the number of *in vivo* studies in which oxoLPP-protein adducts were identified using proteomics approach is relatively low in comparison to the studies performed using standard compounds. Nevertheless, several interesting reports are available. Thus MALDI-MS was used to identify HNE adducts during lupus erytemotosus development and erythrocyte catalase was shown to be modified. [92] Using LC-MS/MS, HNE adducts on heat shock protein 90 were identified in rat model of chronic liver disease. [97] The same approach allowed to identify HNE, ONE and acrolein adducts on several liver proteins using murine model of alcoholic liver disease. [98] HNE Michael adducts on apolipoprotein B-100 were detected in blood plasma by LC-MS/MS analysis. [76] HNE -modified proteins were detected in adipose tissue of lean insulin-sensitive and obese insulin-resistant C57BL/6J mice. [99]

4. APPLICATION OF MASS SPECTROMETRY TO STUDY PHOSPHOLIPID–PEPTIDE/PROTEIN ADDUCTS

In addition to low molecular weight oxoLPP, formed by oxidative cleavage of free or phospholipid (PL) esterified PUFAs, high molecular weight reactive phospholipids (PL) oxidation products with electrophilic properties can be formed by lipid oxidation. [90] Oxidized electrophilic PL with polar head group and modified fatty acyl chain with an aldehyde or a keto moieties (Figure 1) can arise from decomposition of PL hydroperoxides. [7,22,100] Such PL-bound oxoLPP include truncated species resulting from the cleavage on oxidized fatty acyl chain, as well as full length PL carrying newly introduced functional groups (Figure 1).

PL-bound LPP formed during *in vitro* PL oxidation were detected by several research groups. [55,57,101] Moreover, truncated PL-bound LPP were identified in human plasma and atherosclerotic plaques and were proposed to play an important role in the onset of inflammation and immune response. [53] A positive correlation between protein aggregation and PL oxidation was shown for Alzheimer and Parkinson diseases, as well as diabetes and macular degeneration. [102] Using immunoassays, it was proposed that PL-bound oxoLPP react to proteins as well. [103,104] Further *in vitro* studies using head group biotinylated phosphatidylcholine (PC) confirmed that PC-bound electrophilic species can modify small synthetic peptides. Biotin moiety introduced to the PC lipid facilitated enrichment of modified peptides and thus increased the sensitivity of analysis. [105,106]

By similarity to low molecular weight oxoLPP-peptide adducts, reactivity of PL-bound oxoLPP towards different peptides was investigated using *in vitro* biomimetic systems. These models allowed to study ionization, MS detection, CID and ETD fragmentation of PL-bound oxoLPP-peptide adducts. Several adducts between model peptides and oxidized 1-palmitoyl-2-linoleyl-sn-glycero-3-phosphocholine (PLPC) were identified. [107,108] In the study performed by Reis et al., [107] PL-bound oxoLPP-peptide adducts were obtained by co-incubation of leucine encephalin (LeuEnk) with PLPC oxidized by Fenton reaction. Adducts of LeuEnk were identified and characterized by ESI-MS/MS. The oxoLPP reactive towards LeuEnk were identified as truncated oxidized PL carrying terminal aldehyde function derived from oxidative cleavage of LA. The most abundant adducts with N-terminal amino group of LeuEnk were derived from 1-palmitoyl-2-(9-oxo-nonanoyl)-glycerophosphocholine (Schiff adduct), and 1-palmitoyl-2-(8-hydroxy-11-oxo-9-undecenoyl)-glycerophosphocholine (Schiff and Michael adducts).

As mentioned earlier, CID tandem mass spectra of low molecular weight oxoLPP-peptide adducts are usually dominated by ions corresponding to the neutral loss of oxoLPP and also by ions corresponding to peptide backbone cleavage (*y* and *b* ion series). In contrast, under CID conditions oxidized PC-peptide adducts fragment with a loss of trimethylamine (-59 u), PC polar head group (-183 u), and fatty acyl chain from *sn-1* position. Additionally a product ion at m/z 184.1, corresponding to the charged phosphatydilcholine is usually formed. [56,109] CID tandem mass spectra of Schiff base (Fig. 5, A) and Michael (Fig. 5, B) adducts of LeuEnk and 1-palmitoyl-2-(8-hydroxy-11-oxo-9-undecenoyl)-glycerophospho choline are exemplified in Figure 5. Product ions corresponding to the peptide backbone cleavages (*b* and *y* ions) usually are low abundant. Such differences between the CID fragmentation patterns of low molecular weight and PC-bound oxoLPP-peptide adducts are most probably due to preferential charge retention on PC polar head, while in the case of low molecular weight oxoLPP the charge is retained on a peptide backbone.

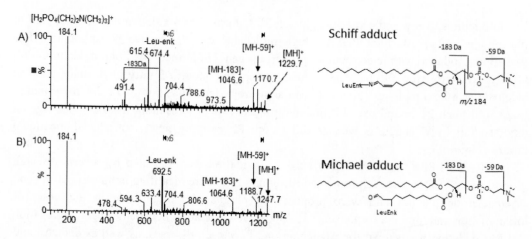

Figure 5. ESI-CID-MS/MS spectra of the [M+H]$^+$ ions corresponding to Schiff base (A; *m/z* 1229.7) and Michael (B; *m/z* 1241.7) adducts of LeuEnk with 2-(8-hydroxy-11-oxo-9-undecenoyl)-glycerophosphocholine.

Using nanoUPLC-MS and model peptides, Milic et al., identified peptide adducts with truncated and oxidized PC species obtained by *in vitro* PLPC oxidation. [108] Using three model peptides (Ac-PAAPAAPAPAEXTPV-OH, where X= Cys, His or Lys), Lys residue was shown to be adducted with 1-palmitoyl-2-(9-hydroxy-12-oxo-dodecendioic acid)- and 1-palmitoyl-2-(9-keto-10,12-octadecadienoic acid)-glycerophosphocholine. Interestingly, adducts between PC-bound oxoLPP and Cys or His residues were not observed. However, adducts with low molecular weight oxoLPP formed by linoleic acid oxidative cleavage were identified on all three nucleophilic amino acid residues.

Using biotinylated oxidized PC species, Porter and coworkers demonstrated that truncated PC-bound oxoLPP can form adducts with model peptide and human serum albumin. [110] These authors also studied adducts between oxidized truncated PC and apolipoprotein A1 (Apo A1) by LC-MS/MS. Plasma samples were supplemented with oxidized biotinylated PC and adducts between Apo A1 and PC-bound 9,12-dioxo-10(E)-dodecenoic acid (KODA), 9-hydroxy, 12-oxo-10(E)-dodecenoic acid (HODA), 7-oxoheptanoic acid, 8-oxooctanoic acid, and 9-oxononanoic acid were identified. [105] Due to the possibility to enrich biotinylated oxoPC-peptide adducts with avidin affinity chromatography, this approach might be very useful for identification of modified proteins in complex biological samples.

5. DERIVATIZATION APPROACHES TO STUDY PROTEINS CARBONYLATED BY OXOLPP

Although mass spectrometric detection of carbonylated proteins and their modification sites does not necessarily require derivatization and can be achieved by considering the corresponding mass increments of modifiable amino acid residues, the derivatization approach often results in increased specificity and sensitivity of MS detection. [26] *In vivo* protein carbonylation is a low abundant post-translational modification and often requires an enrichment step at the protein or peptide level to increase sensitivity. Additionally, carbonylated peptides have lower ionization efficiency due to the modification of nucleophilic sites, which are required for efficient ionization in positive ion mode (e.g., side chain amino group of lysine residues). Among the derivatization reagents used in the field of protein carbonylation, DNPH, biotin hydrazide and aldehyde reactive probe are the most commonly used.

From the classical studies by Levine and Stadmann, DNPH was used for derivatization of protein bound carbonyls, followed by spectrophotometric, HPLC, and finally MS detection. [111] Availability of anti-DNPH antibodies enabled the development of "oxyblot" technique, with is often coupled with MS to identify the protein bands detected on the corresponding Western blots. [112] Despite the widespread applications of "oxyblot" technique, several drawbacks were reported, including the mismatching of DNPH-labelled proteins from the "oxyblot" with unlabeled proteins in corresponding gel used for MS analysis. DNPH labelling can influence the mobility of the proteins in the gel and moreover low abundant carbonylated proteins can be masked by high abundant ones present on the same position in the gel. [113,114] Several gel-free MS approaches based on DNPH-derivatization of carbonylated proteins were developed. [115,116] Recently, we reported a new approach based on the ability of DNPH group to absorb the laser energy in MALDI ionization source. [117] Thus, proteins were digested with trypsin, modified peptides were derivatized with DNPH, separated by hydrophilic interaction chromatography and analyzed by laser desorption ionization (LDI) using DNPH as reactive matrix. DNPH-derivatized carbonylated peptides were preferentially ionized in comparison to unmodified peptides. Such "MS enrichment" allowed to compose an "inclusion list" containing *m/z* values of potentially modified peptides, which was used in consecutive RP-ESI-MS/MS analysis for further separation and identification of modified sequences. Using this approach it was possible to identify more than 200 carbonylated proteins and 643 carbonylation sites in a HeLa cell model of mild oxidative stress. [118]

Another popular derivatization reagent used for the analysis of protein carbonylation is biotin hydrazide, which reacts with carbonyl groups to form the corresponding Schiff bases. These Schiff bases are usually reduced to generate more stable amines, which require an additional sample preparation step. However, introduction of biotin moiety into carbonylated proteins or peptides allows to perform an affinity based enrichment on avidin coated columns. This approach was successfully applied for identification of carbonylated proteins in human plasma from healthy subjects, [119] in blood of diabetic and lean rats, [120] and plasma samples from breast cancer patients.[91] Using this approach, different types of protein carbonyls were identified including the direct oxidation products and reactive oxoLPP adducts. O-(biotinylcarbazoylmethyl) hydroxylamine, known as aldehyde reactive probe

(ARP) represents another example of biotin-conjugated derivatization reagent. The hydroxylamine group of ARP reacts with carbonyls leading to the formation of more stable aldoxime/ketoxime derivatives. ARP derivatization followed by avidin affinity enrichment and ESI-MS/MS detection was applied to study LPP derived modification on thioredoxin incubated with HNE *in vitro* [121] and in THP-1 cell cultures treated with HNE. [122]

Despite the large variety of labelling reagents available to tag carbonylated proteins, several major analytical considerations should be made prior selection of a derivatization strategy. [26] First and foremost, any derivatization reagent should provide quantitative labelling efficiency independent from the structure of the modification (e.g., aldehyde or ketone). This requires selection of optimal reaction conditions. Recently, labelling efficiencies of DNPH, biotin hydrazide and ARP towards aldehydes and ketones were compared using model carbonylated peptides and it was possible to optimize the derivatization conditions to achieve quantitative labelling for ARP. [123] Another important consideration is MS/MS behavior of the derivatized carbonylated peptides since tag-specific ions as well as neutral losses, formed during gas-phase fragmentation, can complicate the data analysis, especially when conventional search engines (e.g., Sequest, Mascot) are used to process high-throughput proteomics data. Using HNE modified model peptides, it was demonstrated that CID fragmentation of biotin hydrazide derivatized peptides result in numerous neutral losses corresponding to biotin hydrazide with or without HNE almost from each *b*- and *y*-fragment ion. This can be avoided when ETD fragmentation is applied. In turn, CID fragmentation of DNPH or ARP derivatized HNE-modified peptides resulted in representative fragment spectra which can be used for the identification of peptide sequences. [123]

CONCLUSION

A broad number of aldehyde and keto compounds can be formed during *in vivo* lipid oxidation, and each of them have the capability to modify nucleophilic amino acid residues via different addition mechanisms. Due to the complexity and large number of peptide/protein-oxoLPP adducts as well as limitations of existing techniques, there is no single analytical approach which can be used for identification of all oxidative modifications in the proteome of cells, tissues or body fluids. Thus, combined and integrated analytical approaches are required to identify proteins modified by oxidized lipids and determine a biological role of such modifications. Numerous MS based techniques were developed to assist identification of modified lipidomes and proteomes. MS is capable to provide information not only about the identity of modified lipid or protein, but also to specify the sites of modifications and, in several cases, to define the structure and propose the mechanism of formation. Recent success of high-throughput "omics" techniques allowed to obtain large datasets indicating non-random nature of lipid and protein carbonylation which can further allow us to understand the pathophysiological mechanisms of "carbonyl stress" related to human disorders.

ACKNOWLEDGMENTS

Thanks are due to Fundação para a Ciência e a Tecnologia (FCT, Portugal), European Union, QREN, FEDER, and COMPETE for funding the QOPNA research unit (project PEst-C/QUI/UI0062/2013; FCOMP-01-0124-FEDER-037296), and RNEM (REDE/1504/REM /2005 that concerns the Portuguese National Mass Spectrometry Network). Financial support from the European Regional Development Fund (ERDF, European Union and Free State Saxony) is gratefully acknowledged. Participants are members of COST Action CM1001.

REFERENCES

[1]   Zarkovic K. 4-Hydroxynonenal and neurodegenerative diseases. *Mol Aspects Med.* 2003; 24: 293–303.

[2]   Mattson MP. Roles of the lipid peroxidation product 4-hydroxynonenal in obesity, the metabolic syndrome, and associated vascular and neurodegenerative disorders. *Exp Gerontol.* 2009 ;44:625-33.

[3]   Spickett CM. The lipid peroxidation product 4-hydroxy-2-nonenal: Advances in chemistry and analysis. *Redox Biol.* 2013;1:145–52.

[4]   Niki E. Biomarkers of lipid peroxidation in clinical material. *BBA- Gen Sub.* 2014; 1840: 809–817.

[5]   Zarkovic N. 4-Hydroxynonenal as a bioactive marker of pathophysiological processes. *Mol Aspects Med.* 2003;24:281–91.

[6]   Stemmer U, Hermetter A. Protein modification by aldehydophospholipids and its functional consequences. *Biochim Biophys Acta.* 2012 ;1818:2436–45.

[7]   Catalá A. Lipid peroxidation of membrane phospholipids generates hydroxy-alkenals and oxidized phospholipids active in physiological and/or pathological conditions. *Chem Phys Lipids.* 2009;157:1–11.

[8]   Chavez JD, Wu J, Bisson W, Maier CS. Site-specific proteomic analysis of lipoxidation adducts in cardiac mitochondria reveals chemical diversity of 2-alkenal adduction. *J Proteomics;* 2011;74:2417–29.

[9]   Bradley MA, Xiong-Fister S, Markesbery WR, Lovell MA. Elevated 4-hydroxyhexenal in Alzheimer's disease (AD) progression. *Neurobiol Aging.* 2012;33:1034–44.

[10]   Perluigi M, Coccia R, Butterfield DA. 4-Hydroxy-2-Nonenal, a Reactive Product of Lipid Peroxidation, and Neurodegenerative Diseases: A Toxic Combination Illuminated by Redox Proteomics Studies. *Antioxidants Redox Signal.* 2012; 1590–609.

[11]   Butterfield DA, Reed T, Sultana R. Roles of 3-nitrotyrosine- and 4-hydroxynonenal-modified brain proteins in the progression and pathogenesis of Alzheimer's disease. *Free Radic Res.* 2011;45:59–72.

[12]   Perluigi M, Sultana R, Cenini G, Di Domenico F, Memo M, Pierce WM, et al. Redox proteomics identification of 4-hydroxynonenal-modified brain proteins in Alzheimer's disease: Role of lipid peroxidation in Alzheimer's disease pathogenesis. *Proteomics Clin Appl.* 2009;3:682–93.

[13]   Dalle-Donne I, Giustarini D, Colombo R, Rossi R, Milzani A. Protein carbonylation in human diseases. *Trends Mol Med.* 2003;9: 169–76.

[14] Baraibar MA, Ladouce R, Friguet B. Proteomic quantification and identification of carbonylated proteins upon oxidative stress and during cellular aging. *J Proteomics.* 2013;92:63–70.

[15] Wang G, Pierangeli SS, Papalardo E, Ansari GAS, Khan MF. Markers of oxidative and nitrosative stress in systemic lupus erythematosus: correlation with disease activity. *Arthritis Rheum.* 2010;62:2064–72.

[16] Petersen DR, Doorn JA. Reactions of 4-hydroxynonenal with proteins and cellular targets. *Free Rad Biol Med.* 2004;37:937–45.

[17] Leonarduzzi G, Robbesyn F, Poli G. Signaling kinases modulated by 4-hydroxynonenal. *Free Radic Biol Med.* 2004;37: 1694–702.

[18] Negre-Salvayre A, Coatrieux C, Ingueneau C, Salvayre R. Advanced lipid peroxidation end products in oxidative damage to proteins. Potential role in diseases and therapeutic prospects for the inhibitors. *Br J Pharmacol.* 2008;153:6–20.

[19] Valacchi G, Pagnin E, Phung A, Nardini M, Schock BC, Cross CE, et al. Inhibition of NFkappaB activation and IL-8 expression in human bronchial epithelial cells by acrolein. *Antioxid Redox Signal.* 2005;7:25–31.

[20] Groeger AL, Freeman BA. Signaling actions of electrophiles: anti-inflammatory therapeutic candidates. *Mol Interv.* 2010;10:39–50.

[21] Domingues MRM, Reis A, Domingues P. Mass spectrometry analysis of oxidized phospholipids. *Chem Phys Lipids.* 2008;156:1–12.

[22] Fruhwirth GO, Loidl A, Hermetter A. Oxidized phospholipids: From molecular properties to disease. *Biochim Biophys Acta - Mol Basis Dis.* 2007;1772 :718–36.

[23] Reis A, Spickett CM. Chemistry of phospholipid oxidation. *Biochim Biophys Acta.* 2012;1818:2374–87.

[24] Ullery JC, Marnett LJ. Protein modification by oxidized phospholipids and hydrolytically released lipid electrophiles: Investigating cellular responses. *Biochim Biophys Acta.* 2012;1818:2424–35.

[25] Teuber K, Fedorova M, Hoffmann R, Schiller J. 2,4-Dinitrophenylhydrazine as a New Reactive Matrix to Analyze Oxidized Phospholipids by MALDI-TOF Mass Spectrometry. *Anal Lett.* 2012;45: 968–76.

[26] Fedorova M, Bollineni RC, Hoffmann R. Protein carbonylation as a major hallmark of oxidative damage: Update of analytical strategies. *Mass Spectrom Rev.* 2014;33:79-97.

[27] Codreanu SG, Zhang B, Sobecki SM, Billheimer DD, Liebler DC. Global analysis of protein damage by the lipid electrophile 4-hydroxy-2-nonenal. *Mol Cell Proteomics.* 2009;8:670–80.

[28] Vasil'ev Y V., Tzeng SC, Huang L, Maier CS. Protein modifications by electrophilic lipoxidation products: Adduct formation, chemical strategies and tandem mass spectrometry for their detection and identification. *Mass Spectrom Rev.* 2014, 33, 157-182.

[29] Carini M, Aldini G, Facino RM. Mass spectrometry for detection of 4-hydroxy-*trans*-2-nonenal (HNE) adducts with peptides and proteins. *Mass Spectrom Rev.* 2004;23:281–305.

[30] Sayre LM, Lin D, Yuan Q, Zhu X, Tang X. Protein adducts generated from products of lipid oxidation: focus on HNE and one. *Drug Metab Rev.* 2006;38:651–75.

[31] Ishii T, Kumazawa S, Sakurai T, Nakayama T, Uchida K. Mass spectroscopic characterization of protein modification by malondialdehyde. *Chem Res Toxicol.* 2006;19:122–9.

[32] Aldini G, Orioli M, Carini M. Protein modification by acrolein: Relevance to pathological conditions and inhibition by aldehyde sequestering agents. *Mol Nutr Food Res.* 2011;55: 1301–19.

[33] Reis A, Spickett CM. Chemistry of phospholipid oxidation. *Biochim Biophys Acta.* 2012;1818:2374–87.

[34] Catalá A. Five Decades with Polyunsaturated Fatty Acids: Chemical Synthesis, Enzymatic Formation, Lipid Peroxidation and Its Biological Effects. *J Lipids.* 2013:710290.

[35] Niki E, Yoshida Y, Saito Y, Noguchi N. Lipid peroxidation: Mechanisms, inhibition, and biological effects. *Biochem Biophys Res Commun.* 2005;338:668–76.

[36] Oeste CL, Pérez-Sala D. Modification of cysteine residues by cyclopentenone prostaglandins: Interplay with redox regulation of protein function. *Mass Spectrom Rev.* 2014;33:110–25.

[37] Baker LMS, Baker PRS, Golin-Bisello F, Schopfer FJ, Fink M, Woodcock SR, et al. Nitro-fatty acid reaction with glutathione and cysteine. Kinetic analysis of thiol alkylation by a Michael addition reaction. *J Biol Chem.* 2007;282:31085–93.

[38] Madian AG, Regnier FE. Proteomic identification of carbonylated proteins and their oxidation sites. *J Proteome Res.* 2010;9:3766–80.

[39] Esterbauer H, Schaur RJ, Zollner H. Chemistry and Biochemistry of 4-hydroxynonenal, malonaldehyde and related aldehydes. *Free Radic Biol Med.* 1991; 9: 81–128.

[40] Esterbauer H, Zollner H Methods for determination of aldehydic lipid peroxidation *Free Radic Biol Med..* 1989;7:197-203

[41] Kölliker S, Oehme M, Dye C. Structure Elucidation of 2,4-Dinitrophenylhydrazone Derivatives of Carbonyl Compounds in Ambient Air by HPLC/MS and Multiple MS/MS Using Atmospheric Chemical Ionization in the Negative Ion Mode. *Anal Chem.* 1998;70:1979–85.

[42] Fitzmaurice PS, Tong J, Yazdanpanah M, Liu PP, Kalasinsky KS, Kish SJ. Levels of 4-hydroxynonenal and malondialdehyde are increased in brain of human chronic users of methamphetamine. *J Pharmacol Exp Ther.* 2006;319:703–9.

[43] Halket JM, Waterman D, Przyborowska AM, Patel RKP, Fraser PD, Bramley PM. Chemical derivatization and mass spectral libraries in metabolic profiling by GC/MS and LC/MS/MS. *J Exp Bot.* 2005;56:219–43.

[44] Kawai Y, Takeda S, Terao J. Lipidomic analysis for lipid peroxidation-derived aldehydes using gas chromatography-mass spectrometry. *Chem Res Toxicol.* 2007;20:99–107.

[45] Bradley MA, Markesbery WR, Lovell MA. Increased levels of 4-hydroxynonenal and acrolein in the brain in preclinical Alzheimer disease. *Free Radic Biol Med.* 2010;48:1570–6.

[46] Milic I, Hoffmann R, Fedorova M. Simultaneous detection of low and high molecular weight carbonylated compounds derived from lipid peroxidation by electrospray ionization-tandem mass spectrometry. *Anal Chem.* 2013;85:156–62.

[47]   Zurek G, Karst U. Liquid chromatography-mass spectrometry method for the determination of aldehydes derivatized by the Hantzsch reaction. *J Chromatogr A.* 1999;864:191–7.

[48]   Williams TI, Lovell MA, Lynn BC. Analysis of derivatized biogenic aldehydes by LC tandem mass spectrometry. *Anal Chem.* 2005;77:3383–9.

[49]   O'Brien-Coker IC, Perkins G, Mallet AI. Aldehyde analysis by high performance liquid chromatography/tandem mass spectrometry. *Rapid Commun Mass Spectrom.* 2001;15:920–8.

[50]   Johnson DW. A modified Girard derivatizing reagent for universal profiling and trace analysis of aldehydes and ketones by electrospray ionization tandem mass spectrometry. *Rapid Commun Mass Spectrom.* 2007;21:2926–32.

[51]   Berdyshev E V. Mass spectrometry of fatty aldehydes. BBA - *MolCell Biol Lipids.* 2011; :680–93.

[52]   Fruhwirth GO, Loidl A, Hermetter A. Oxidized phospholipids: From molecular properties to disease. *BBA - Mol Basis Disease.* 2007; 1772: 718–36.

[53]   Bochkov VN, Oskolkova O V, Birukov KG, Levonen A-L, Binder CJ, Stöckl J. Generation and biological activities of oxidized phospholipids. *Antioxid Redox Signal.* 2010;12:1009–59.

[54]   Reis A, Domingues P, Ferrer-Correia AJ V, Domingues MRM. Tandem mass spectrometry of intact oxidation products of diacylphosphatidylcholines: evidence for the occurrence of the oxidation of the phosphocholine head and differentiation of isomers. *J Mass Spectrom.* 2004;39:1513–22.

[55]   Domingues MRM, Simões C, da Costa JP, Reis A, Domingues P. Identification of 1-palmitoyl-2-linoleoyl-phosphatidylethanolamine modifications under oxidative stress conditions by LC-MS/MS. *Biomed Chromatogr.* 2009;23:588–601.

[56]   Reis A, Domingues P, Ferrer-Correia AJ V, Domingues MRM. Fragmentation study of short-chain products derived from oxidation of diacylphosphatidylcholines by electrospray tandem mass spectrometry: Identification of novel short-chain products. *Rapid Commun Mass Spectrom.* 2004;18:2849–58.

[57]   Reis A, Domingues P, Domingues MRM. Structural motifs in primary oxidation products of palmitoyl-arachidonoyl-phosphatidylcholines by LC-MS/MS. *J Mass Spectrom.* 2013;48:1207–16.

[58]   Maciel E, da Silva RN, Simoes C, Melo T, Ferreira R, Domingues P, Domingues MRM. Liquid chromatography-tandem mass spectrometry of phosphatidylserine advanced glycated end products. *Chem Phys Lipids.* 2013;174:1–7.

[59]   Maciel E, Da Silva RN, Simões C, Domingues P, Domingues MRM. Structural characterization of oxidized glycerophosphatidylserine: Evidence of polar head Oxidation. *J Am Soc Mass Spectrom.* 2011;22:1804–14.

[60]   Reis A, Domingues MRM, Amado FML, Ferrer-Correia AJ, Domingues P. Radical peroxidation of palmitoyl-lineloyl-glycerophosphocholine liposomes: Identification of long-chain oxidised products by liquid chromatography-tandem mass spectrometry. *Chem Phys Lipids.* 2007;855:186–99.

[61]   Maciel E, Faria R, Santinha D, Domingues MR, Domingues P. Evaluation of oxidation and glyco-oxidation of 1-palmitoyl-2-arachidonoyl-phosphatidylserine by LC-MS/MS. *J Chromatogr B Anal Technol Biomed Life Sci.* 2013;929:76–83.

[62] Mirzaei H, Regnier F. Identification and quantification of protein carbonylation using light and heavy isotope labeled Girard's P reagent. *J Chromatogr A.* 2006;1134:122–33.

[63] Vila A, Tallman KA, Jacobs AT, Liebler DC, Porter NA, Marnett LJ. Identification of protein targets of 4-hydroxynonenal using click chemistry for ex vivo biotinylation of azido and alkynyl derivatives. *Chem Res Toxicol.* 2008;21:432–44.

[64] Kim H-YH, Tallman KA, Liebler DC, Porter NA. An azido-biotin reagent for use in the isolation of protein adducts of lipid-derived electrophiles by streptavidin catch and photorelease. *Mol Cell Proteomics.* 2009;8:2080–9.

[65] Codreanu SG, Kim HH, Porter NA, Liebler DC. Biotinylated Probes for the Analysis of Protein Modification by Electrophiles. *Methods Mol Biol.* 2012;803:77-95.

[66] Han B, Stevens JF, Maier CS. Design, synthesis, and application of a hydrazide-functionalized isotope-coded affinity tag for the quantification of oxylipid-protein conjugates. *Anal Chem.* 2007;79:3342–54.

[67] Colzani M, Criscuolo A, De Maddis D, Garzon D, Yeum K-J, Vistoli G, et al. A novel high resolution MS approach for the screening of 4-hydroxy-trans-2-nonenal sequestering agents. *J Pharm Biomed Anal.* 2014 Mar;91:108–18.

[68] Zhu X, Tang X, Anderson VE, Sayre LM. Mass spectrometric characterization of protein modification by the products of nonenzymatic oxidation of linoleic acid. *Chem Res Toxicol.* 2009;22:1386–97.

[69] Colzani M, Aldini G, Carini M. Mass spectrometric approaches for the identification and quantification of reactive carbonyl species protein adducts. *J Proteomics.* 2013;92:28–50.

[70] Fenaille F, Tabet J-C, Guy PA. Identification of 4-hydroxy-2-nonenal-modified peptides within unfractionated digests using matrix-assisted laser desorption/ionization time-of-flight mass spectrometry. *Anal Chem.* 2004;76:867–73.

[71] Silva AMN, Borralho AC, Pinho SA, Domingues MRM, Domingues P. Cross-oxidation of angiotensin II by glycerophosphatidylcholine oxidation products. *Rapid Commun Mass Spectrom.* 2011;25:1413–21.

[72] Orioli M, Aldini G, Beretta G, Facino RM, Carini M. LC-ESI-MS/MS determination of 4-hydroxy-trans-2-nonenal Michael adducts with cysteine and histidine-containing peptides as early markers of oxidative stress in excitable tissues. *J Chromatogr B Anal Technol Biomed Life Sci.* 2005;827:109–18.

[73] Tang X, Sayre LM, Tochtrop GP. A mass spectrometric analysis of 4-hydroxy-2-(E)-nonenal modification of cytochrome C. *J Mass Spectrom.* 2011;46:290–7.

[74] Liu Z, Minkler PE, Sayre LM. Mass spectroscopic characterization of protein modification by 4-hydroxy-2-(E)-nonenal and 4-oxo-2-(E)-nonenal. *Chem Res Toxicol.* 2003;16:901–11.

[75] Zhu X, Sayre LM. Mass spectrometric evidence for long-lived protein adducts of 4-oxo-2-nonenal. *Redox Rep.* 2007;12:45-9.

[76] Obama T, Kato R, Masuda Y, Takahashi K, Aiuchi T, Itabe H. Analysis of modified apolipoprotein B-100 structures formed in oxidized low-density lipoprotein using LC-MS/MS. *Proteomics.* 2007;7:2132–41.

[77] Fritz KS, Kellersberger K a, Gomez JD, Petersen DR. 4-HNE adduct stability characterized by collision-induced dissociation and electron transfer dissociation mass spectrometry. *Chem Res Toxicol.* 2012 ;25:965–70.

[78]   Bolgar MS, Yang CY, Gaskell SJ. First direct evidence for lipid/protein conjugation in oxidized human low density lipoprotein. *J Biol Chem.* 1996;271:27999–8001.

[79]   Aldini G, Regazzoni L, Orioli M, Rimoldi I, Facino RM, Carini M. A tandem MS precursor-ion scan approach to identify variable covalent modification of albumin Cys34: a new tool for studying vascular carbonylation. *J Mass Spectrom.* 2008;43:1470–81.

[80]   Rauniyar N, Stevens SM, Prokai-Tatrai K, Prokai L. Characterization of 4-hydroxy-2-nonenal-modified peptides by liquid chromatography-tandem mass spectrometry using data-dependent acquisition: neutral loss-driven MS3 versus neutral loss-driven electron capture dissociation. *Anal Chem.* 2009;81:782–9.

[81]   Jr SMS, Rauniyar N, Prokai L. Rapid characterization of covalent modifications to rat brain mitochondrial proteins after ex vivo exposure to 4-hydroxy-2-nonenal by liquid chromatography – tandem mass spectrometry using data-dependent and neutral loss-driven MS 3. *J Mass Spectrom.* 2007;1599–605.

[82]   Guo J, Prokai L. To tag or not to tag: a comparative evaluation of immunoaffinity-labeling and tandem mass spectrometry for the identification and localization of posttranslational protein carbonylation by 4-hydroxy-2-nonenal, an end-product of lipid peroxidation. *J Proteomics.;* 2011;74:2360–9.

[83]   Guo J, Prokai-Tatrai K, Nguyen V, Rauniyar N, Ughy B, Prokai L. Protein targets for carbonylation by 4-hydroxy-2-nonenal in rat liver mitochondria. *J Proteomics.;* 2011;74:2370–9.

[84]   Rauniyar N, Prokai L. Detection and identification *Proteomics.* 2009 ;9:5188-93.

[85]   Roe MR, Xie H, Bandhakavi S, Griffin TJ. Proteomic mapping of 4-hydroxynonenal protein modification sites by solid-phase hydrazide chemistry and mass spectrometry. *Anal Chem.* 2007;79:3747–56.

[86]   Fritz KS, Kellersberger K a, Gomez JD, Petersen DR. 4-HNE adduct stability characterized by collision-induced dissociation and electron transfer dissociation mass spectrometry. *Chem Res Toxicol.* 2012;25:965–70.

[87]   Lee SH, Takahashi R, Goto T, Oe T. Mass spectrometric characterization of modifications to angiotensin II by lipid peroxidation products, 4-oxo-2(E)-nonenal and 4-hydroxy-2(E)-nonenal. *Chem Res Toxicol.* 2010;23:1771–85.

[88]   Aldini G, Gamberoni L, Orioli M, Beretta G, Regazzoni L, Maffei Facino R, et al. Mass spectrometric characterization of covalent modification of human serum albumin by 4-hydroxy-trans-2-nonenal. *J Mass Spectrom.* 2006;41:1149–61.

[89]   Ishii T, Ito S, Kumazawa S, Sakurai T, Yamaguchi S, Mori T, et al. Site-specific modification of positively-charged surfaces on human serum albumin by malondialdehyde. *Biochem Biophys Res Commun.* 2008;371:28–32.

[90]   Domingues RM, Domingues P, Melo T, Pérez-Sala D, Reis A, Spickett CM. Lipoxidation adducts with peptides and proteins: Deleterious modifications or signaling mechanisms? *J Proteomics.* 2013;92:110–31.

[91]   Madian AG, Diaz-Maldonado N, Gao Q, Regnier FE. Oxidative stress induced carbonylation in human plasma. *J Proteomics.* 2011;74:2395–416.

[92]   D'souza A, Kurien BT, Rodgers R, Shenoi J, Kurono S, Matsumoto H, Hensley K, Nath SK, Scofield RH.. Detection of catalase as a major protein target of the lipid peroxidation product 4-HNE and the lack of its genetic association as a risk factor in SLE. *BMC Med Genet.* 2008;9:62.

[93] Guichardant M, Chen P, Liu M, Calzada C, Colas R, Véricel E, et al. Functional lipidomics of oxidized products from polyunsaturated fatty acids. *Chem Phys Lipids.* 2011;164:544–8.

[94] Liu Z, Minkler PE, Sayre LM. Mass spectroscopic characterization of protein modification by 4-hydroxy-2-(E)-nonenal and 4-oxo-2-(E)-nonenal. *Chem Res Toxicol.* 2003;16:901–11.

[95] Ishii T, Tatsuda E, Kumazawa S, Nakayama T, Uchida K. Molecular basis of enzyme inactivation by an endogenous electrophile 4-hydroxy-2-nonenal: identification of modification sites in glyceraldehyde-3-phosphate dehydrogenase. *Biochemistry.* 2003;42:3474–80.

[96] Zhu X, Tang X, Zhang J, Tochtrop GP, Anderson VE, Sayre LM. Mass spectrometric evidence for the existence of distinct modifications of different proteins by 2(E),4(E)-decadienal. *Chem Res Toxicol.* 2010 ;23:467–73.

[97] Carbone DL, Doorn JA, Kiebler Z, Petersen DR. Cysteine modification by lipid peroxidation products inhibits protein disulfide isomerase. *Chem Res Toxicol.* 2005;18:1324–31.

[98] Galligan JJ, Smathers RL, Fritz KS, Epperson LE, Hunter LE, Petersen DR. Protein carbonylation in a murine model for early alcoholic liver disease. *Chem Res Toxicol.* 2012;25:1012–21.

[99] Grimsrud PA, Picklo MJ, Griffin TJ, Bernlohr DA. Carbonylation of adipose proteins in obesity and insulin resistance: identification of adipocyte fatty acid-binding protein as a cellular target of 4-hydroxynonenal. *Mol Cell Proteomics.* 2007;6:624–37.

[100] Spiteller G.Peroxyl radicals: inductors of neurodegenerative and other inflammatory diseases. Their origin and how they transform cholesterol, phospholipids, plasmalogens, polyunsaturated fatty acids, sugars, and proteins into deleterious products. *Free Radic Biol Med.* 2006;41:362-87.

[101] O'Donnell VB.Mass spectrometry analysis of oxidized phosphatidylcholine and phosphatidylethanolamine. *Biochim Biophys Acta.* 2011;1811:818-26.

[102] Kinnunen PKJ, Kaarniranta K, Mahalka AK. Protein-oxidized phospholipid interactions in cellular signaling for cell death: from biophysics to clinical correlations. *Biochim Biophys Acta.* 2012;1818:2446–55.

[103] Pegorier S, Stengel D, Durand H, Croset M, Ninio E. Oxidized phospholipid: POVPC binds to platelet-activating-factor receptor on human macrophages. Implications in atherosclerosis. *Atherosclerosis.* 2006;188:433–43.

[104] Hörkkö S, Bird DA, Miller E, Itabe H, Leitinger N, Subbanagounder G, et al. Monoclonal autoantibodies specific for oxidized phospholipids or oxidized phospholipid-protein adducts inhibit macrophage uptake of oxidized low-density lipoproteins. *J Clin Invest.* 1999;103:117–28.

[105] Szapacs ME, Kim HH, Porter NA, Liebler DC. Identification of Proteins Adducted by Lipid Peroxidation Products in Plasma and Modifications of Apolipoprotein A1 with a Novel Biotinylated Phospholipid Probe research articles. 2008;4237–46.

[106] Gugiu BG, Mouillesseaux K, Duong V, Herzog T, Hekimian A, Koroniak L, et al. Protein targets of oxidized phospholipids in endothelial cells. *J Lipid Res.* 2008;49:510–20.

[107] Reis A, Domingues P, Ferrer-Correia AJ V, Domingues MRM. Peptide-Phospholipid Cross-Linking Reactions: Identification of Leucine Enkephalin-Alka(e)nal-

Glycerophosphatidylcholine Adducts by Tandem Mass Spectrometry. *J Am Soc Mass Spectrom.* 2006;17:657–60.

[108] Milic I, Fedorova M, Teuber K, Schiller J, Hoffmann R. Characterization of oxidation products from 1-palmitoyl-2-linoleoyl-sn-glycerophosphatidylcholine in aqueous solutions and their reactions with cysteine, histidine and lysine residues. *Chem Phys Lipids.* 2012;165:186–96.

[109] Domingues P, Domingues MRM, Amado FML, Ferrer-Correia AJ. Characterization of sodiated glycerol phosphatidylcholine phospholipids by mass spectrometry. *Rapid Commun Mass Spectrom.* 2001;15:799–804.

[110] Tallman KA, Kim HH, Ji J, Szapacs ME, Yin H, Mcintosh TJ, et al. Phospholipid - Protein Adducts of Lipid Peroxidation: *Synthesis and Study of New Biotinylated Phosphatidylcholines.* 2007;227–34.

[111] Levine RL, Garland D, Oliver CN, Amici A, Climent I, Lenz AG, et al. Determination of carbonyl content in oxidatively modified proteins. *Methods Enzymol.* 1990;186:464–78.

[112] Goto S, Nakamura A, Radak Z, Nakamoto H, Takahashi R, Yasuda K, et al. Carbonylated proteins in aging and exercise: Immunoblot approaches. *Mechanisms of Ageing Develop.* 1999;107: 245–53.

[113] Castegna A, Aksenov M, Thongboonkerd V, Klein JB, Pierce WM, Booze R, et al. Proteomic identification of oxidatively modified proteins in Alzheimer's disease brain. Part II: dihydropyrimidinase-related protein 2, alpha-enolase and heat shock cognate 71. *J Neurochem.* 2002;82:1524–32.

[114] Tezel G, Yang X, Cai J. Proteomic identification of oxidatively modified retinal proteins in a chronic pressure-induced rat model of glaucoma. *Invest Ophthalmol Vis Sci.* 2005;46:3177–87.

[115] Kristensen BK, Askerlund P, Bykova N V., Egsgaard H, Miller IM. Identification of oxidised proteins in the matrix of rice leaf mitochondria by immunoprecipitation and two-dimensional liquid chromatography-tandem mass spectrometry. *Phytochemistry.* 2004;65:1839–51.

[116] Bollineni RC, Fedorova M, Hoffmann R. Identification of carbonylated peptides by tandem mass spectrometry using a precursor ion-like scan in negative ion mode. *J Proteomics.* 2011;74:2351–9.

[117] Bollineni RC, Hoffmann R, Fedorova M. Identification of protein carbonylation sites by two-dimensional liquid chromatography in combination with MALDI- and ESI-MS. *J Proteomics.* 2011;74:2338–50.

[118] Bollineni RC, Hoffmann R, Fedorova M. Proteome-wide profiling of carbonylated proteins and carbonylation sites in HeLa cells under mild oxidative stress conditions. *Free Radic Biol Med.* 2014;68:186–95.

[119] Madian AG, Regnier FE. Profiling Carbonylated Proteins in Human Plasma research articles. *J Proteome Res.* 2010;9:1330–43.

[120] Madian AG, Myracle AD, Diaz-Maldonado N, Rochelle NS, Janle EM, Regnier FE. Differential Carbonylation of Proteins as a Function of in vivo Oxidative Stress. *J Proteome Res.* 2011;10:3959–72.

[121] Chavez J, Wu J, Han B, Chung W-G, Maier CS. New role for an old probe: affinity labeling of oxylipid protein conjugates by N'-aminooxymethylcarbonylhydrazino d-biotin. *Anal Chem.* 2006;78:6847–54.

[122] Chavez J, Chung W-G, Miranda CL, Singhal M, Stevens JF, Maier CS. Site-specific protein adducts of 4-hydroxy-2(E)-nonenal in human THP-1 monocytic cells: protein carbonylation is diminished by ascorbic acid. *Chem Res Toxicol.* 2010;23:37–47.

[123] Bollineni RC, Fedorova M, Hoffmann R. Qualitative and quantitative evaluation of derivatization reagents for different types of protein-bound carbonyl groups. *Analyst.* 2013;138:5081–8.

In: Reactive Oxygen Species, Lipid Peroxidation …
Editor: Angel Catalá

ISBN: 978-1-63321-886-4
© 2015 Nova Science Publishers, Inc.

Chapter 4

DIAGONAL GEL ELECTROPHORETIC ANALYSIS OF PROTEIN DISULFIDES: PRINCIPLES AND APPLICATIONS

*Xiaoting Luo[1,2], Rongrong Li[2] and Liang-Jun Yan[*2]*

[1]Department of Biochemistry and Molecular Biology, Gannan Medical University, Ganzhou, Jiangxi Province, China
[2]Department of Pharmaceutical Sciences, UNT System College of Pharmacy, University of North Texas Health Science Center, Fort Worth, Texas, US

ABSTRACT

Protein cysteine residues are constantly undergoing redox modifications, and many of them are involved in disulfide formation. In this chapter, we first give an overview of the diagonal gel analysis method for the identification of protein disulfides followed by the application of the method for the identification of mitochondrial proteins that have endogenous disulfide bonds or form disulfide bonds upon oxidative stress. Data that show that the albumin precursor protein could be identified by this method, and that many proteins form disulfide bonds after treatment with diamide are presented. The data presented in this chapter indicate that this diagonal gel analytical method, when used in conjunction with mass spectrometric peptide sequencing, can provide a powerful tool for studying protein disulfide proteomics.

Keywords: Diagonal gel electrophoresis, disulfides, mass spectrometry, mitochondria, redox modifications

---

[*] Corresponding author: Department of Pharmaceutical Sciences, UNT System College of Pharmacy, University of North Texas Health Science Center, 3500 Camp Bowie Blvd, RES-314E, Fort Worth TX 76107, Phone 817-735-2386, Fax 817-735-2603, Email: liang-jun.yan@unthsc.edu.

INTRODUCTION

Protein disulfides are an integral feature of a given proteome [1-3]. They are not only an inherent part of protein structure and function, but also involved in redox signaling and protein-protein interactions [4,5]. While endogenous disulfides are indispensable for numerous redox-sensitive proteins and enzymes [1,6,7], those formed upon oxidative stress are usually involved in stress response and redox signaling [6,8-10]. There are many methods that can be used for the analysis of protein disulfides [11-13]. The diagonal gel analysis has gained increasing attention [13-18].

PRINCIPLES OF DIAGONAL GEL ELECTROPHORESIS

The method is very simple and straight forward, though sometimes tedious. In our opinion, it should have received more applications than it has. Essentially, the approach involves two-dimensional SDS-PAGE [13,16]. Samples for the first dimension are usually not treated with any disulfide-reducing reagent (non-reducing) prior to gel loading and samples for the second dimension usually are treated by a disulfide-reducing reagent (reducing). Following the first dimensional non-reducing gel analysis, the bands are excised and incubated in a reducing buffer that contains a reductant such as dithiothreitol or β-mercaptoethanol. The bands are then over-laid horizontally onto a second dimensional SDS-PAGE. Hence, the two steps of gel analysis are often called non-reducing and reducing. Based on the nature of disulfides that are formed, the diagonal gel can elegantly characterize whether the disulfides are intra- or inter-proteins [13,16]. This is because intra disulfide protein will end up above the diagonal line, while that formed between protein and protein will fall below the diagonal line, and proteins that do not respond to exogenous reductants will stay perfectly on the diagonal line [13,16].

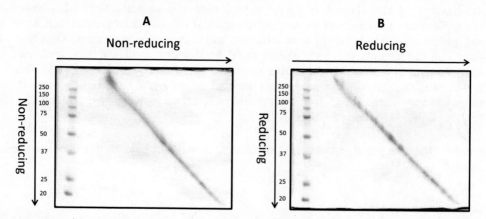

Figure 1. Diagonal gel analysis of kidney mitochondrial proteins. Shown are (**A**): Non-reducing/non-reducing; (**B**) Reducing/reducing. In **A**, protein samples were not treated by β-mercaptoethanol before gel loading, nor the resulting gel bands before applying onto the second dimensional gel. In **B**, samples for both dimensions were treated by β-mercaptoethanol.

APPLICATIONS

1. Analysis of Endogenous Disulfides

To demonstrate the application of this diagonal gel analysis, we first did two controls. One is non-reducing/non-reducing, and the other is reducing/reducing. As shown in Figure 1, the conditions of the experiment did not yield any protein spots that deviate from the diagonal line. Instead, a perfect linear line under both conditions could be visualized (Figure 1).

To analyze whether there are any proteins possessing any endogenous disulfides that can be analyzed by this method, we used liver mitochondria isolated from rats. Mitochondrial samples underwent non-reducing and reducing in the respective dimensions. As shown in Figure 2A, a distinct spot ran above the diagonal line. This spot was then excised and subjected to mass spectrometric peptide sequencing, a total of 17 peptides were obtained that matched the albumin precursor protein (Table 1, left side), indicating the existence of albumin precursor protein in this spot. To confirm further that albumin precursor protein indeed exists in mitochondria, we then analyzed rat kidney mitochondria under the same experimental conditions. As shown in Figure 2B, there was also a spot above the line, which was also sequenced. As a result, 15 peptides were obtained that also matched the albumin precursor protein (Table 1, right side). These findings are in agreement with previous studies that albumin precursor can be localized to mitochondria [19]. Therefore, for the first time, we have shown that mitochondrial albumin precursor protein has endogenous disulfide bonds that can be analyzed by this analytical method. It should be noted that the albumin precursor has 35 cysteine residues, 34 of which are in the form of disulfides. It is likely that the second dimensional reducing gel analysis broke more than one disulfide bridge; nonetheless, it appears that we could only observe one spot above the diagonal line under our experimental conditions. There were other proteins present in each spot, but the abundance of which was much less than that of the albumin precursor protein based on spectral count number that reflects the number of peptides sequenced [20,21]. It should also be noted that the albumin precursor protein has a single free cysteine residue that is highly redox sensitive [22,23]. This cysteine residue theoretically can form a disulfide bond with the same cysteine residue from another albumin precursor molecule, but we could not detect this type of disulfide in our gel analysis.

2. Analysis of Oxidative Stress - Induced Disulfide Formation

To demonstrate the application of this gel method further, we also conducted studies using kidney mitochondria treated with diamide, which is a well-known chemical that can induce the formation of disulfide bonds within the same proteins or between different proteins [24,25]. As shown in Figure 3 after silver staining, which is more sensitive than Coomassie blue staining, many proteins dropped below the diagonal line after treatment with 10 mM (final concentration) of diamide for 1 hour at room temperature. We then selected five spots for mass spectrometric identification. The results are given in table 2. As can be seen in this table, there was only one protein in spot 3 and spot 4, which was ATP synthase subunit b and ADP/ATP translocase 2, respectively. All other spots had more than one protein with spot one containing the highest number of proteins that could be identified. Interestingly, many of these proteins are redox sensitive. For example, actin is known to undergo cysteine oxidation under a variety of experimental conditions [17,26]. Similarly, the cysteine residues of ATP synthase subunit b [27,28] and voltage dependent anion channel-1 are also known to be susceptible to oxidative modifications [29].

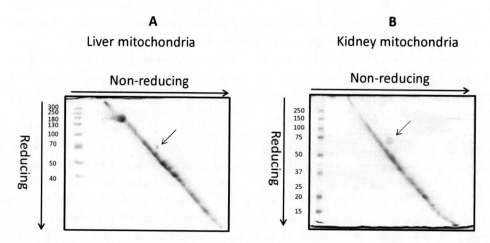

Figure 2. Identification of the albumin precursor protein in both liver (**A**) and kidney (**B**) mitochondria. The arrow indicates the spot excised for mass spectrometric identification. For liver mitochondria, the spot yielded 17 peptides that matched the albumin precursor protein; while for kidney mitochondria, the spot produced 15 peptides that matched the albumin precursor protein.

**Table 1. Peptides obtained from gel spots indicated in Figure 2,
Panels A and B, respectively**

Liver mitochondrial spot (17 peptides)	Kidney mitochondrial spot (15 peptides)
KYEATLEK	LSQKFPK
YEATLEK	DLGEEHFK
FKDLGEQHFK	FKDLGEEHFK
APQVSTPTLVEAAR	HLVDEPQNLIK
LVQEVTDFAK	LKHLVDEPQNLIK
APQVSTPTLVEAAR	KVPQVSTPTLVEVSR
SIHTLFGDK	LVNELTEFAK
QTALAELVK	RHPEYAVSVLLR
FPNAEFAEITK	RHPEYAVSVLLR
RHPDYSVSLLLR	KQTALVELLK
LGEYGFQNAILVR	QTALVELLK
RHPYFYAPELLYYAEK	LGEYGFQNALIVR
RHPYFYAPELLYYAEK	RHPYFYAPELLYYANK
RHPYFYAPELLYYAEK	HPYFYAPELLYYANK
HPYFYAPELLYYAEK	DAFLGSFLYEYSR
DVFLGTFLYEYSR	
GLVLIAFSQYLQK	

Table 2. Proteins identified in the spots indicated in Figure 3

Protein name	MW (Da)	Access number (NCBI)	Spectral count number
Spot 1 (rat)			
Actin	42051.85	46397316	23
Creatine kinase	47331.41	81888398	6
Long-chain specific acyl-CoA dehydrogenase	48241.58	113016	5
Medium-chain specific acyl-CoA dehydrogenase	46924.95	113018	4
Isovaleryl-CoA dehydrogenase	46861.93	125052	3
Cystathionine gamma-lyase	44261.57	1705789	3
3-ketoacyl-CoA thiolase	42243.61	135762	3
Creatine kinase B-type	42983.42	122065316	3
4-hydroxyphenylpyruvate dioxygenase	45311.98	83303639	2
Glutamine synthetase	42981.6	121376	2
Spot 2 (rat)			
ATP synthase subunit gamma	30228.72	728931	3
Voltage-dependent anion channel protein 1	30850.6	46397782	2
Spot 3 (rat)			
ATP synthase subunit b	28964.52	114625	3
Spot 4 (rat)			
ADP/ATP translocase 2	33108.22	728810	2
Spot 5 (rat)			
Peroxiredoxin-3	28566.55	149040547	5
Peroxiredoxin-1	22323.4	2499470	2

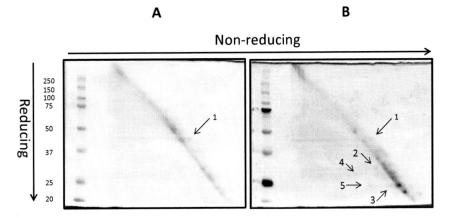

Figure 3. Identification of kidney mitochondrial proteins cross-linked by diamide. Mitochondrial proteins (1 mg/ml) were treated with 10 mM diamide (final concentration) at room temperature for 1 h followed by non-reducing/reducing diagonal gel electrophoresis. The gel was initially visualized by Coomassie blue staining (A), which was followed by silver staining that rendered more protein spots visible (B). Numbers indicate the spots excised for protein identification by mass spectrometric peptide sequencing.

It should be noted that one caveat of this method is that it cannot analyze a mixed disulfide that is formed between glutathione and proteins. This is probably because the glutathione is too small and the mixed disulfide bond is broken; the running pattern of the protein that forms the mixed disulfide bond may not change. Therefore, the method can only analyze protein-protein disulfides.

SUMMARY

In this chapter, we have overviewed the diagonal gel method and demonstrated its utilization by identifying mitochondrial proteins involved in disulfide bond formation. Particularly, we have shown that the albumin precursor protein exists in mitochondria and the inherent disulfide bonds of this protein dictates its running behavior on the diagonal gel as the protein clearly runs above the diagonal line for both kidney and liver mitochondria (Figure 2). Moreover, we also demonstrated that many mitochondrial proteins form disulfide bridges upon treatment with diamide (Figure 3 and Table 2). While the analysis of each identified protein's function is beyond the scope of this chapter, many of the identified proteins have been reported to be redox sensitive in the literature. Nevertheless, it would be interesting to follow some of the identified proteins in future studies, especially in the context of aging and aging-related diseases as well as in ischemic tolerance [30].

ACKNOWLEDGMENTS

Work presented in this chapter was supported in part by National Institutes of Health (R01NS079792 to L.J.Y.). The authors thank Dr. Drake Zhang at ProtTech Inc. for mass spectrometric peptide sequencing.

REFERENCES

[1]   Jacob, C; Battaglia, E; Burkholz, T; Peng, D; Bagrel, D; Montenarh, M. Control of oxidative posttranslational cysteine modifications: from intricate chemistry to widespread biological and medical applications. *Chem Res Toxicol*, 25, (2012), 588-604.

[2]   Go, YM; Jones, DP. Thiol/disulfide redox states in signaling and sensing. *Crit Rev Biochem Mol Biol*, 48, (2013), 173-181.

[3]   Cai, Z; Yan, LJ. Protein oxidative modifications: Beneficial roles in disease and health. *Journal of Biochemical and Pharmacological Research*, 1, (2013), 15-26.

[4]   Yan, LJ. Analysis of oxidative modification of proteins. *Curr Protoc Protein Sci Chapter*, 14, (2009), Unit14 14.

[5]   Go, YM; Jones, DP. The redox proteome. *J Biol Chem*, 288, (2013), 26512-26520.

[6]   Cremers, CM; Jakob, U. Oxidant sensing by reversible disulfide bond formation. *J Biol Chem*, 288, (2013), 26489-26496.

[7] Lizama-Manibusan, B; McLaughlin, B. Redox modification of proteins as essential mediators of CNS autophagy and mitophagy. *FEBS Lett*, 587, (2013), 2291-2298.

[8] Bourdon, E; Blache, D. The importance of proteins in defense against oxidation. *Antioxid Redox Signal*, 3, (2001), 293-311.

[9] Forman, HJ; Fukuto, JM; Miller, T; Zhang, H; Rinna, A; Levy, S. The chemistry of cell signaling by reactive oxygen and nitrogen species and 4-hydroxynonenal. *Arch Biochem Biophys*, 477, (2008), 183-195.

[10] Forman, HJ; Fukuto, JM; Torres, M. Redox signaling: thiol chemistry defines which reactive oxygen and nitrogen species can act as second messengers. *Am J Physiol Cell Physiol*, 287, (2004), C246-256.

[11] Rogers, LK; Leinweber, BL; Smith, CV. Detection of reversible protein thiol modifications in tissues. *Anal Biochem*, 358, (2006), 171-184.

[12] Hochgrafe, F; Mostertz, J; Albrecht, D; Hecker, M. Fluorescence thiol modification assay: oxidatively modified proteins in Bacillus subtilis. *Mol Microbiol*, 58, (2005), 409-425.

[13] McDonagh, B. Diagonal electrophoresis for the detection of protein disulfides. *Methods Mol Biol*, (2012), 309-315.

[14] Xia, K; Manning, M; Hesham, H; Lin, Q; Bystroff, C; Colon, W. Identifying the subproteome of kinetically stable proteins via diagonal 2D SDS/PAGE. *Proc Natl Acad Sci U S A*, 104, (2007), 17329-17334.

[15] Winger, AM; Taylor, NL; Heazlewood, JL; Day, DA; Millar, AH. Identification of intra- and intermolecular disulphide bonding in the plant mitochondrial proteome by diagonal gel electrophoresis. *Proteomics*, 7, (2007), 4158-4170.

[16] Samelson, LE. Diagonal gel electrophoresis. *Curr Protoc Immunol Chapter*, 8, (2001), Unit 8 6.

[17] Fedorova, M; Kuleva, N; Hoffmann, R. Reversible and irreversible modifications of skeletal muscle proteins in a rat model of acute oxidative stress. *Biochim Biophys Acta*, 1792, (2009), 1185-1193.

[18] McDonagh, B; Sheehan, D. Effect of oxidative stress on protein thiols in the blue mussel Mytilus edulis: proteomic identification of target proteins. *Proteomics*, 7, (2007), 3395-3403.

[19] Kiri, AN; Tran, HC; Drahos, KL; Lan, W; McRorie, DK; Horn, MJ. Proteomic changes in bovine heart mitochondria with age: using a novel technique for organelle separation and enrichment. *J Biomol Tech*, 16, (2005), 371-379.

[20] Yan, LJ; Forster, MJ. Resolving mitochondrial protein complexes using nongradient blue native polyacrylamide gel electrophoresis. *Anal Biochem*, 389, (2009), 143-149.

[21] Thangthaeng, N; Sumien, N; Forster, MJ; Shah, RA; Yan, LJ. Nongradient blue native gel analysis of serum proteins and in-gel detection of serum esterase activities. *J Chromatogr B Analyt Technol Biomed Life Sci*, 879, (2011), 386-394.

[22] Fabisiak, JP; Sedlov, A; Kagan, VE. Quantification of oxidative/nitrosative modification of CYS(34) in human serum albumin using a fluorescence-based SDS-PAGE assay. *Antioxid Redox Signal*, 4, (2002), 855-865.

[23] Holderman, MT; Miller, KP; Dangott, LJ; Ramos, KS. Identification of albumin precursor protein, Phi AP3, and alpha-smooth muscle actin as novel components of redox sensing machinery in vascular smooth muscle cells. *Mol Pharmacol*, 61, (2002), 1174-1183.

[24] Yan, LJ; Yang, SH; Shu, H; Prokai, L; Forster, MJ. Histochemical staining and quantification of dihydrolipoamide dehydrogenase diaphorase activity using blue native PAGE. *Electrophoresis*, 28, (2007), 1036-1045.

[25] Brennan, JP; Wait, R; Begum, S; Bell, JR; Dunn, MJ; Eaton, P. Detection and mapping of widespread intermolecular protein disulfide formation during cardiac oxidative stress using *proteomics* with diagonal electrophoresis. *J Biol Chem*, 279, (2004), 41352-41360.

[26] Graceffa, P; Lee, E; Stafford, WF. Disulfide cross-linked antiparallel actin dimer. *Biochemistry*, 52, (2013), 1082-1088.

[27] McLachlin, DT; Dunn, SD. Disulfide linkage of the b and delta subunits does not affect the function of the Escherichia coli ATP synthase. *Biochemistry*, 39, (2000), 3486-3490.

[28] DeLeon-Rangel, J; Ishmukhametov, RR; Jiang, W; Fillingame, RH; Vik, SB. Interactions between subunits a and b in the rotary ATP synthase as determined by cross-linking. *FEBS Lett*, 587, (2013), 892-897.

[29] Dias, GM; Lopez, ML; Ferreira, AT; Chapeaurouge, DA; Rodrigues, A; Perales, J; Retamal, CA. Thiol-disulfide proteins of stallion epididymal spermatozoa. *Anim Reprod Sci*, (2013).

[30] Yan, L-J Positive oxidative stress in aging and aging-related disease tolerance. *Redox Biology*, 2, (2014), 165-169.

In: Reactive Oxygen Species, Lipid Peroxidation …
Editor: Angel Catalá

ISBN: 978-1-63321-886-4
© 2015 Nova Science Publishers, Inc.

Chapter 5

PARTICIPATION OF REACTIVE OXYGEN SPECIES IN THE TOXICITY OF COBALT, NICKEL, CADMIUM AND MERCURY

Sandra Viviana Verstraeten[*]

Department of Biological Chemistry, IQUIFIB (UBA-CONICET),
School of Pharmacy and Biochemistry,
University of Buenos Aires, Argentina

ABSTRACT

Upon the industrial revolution in the XVIII century, the mobilization of metals from their natural reservoirs as well as their use increased exponentially. As a result, many heavy metals were mobilized towards the Earth's surface, contaminated the soils, water and air, and became available for living organisms. Among others, Co, Ni, Cd and Hg are highly toxic metals for humans, and their mechanisms of toxicity are still under elucidation. However, they share with other metals a common mechanism of toxicity that involves the alteration of the intracellular redox status. This may be caused by increased generation of oxidant species, the impairment of the antioxidant defense system, or both. Among the oxidant species, the generation of reactive oxygen species (ROS) seems to be a common feature in the toxicity of most heavy metals, regardless of their redox-active or redox-inactive condition. The excessive production of ROS, together with the inhibition of certain components of the antioxidant defense system leads to the oxidative damage of key intracellular components, such as lipids, proteins and DNA. Moreover, by promoting oxidative stress these metals induce cell death via apoptosis or necrosis. In the present work, the current knowledge regarding the mechanisms involved in Co, Ni, Cd, and Hg-mediated oxidative stress will be discussed.

[*] Corresponding author: Dr Sandra V. Verstraeten, Departamento de Química Biológica, IQUIFIB (UBA-CONICET), Facultad de Farmacia y Bioquímica, Universidad de Buenos Aires, Junín 956, C1113AAD, Buenos Aires, Argentina. Phone: 54-11-4964-8290 (ext. 143). Fax: 54-11-4962-5457. E-mail: verstraeten@ffyb.uba.ar.

ABBREVIATIONS

8-OHdG: 8-hydroxy-2'-deoxyguanosine
AIF: apoptosis inducing factor
B.W.: body weight
BSO: L-buthionine-[S,R]-sulfoximine
CAT: catalase
CFTR: Cystic fibrosis transmembrane conductance regulator
DCF: dichlorofluorescein diacetate
DMPO: 5,5-dimethyl-1-pyrroline N-oxide
DMPOX: 5,5-dimethyl-1-pyrrolidone-2-oxyl
DPI: diphenyleniodonium
eNOS: endothelial nitric oxide synthase
ESR: electronic spin resonance
GPx: glutathione peroxidase
GSH: glutathione
HO-1: hemeoxygenase-1
JNK: Jun N-terminal kinase
LDL: low density lipoprotein
MAPK: mitogen-activated protein kinase
Me$_2$Hg: dimethylmercury
MeHg$^+$: methylmercury
MTT: 3-[4, 5-dimethylthiazol-2-yl]-2, 5-diphenyl-tetrazolium bromide
NAC: N-acetyl-cysteine
Prx: peroxiredoxin
ROS: reactive oxygen species
SOD: superoxide dismutase
Trx: thioredoxin
TrxR: thioredoxin reductase

INTRODUCTION

Exposure to heavy metals is a frequent phenomenon in the industrialized world. Their accumulation in the body produces multiple toxic effects, including neurotoxicity, genotoxicity and carcinogenicity. Therefore, not only the characterization of the clinical symptoms associated with metals intoxication, but also the knowledge of the biochemical mechanisms underlying their toxicity are required to establish appropriate therapies and health policies. The term "heavy metals" is commonly used to denominate the group of toxic metals. However, the use of this term has been discouraged because it is inexact from a chemical point of view (Duffus, 2002). A more accurate classification is based on the last electron subshell in the atom to be occupied (Duffus, 2002). On this basis, metals are grouped into the s-, p-, d- and f-blocks. Particularly, the d-block comprises a set of 35 elements including the transition metals. Among them, the number of biologically relevant metals is small, and includes iron, copper, manganese, cobalt, zinc and molybdenum. The first three metals are redox-active and participate in enzymatic oxido-reduction reactions. Cobalt is also a redox-active metal that forms the organometallic complex vitamin B12, which is the cofactor for certain isomerases, dehalogenases and methyltransferases. Zinc and molybdenum are also present in the active site of numerous enzymes, although these metals lack redox capacity under biological conditions. Despite being biologically relevant, the concentration of all these metals within cells must be strictly regulated, as their absence or excessive accumulation are both cytotoxic. The remaining metals that belong to the d-block have no biological functions. In fact, even in low amounts these metals result prejudicial for the normal functioning of the affected organs and systems.

Toxic metals have noxious effects on almost every cellular organelle and component, including the membranes, mitochondria, lysosomes, endoplasmic reticula, and nuclei. In addition, either directly or indirectly, these metals affect the catalytic properties of several enzymes that are involved in the metabolism, detoxification, and damage repair (Wang and Shi, 2001). Accumulating evidence indicates that a common mechanism underlying metals toxicity involves a misbalanced generation of the reactive oxygen species (ROS). This group of chemical species includes hydrogen peroxide (H_2O_2), superoxide anion ($O_2^{\bullet-}$), hydroxyl radical ($HO^{\bullet}$), peroxyl radical ($ROO^{\bullet}$), and alcoxyl radical ($RO^{\bullet}$). In addition, other radical species can also be formed, such as thiyl radicals ($RS^{\bullet}$), and the nitrogen reactive species nitric oxide (NO) and peroxynitrite anion ($ONOO^{\bullet-}$). All these reactive species play a major role in mediating metal-induced cellular responses. Even more, several lines of investigation relate the increased ROS production to the downstream activation of inflammatory signaling cascades, the production of chemo attractant molecules, and carcinogenesis (Jomova and Valko, 2011; Ivanova et al., 2013; Saeidnia and Abdollahi, 2013; Choi et al., 2014). For example, $HO^{\bullet-}$ activates the transcription factor NF-κB, which is involved in the inflammatory response (Morgan; Kauppinen et al., 2013). On the other hand, H_2O_2 has gained the role of second messenger, as it participates in the release of insulin, the signal transduction triggered by the interaction of growth factors with their corresponding membrane receptors, the activation of protein kinase B (Akt) and mitogen-activated protein kinases (MAPK), among others (for a recent review on this topic, see Sies, 2014). However, when H_2O_2 production is exacerbated beyond the physiological limits, this molecule induces programmed cell death (apoptosis) or necrosis (Gough and Cotter, 2011).

This chapter provides an overview of the current knowledge regarding the mechanisms underlying the oxidative stress mediated by toxic metals belonging to the d-block. Since the list of metals that has been demonstrated to cause oxidative damage is extensive, cobalt (Co), nickel (Ni), cadmium (Cd) and mercury (Hg) have been selected, as they are frequently found in contaminated areas and they generate public health concerns.

COBALT

a. Chemical Properties and Uses

Cobalt is a silver-gray, strongly ferromagnetic metal (Co, atomic number 27, atomic weight 58.93) that belongs to element group 9. The most common oxidation states of Co are 2+ and 3+, but 1-, 0 and 1+ states are also known.

Co is the 33rd most abundant metal in the Earth's crust (ATSDR, 2004). The average concentration of Co in the continental crust was estimated in 24 ppm (Wedepohl, 1995) as a component of minerals such as linnaeite (Co_3S_4), carrolite ($CuCo_2S_4$), erythrite ($Co_3(AsO_4)_2.8$ H_2O), sulfidic cobaltite (CoAsS), safflorite ($CoAs_2$), glaucodot ((Co,Fe)AsS), and skutterudite ($CoAs_3$) (ATSDR, 2004). The annual world consumption of Co was estimated in 24,000 tons (Wedepohl, 2008). Although Co salts have been used for centuries to obtain colored glass and ceramics, the element was first isolated and identified in 1792 by H. Brandt (Schrauzer, 2008). Co is currently used for the fabrication of the so-called superalloys destined for the fabrication of engine parts that must operate under high temperatures. Due to its ferromagnetic properties, metallic Co is also used for manufacturing magnetic steels and aluminum alloys. Co salts are used in the chemical industry in the preparation of pigments, catalysts and to promote the hardening of silicon resins, among other applications (Schrauzer, 2008).

Co can be released to the environment from combustion of coal and oils, and as result of certain industrial processes. In non-contaminated areas, the concentration of Co in rivers is approximately 0.2 ppb, while in oceanic waters the concentration is ~100-fold lower (Wedepohl, 2008). However, in polluted rivers the concentration of Co may reach values as high as 4,500 ppb. The most frequent route of human exposure to Co is the inhalation of airborne particles, mostly containing metallic Co, alone or combined with other metals. These ultrafine particles can be distributed through the lymph and blood, and during their transit, soluble Co ions can be released and absorbed by the organs and tissues.

b. Effects on Human Health

Co is considered an essential element because it is required for vitamin B12 synthesis, but only trace amounts of Co are necessary to fulfill that requirement (Paustenbach et al., 2013). When ingested, it is readily absorbed in the gastrointestinal tract, and most of the amount absorbed will be released through the urine. The use of radioactive Co (^{60}Co) allowed the characterization of Co kinetics. In a study performed with healthy humans that received a single dose of Co, it was reported that 40% of the initial dose was excreted within the first 24 h, but the excretion progressively decreased and 10% of the dose remained in the body 1 y after Co administration (Simonsen et al., 2012 and references therein). Thus, Co accumulates in several organs, including the liver, kidneys, pancreas and heart (Simonsen et al., 2012).

The adverse effects of Co accumulation include the dysfunction of thyroid gland, asthma, allergic contact dermatitis, alterations in the immune and hematological systems, and carcinogenesis. For complete and recent reviews on the effects of Co on humans health, see Simonsen et al. (2012) and Paustenbach et al. (2013).

c. Co and Oxidative Stress

It has been proposed that the generation of free radicals mediated by Co^{2+} contributes to the toxicity and carcinogenicity of this metal. Early studies of Hasan and Ali (1981) showed that the daily administration of 2 mg Co^{2+}/kg body weight (b.w.) to rats caused an increase in the content of lipid peroxidation products in the brain, brain stem and cerebellum after a week. More recently, Kubrak et al. (2011) evaluated the impact of Co^{2+} concentration in water on the oxidative damage to lipids and proteins in goldfish (*Carassius auratus*). After 96 h of Co^{2+} exposure, increased levels of lipid peroxidation products were detected in the brain and liver and this effect was positively related to Co concentration in the water (Kubrak et al., 2011). Although no changes in the concentration of lipid peroxidation products were found in the kidneys, the extent of the oxidative damage to kidney proteins was greater than that measured in the brain and liver (Kubrak et al., 2011). The exposure of human lung epithelial (H460) cells to $CoCl_2$ for 6 h resulted in 2.5-fold increased production of intracellular oxidant species as evidenced by the oxidation of the probe dichlorofluorescein diacetate (DCF) (Patel et al., 2012). This effect was partially prevented by cell incubation with the precursor of GSH synthesis, N-acetyl-cysteine (NAC), prior to their exposure to Co^{2+}, suggesting the participation of GSH in the attenuation of the oxidative stress due to Co^{2+} (Patel et al., 2012). Similar results were previously reported by Zou et al. (2001) who, using rat pheochromocytoma (PC12) cells, observed that cell treatment with NAC or dithiothreitol previous to the exposure to 500 µM Co^{2+} prevented not only the oxidation of DCF but also the induction of apoptosis by this metal.

Using the spin trap 5,5-dimethyl-1-pyrroline N-oxide (DMPO) Hanna et al. (1992) found that, unlike Fe^{2+}, Co^{2+} does not generate per se $HO^{•}$ radicals from H_2O_2. However, when Co^{2+} was complexed with compounds such as nitrilotriacetate, a strong electronic spin resonance (ESR) signal corresponding to the DMPO-OOH adduct was observed (Hanna et al., 1992). Such ESR signal was absent when the enzyme superoxide dismutase (SOD) was added to the medium, suggesting that $O_2^{•-}$ was generated along the reaction. In contrast to Co^{2+}, aqueous suspensions of metallic Co (Co^{0}) are capable –in the absence of further oxidants– to oxidize DMPO. In this case, the final product is the radical 5,5-dimethyl-1-pyrrolidone-2-oxyl (DMPOX) whose presence is an indirect evidence of peroxyl radicals ($ROO^{•}$) generation (Leonard et al., 1998). The addition of SOD to the system resulted in the generation of $HO^{•}$ instead of $ROO^{•}$. On the basis of that evidence, Leonard et al. (1998) proposed that the following reaction does not proceed in aqueous solution at a significant rate:

$$Co^{0} + H_2O_2 \rightarrow Co^{+} + HO^{•} + HO^{-}$$

Instead, Co^{0} reacts with molecular oxygen generating a Co^{+}-bound $O_2^{•-}$ adduct with strong oxidant capacity:

$$Co^{0} + O_2 \rightarrow Co^{+}\text{-}OO^{•}$$

In the presence of SOD, this reaction renders H_2O_2 as follows:

$$Co^{+}\text{-}OO^{•} \xrightarrow{\text{SOD}} H_2O_2 + Co^{+}$$

Finally, H_2O_2 can react with Co^{+} via a Fenton-like reaction:

$$Co^{+} + H_2O_2 \rightarrow Co^{2+} + HO^{•} + HO^{-}$$

Although free Co^{2+} cannot react with H_2O_2, complexes of Co^{2+} with small peptides such as GSH (γ-Glu-Cys-Gly), anserine (βAla-3-methyl-L-His) or Gly-Gly-His can, as described by Leonard et al. (1998):

$$Co^{2+}\text{-complex} + H_2O_2 \rightarrow Co^{3+}\text{-complex} + HO^{\bullet} + HO^{-}$$

This is an interesting finding because GSH and anserine are both biologically relevant antioxidants (Jozefczak et al., 2012; Song et al., 2014). Therefore, in biological systems exposed to Co^{2+} it is plausible that GSH and anserine may act as pro-oxidants and enhance the oxidative stress caused by Co^{2+}. Supporting that, Mao et al. (1996) showed that Co^{2+} in the presence of anserine and H_2O_2 generates both $^1O_2$ and $HO^{\bullet}$, and that these oxidants were directly involved in the in vitro oxidation of DNA, as evidenced by the formation of oxidized base 8-hydroxy-2'-deoxyguanosine (8-OHdG). The possibility that Co^{2+} may generate $ROO^{\bullet}$ was also evaluated in an in vivo model of Co^{2+} administration. When rats received $CoCl_2$ (10-500 mM) and ascorbate (100 mM) simultaneously, the generation of ascorbyl radical in blood was detected by ESR (Wang et al., 1993). Ascorbic acid is the main soluble antioxidant present in plasma and it efficiently traps $ROO^{\bullet}$ in the aqueous phase, generating ascorbyl radicals. Interestingly, the concentration of ascorbyl radicals in rat plasma was markedly higher upon administration of ascorbate plus Co^{2+} than the one attained with an equivalent amount of ferric citrate, a recognized generator of $ROO^{\bullet}$ in plasma (Wang et al., 1993). This work provided for the first time direct *in vivo* evidence of free radical generation upon Co^{2+} administration and supported the participation of oxidative stress as a potential contributor to Co^{2+} toxicity.

As mentioned before, although the experimental evidence reported in the literature is still not conclusive, Co^{2+} might cause DNA oxidation. The incubation of intact human lymphocytes for 15 min in the presence of Co^{2+} or tungsten carbide-Co particles (WC-Co) resulted in increased DNA single-strand breaks in a time- and concentration-dependent manner (Anard et al., 1997). The finding that DNA damage by Co^{2+} or WC-Co was prevented by the $HO^{\bullet}$ scavenger formate supports the hypothesis of ROS participation in Co genotoxicity (Anard et al., 1997). In experiments performed in vitro, Ivancsits et al. (2002) reported that calf-thymus DNA incubated in the presence of Co^{2+} alone had slightly increased 8-OHdG contents. However, the addition of H_2O_2 to samples markedly increased the concentration of 8-OHdG and this effect depended on the concentration of both, H_2O_2 and Co^{2+} (Ivancsits et al., 2002). Conversely, when the experiments were performed using intact human fibroblasts instead of isolated DNA, Co^{2+} caused no additional increase in the levels of 8-OHdG respect to the values measured in cells treated with H_2O_2 alone (Ivancsits et al., 2002). Considering that H_2O_2 diffuses passively through the bilayer while Co^{2+} requires an active transport, it is possible that the accumulation of Co^{2+} was insufficient to cause a differential effect respect to the cells treated with H_2O_2 alone, or that Co^{2+} was sequestered in the intracellular compartments. Moreover, the chelation of Co^{2+} by intracellular molecules and/or the removal of H_2O_2 by the antioxidants may limit their access to cell nuclei and prevent DNA oxidation. The fact that Co^{2+} inhibits the DNA repairing system (Beyersmann and Hartwig, 2008) contributes to the accumulation of damaged DNA bases, which may lead to carcinogenesis (Paustenbach et al., 2013).

The generation of oxidant species by Co^{2+} has also been related to alterations in mitochondrial functionality. Working with isolated rat liver mitochondria, Battaglia et al.

(2009) observed that micromolar concentrations of Co^{2+} caused mitochondrial swelling in a Co^{2+} concentration-dependent manner. In addition, Co^{2+} caused an increase in H_2O_2 production, the collapse of mitochondrial potential, the decrease in NADPH concentration, and the release of the mitochondrial apoptotic factors AIF (apoptosis inducing factor) and cytochrome c (Battaglia et al., 2009). All these effects of Co^{2+} were prevented by certain antioxidants, such as NAC, dithioerythritol or butylhydroxytoluene, indicating a clear relationship between the pro-apoptotic effects of Co^{2+} and the increased levels of oxidants (Battaglia et al., 2009). In addition to mitochondrial damage, Co^{2+} also affects lysosomes. Working with isolated rat hepatocytes, Pourahmad et al. (2003) found that Co^{2+} caused a time-dependent alteration of lysosomal membrane integrity, as evidenced by the redistribution of the lysosomotropic dye acridine orange. Again, this effect of Co^{2+} was partially prevented by antioxidants such as SOD, catalase (CAT), dimethyl sulfoxide and the scavenger of $HO^{\bullet}$ mannitol (Pourahmad et al., 2003). In addition, the presence of inhibitors of the cathepsins, a group of lysosomal proteases that induce apoptosis upon their release to cytoplasm, prevented Co^{2+}-mediated cell damage (Pourahmad et al., 2003). Interestingly, the Fe^{3+} chelator desferroxamine also prevented Co^{2+}-mediated loss of lysosome integrity. This finding suggests that Co^{2+} may cause the release of Fe^{3+} from the lysosomal stores. The oxidative capability of iron relies mostly in the generation of the highly reactive species $HO^{\bullet}$ through the classic Haber-Weiss and Fenton reactions, which can be summarized as follows:

$$Fe^{2+} + H_2O_2 \rightarrow Fe^{3+} + HO^- + HO^{\bullet}$$

Altogether, the experimental evidence points to mitochondria and lysosomes as the prime targets of Co^{2+}-induced oxidative stress with the subsequent damage to other cell components.

Oxidative stress being a result from oxidant species generation and removal, the pro-oxidant effects of Co^{2+} may be enhanced by Co-mediated alterations in the antioxidant defense system, as well. Supporting that, the administration of an acute dose of $CoCl_2$ (60 mg/kg b.w.) to rats decreased the liver activities of glutathione peroxidase (GPx), SOD and CAT by 13, 30 and 36%, respectively (Christova et al., 2001). In contrast, when $CoCl_2$ was administered chronically, the only enzymes affected were SOD and CAT, with no significant changes observed for GPx (Christova et al., 2001). The activity of hemeoxygenase-1 (HO-1) rapidly increased, reaching a maximum after 24 h of Co^{2+} administration and persisted elevated for at least 6 days (Christova et al., 2001). In the model of goldfish exposure to Co^{2+} mentioned above, the enzymes of the antioxidant defense system were also altered (Kubrak et al., 2011). In that model, the activities of SOD and CAT were decreased in the brain and liver and slightly increased in the kidneys, while the activity of GRed was increased in the three organs (Kubrak et al., 2011). Working with cultured human (MG-63) osteoblasts, Fleury et al. (2006) found that Co^{2+} down-regulated the expression of CAT in a time-dependent fashion. In these cells, the expression of GPx progressively increased between 24 and 72 h of cell exposure to Co^{2+}, while the expression of HO-1 rapidly increased after 24 h and progressively decreased afterwards (Fleury et al., 2006). HO-1, which catalyzes the transformation of heme into biliverdin, carbon monoxide and catalytic iron, has antioxidant properties in diverse experimental models (Hoekstra et al., 2004). Therefore, and on the basis of its early activation, HO-1 is now included in the first line of enzymatic defense against Co^{2+}-mediated oxidative stress.

NICKEL

a. Chemical Properties and Uses

Nickel is a silvery-white metal (Ni, atomic number 28, atomic weight 58.69) that belongs to the element group 10. The oxidation states of Ni are 1-, 0, 1+, 2+, 3+ and 4+, with 0 and 2+ being the most frequent valences (ATSDR, 2005).

The average concentration of Ni in the Earth's crust is 56 ppm (Wedepohl, 1995; Wedepohl, 2008), forming minerals with sulfide (millerite), arsenic (nickeline), sulfure and iron (pentlandite), and sulfide and arsenic (galena), among several others. The annual world consumption of Ni was estimated in 78,000 tons (Wedepohl, 2008). Metallic Ni and its ionic compounds have many industrial uses, such as the production of stainless steel, Ni-Cd batteries, and the fabrication of alloys with high resistance against corrosion and temperature (Cempel and Nikel, 2006). Thus, Ni and its alloys are widely used in the metallurgical, chemical and food processing industries (Cempel and Nikel, 2006).

Similar to what occurs with most heavy metals, certain anthropogenic activities are the main source of environmental contamination with Ni. In non-contaminated areas, the concentration of Ni in river and sea water ranges 0.3-0.9 ppb (Wedepohl, 2008). Ni can be found in the air as a result of the combustion of coal, along with diesel and fuel oils (Cempel and Nikel, 2006). These airborne particles can be inhaled, absorbed in the lungs and distributed throughout the body via the bloodstream. Other sources of Ni exposure constitute tobacco smoking, dental or orthopedic implants, stainless steel cookware, and Ni-containing jewelry (Cempel and Nikel, 2006). Specially, tobacco contains around 0.6-4.4 µg Ni per cigarette (Caruso et al., 2014), and approximately 10-20% of that amount is inhaled during smoking. One of the most toxic species is nickel carbonyl, which upon inhalation passes very rapidly through the alveolar barrier and reaches the bloodstream (Sunderman and Selin, 1968). The presence of Ni carbonyl has been proposed in tobacco smoke, although it has not been univocally demonstrated yet. Although Ni is partially eliminated through urine (Stojanovic et al., 2004), it also accumulates in most organs and tissues. Another route of entry is the ingestion of foods and water containing Ni. It has been calculated that approximately 1-10% of the ingested Ni is absorbed in the gastrointestinal tract. For excellent reviews about Ni metabolism and toxicokinetics, see Cempel and Nikel (2006) and Sunderman (2008).

b. Effects on Human Health

Occupational exposure to Ni occurs in mining, refining, production of alloys and welding, among others (Denkhaus and Salnikow, 2002). In the general population, Ni is the causal agent of most allergic skin reactions through numerous common objects that contain Ni, such as coins and jewelry. In the last years, some cases of facial dermatitis in adolescents have been associated with the use of mobile phones (Wohrl, 2007; Moennich et al., 2009). Ni has also been related to asthma, conjunctivitis, systemic reactions after the administration of parenteral solutions containing Ni compounds, and inflammatory reactions against prostheses and implants (Cempel and Nikel, 2006). Both epidemiological and experimental reports strongly relate Ni with certain kinds of cancer, and thus it has been classified as a carcinogen (Magnus et al., 1982; Kasprzak et al., 2003; Cempel and Nikel, 2006; Sunderman, 2008; Phillips et al., 2010; Cameron et al., 2011; Magaye and Zhao, 2012; Zambelli and Ciurli, 2013). A very important aspect of Ni toxicity is that this metal can cross both the blood-testis barrier and the placenta and therefore, it can affect male fertility and the proper development of embryos (Das and Dasgupta, 2000).

c. Ni and Oxidative Stress

Ni causes oxidative stress both in vitro and in vivo, and the enhancement of lipid peroxidation was postulated as a major mechanism involved in Ni acute toxicity (Sunderman Jr, 1987). For example, rats that received a single dose of 500 μmol $NiCl_2$/kg b.w. had increased contents of lipid peroxidation products in the liver, kidney and lungs only 24 h after Ni administration, although no changes were found in the brain, testis, heart or spleen (Sunderman Jr, 1987). This effect on promoting liver lipid peroxidation was time- and concentration-dependent and correlated well with the increase in aspartate transaminase activity in the plasma, indicative of liver damage (Sunderman Jr, 1987). Similar results were reported by Chen et al. (1998), who administered $NiCl_2$ (50-170 μmol/kg b.w.) to mice and observed that the levels of lipid peroxidation in the liver were increased. Similarly to the previous observations in rats, in this model the kinetics of lipid peroxidation products generation peaked around 24 h after Ni administration and decreased afterwards (Chen et al., 1998). Interestingly, the accumulation of Ni in the liver was accompanied by increased contents of iron and, to a lesser extent, of copper (Athar et al., 1987; Misra et al., 1990; Chen et al., 1998). A reanalysis of the results obtained by Athar et al. (1987) shows linear relationships between the increase in liver iron content and the dose of Ni administered ($r^2 =$ 0.99), and between liver iron and lipid peroxidation products contents ($r^2 = 0.98$). Using a fixed dose of 170 μmol/kg b.w., Chen et al. (1998) found that the content of iron in liver increased exponentially as a function of time, reaching a maximum after 24 h of Ni administration and persisting at least until 48 h. On the other hand, the content of lipid peroxidation products in this model increased linearly during the first 24 h after Ni administration and decreased at prolonged times (Chen et al., 1998). Together, these results indicate that the mobilization of iron plays a key role in the liver damage observed in Ni intoxication.

Free Ni^{2+} cannot generate $HO^{\bullet}$ in solution. Nevertheless, when forming complexes with certain peptides, such as $(Gly)_4$, Asp-Ala-His-Lys, Gly-Gly-His or βAla-His, Ni^{2+} enhances the production of $HO^{\bullet}$. Using the spin trap DMPO, Cotelle et al. (1992) observed that Ni^{2+}-peptides complexes incubated in the presence of a generator of $O_2^{\bullet-}$ generated the DMPO-OOH adduct. In addition, when these compounds were incubated in the presence of H_2O_2, a characteristic ESR signal corresponding to DMPO-OH adduct was observed. Supporting this, Joshi et al. (2005) suggested that Ni complexation with GSH, L-His or L-Cys catalyzed the disproportionation of H_2O_2, resulting in the generation of $HO^{\bullet}$. L-His, L-Cys and GSH are molecules with recognized antioxidant capacity. However, when complexed with Ni they have a biphasic behavior, promoting $HO^{\bullet}$ generation at high Ni:peptide ratios (2:1 for His and GSH, and 4:1 for Cys), and abolishing it at low Ni:peptide ratios (Joshi et al., 2005). The following sequence of reactions was proposed to describe the generation of $HO^{\cdot\cdot}$ by Ni^{2+}-peptide complexes:

$$H_2O_2 + Ni^{2+}\text{-peptide} \rightarrow Ni^{3+}\text{-peptide} + O_2^{\cdot\cdot} + HO^- + HO^{\cdot\cdot}$$
$$Ni^{3+}\text{-peptide} + O_2^{\cdot\cdot} \rightarrow Ni^{2+}\text{-peptide} + O_2$$
$$H_2O_2 + O_2^{\cdot\cdot} \rightarrow HO^- + HO^{\cdot\cdot}$$

As mentioned before, Ni^{2+} crosses the blood-testis barrier and accumulates in the testis. Specially, Ni^{2+} binds to protamine P2 (Bal et al., 1997a), a nuclear protein that replaces histones in the haploid phase of spermatogenesis. Protamine P2-bound Ni^{2+} generates $HO^{\cdot\cdot}$ and $O_2^{\cdot\cdot}$ from H_2O_2, following a mechanism similar to that described above (Bal et al., 1997b; Liang et al., 1999). Therefore, either from the release of iron from its intracellular storage pools, or via its complexation with intracellular aminoacids, small peptides or metal-binding proteins, Ni^{2+} is capable to induce the production of $HO^{\cdot\cdot}$, which will be responsible for the oxidative damage to biologically relevant macromolecules.

Once in cell nuclei, Ni causes DNA oxidation as evidenced by the increase in single-strand breaks amounts and the cross linking between DNA and nuclear proteins (Ciccarelli and Wetterhahn, 1982; Costa and Heck, 1984; Sen and Costa, 1986). Interestingly, Ni^{2+} induces the oxidation of DNA bases in chromatin due to the capacity of peptide-bound Ni^{2+} to generate free radicals from molecular oxygen (Nackerdien et al., 1991). The lack of an effect of added CAT on DNA oxidation by Ni^{2+} suggests that H_2O_2 does not participate in this process (Nackerdien et al., 1991). In contrast, the presence of H_2O_2 was strictly required when assessing isolated DNA (Kawanishi et al., 1989; Nackerdien et al., 1991). The oxidation of DNA by Ni^{2+} was prevented by EDTA (Lloyd and Phillips, 1999) indicative of a weak Ni bonding to DNA, which occurs mostly with the phosphate groups on DNA backbone (Eichhorn and Shin, 1968). In addition, the effect of Ni^{2+} was partially prevented by certain $HO^{\cdot\cdot}$ scavengers, which suggests the participation of this highly oxidant species in the process (Kawanishi et al., 1989; Nackerdien et al., 1991). Ni^{2+} not only induced the generation of DNA strand breaks but also efficiently inhibited the DNA repairing system even at low, non-cytotoxic concentrations (Dally and Hartwig, 1997; Lynn et al., 1997). Therefore, Ni^{2+} induces DNA damage by these two mechanisms, the oxidation of the DNA and/or the inhibition of the DNA repairing system, and the progressive accumulation of altered DNA bases could contribute to the carcinogenic effect of this metal.

The generation of Ni^{2+} complexes with GSH has been widely characterized. By X-ray powder diffraction studies, Singh et al. (2007) showed the formation of a Ni^{2+}-GSH complex with square planar geometry, which results from metal coordination with the sulfhydryl group of Cys and the carboxylate of glutamic acid. At physiological pH, the most abundant species are $[NiH(GSH)_2]^{3-} > [NiHGSH] >>> [Ni_2(GSH)_2]^{2-}$ (Krezel and Bal, 2004). Of these three complexes, the first one is the most effective in facilitating GSH aerobic oxidation when in the absence of further oxidants (Krezel and Bal, 2004). There are several reports showing that Ni^{2+} causes a significant decrease in GSH content, both in models of animal intoxication and in cultured cells exposed to Ni^{2+}. For example, working with HeLa cells incubated for 4 h in the presence of 10 μM Ni^{2+}, Hansen et al. (2006) found a 15% decrease in GSH concentration which was accompanied by a similar increase in GSSG content. The change in GSH and GSSG concentrations increased up to 35% when cells were incubated in the presence of 100 μM Ni^{2+} (Hansen et al., 2006). Similar results were previously reported by Salnikow et al.

(1994) who found 40 and 68% decrease in GSH concentration in 3T3 mouse cells incubated for 6 h in the presence of 0.5 or 1 mM $NiCl_2$, respectively. In human erythrocytes incubated for 2 h in the presence of 1 mM $NiCl_2$, De Luca et al. (2007) found a 30% increase in the amount of GSSG which was accompanied by a 25% decrease in the GSH/GSSG ratio. More recently, Murawska-Cialowicz et al. (2012) observed that upon submitting rats and mice to a similar protocol of intoxication with Ni^{2+} (one dose of 5 mg Ni/kg b.w.), the decrease in GSH concentration in mice testis (-20%) was markedly higher than that observed in rat testis (-7%). This finding correlated well with the amount of protamine P2 in rat and mice sperm cells, with protamine P2 concentration in rat sperm cells representing approximately 2 to 5% of the amount observed in mice (Bunick et al., 1990). Therefore, in this experimental model, the decrease in GSH may be secondary to the enhanced production of $HO^{\cdot}$ and $O_2^{\cdot-}$ that results from H_2O_2 disproportionation caused by protamine P2-bound Ni^{2+}.

Ni^{2+} can also affect the activity of the enzymes that constitute the antioxidant defense system. For example, in rats that received $NiSO_4$ (20 mg/kg b.w.) the activities of SOD, CAT and GPx were decreased in the testis and lungs, and increased in the erythrocytes (Gupta et al., 2006; Das et al., 2007; Gupta et al., 2007). Similar results were obtained by Cartañà et al. (1992) who found that 2 h after the administration of a single dose of Ni^{2+} (4 mg /kg b.w.) to rats, the activities of GR and GPx were decreased in the liver. In this model, the activities of both enzymes were fully recovered after 24 h of Ni^{2+} administration. The kinetics of Ni^{2+} content in the liver and kidneys reached a maximum after 3 h of the administration of 107 µmol (26.5 mg) Ni^{2+} acetate/kg b.w., and this effect was accompanied by decreased activities of CAT, GPx and GR (Misra et al., 1990). In a study performed in 69 Ni plating workers, the plasma concentration of lipid peroxidation products were 1.34-times higher than in non-exposed workers whereas the activities of SOD and GPx in their erythrocytes were 1.5 and 9% lower, respectively (Kalahasthi et al., 2006). Both, the increase in lipid peroxidation products and the decrease in the activity of the antioxidant enzymes, significantly correlated with the concentration of Ni in urine (Kalahasthi et al., 2006). Until now, no evidence has been found suggesting a direct interaction of Ni^{2+} with the antioxidant enzymes that would modify their activity. On the contrary, it seems that the alterations in these enzymes found in different models of Ni^{2+} intoxication are secondary to the increased levels of oxidants (H_2O_2 and $HO^{\cdot}$) generated. Supporting this, Misra et al. (1990) observed that those strains of mice that constitutively have higher contents of GSH and higher activities of the antioxidant enzymes are more resistant to renal damage upon Ni^{2+} intoxication.

CADMIUM

a. Chemical Properties and Uses

Cadmium (Cd, atomic number 48, atomic weight 112.41) belongs to element group 12. Cd is a bluish-white soft metal with only one oxidation state (+2) and therefore, it has no redox capacity in biological conditions.

Cd has a concentration of approximately 0.08-0.1 ppm in the Earth's crust (Wedepohl, 2008), where it forms minerals with sulfide (greenockite and hawlyite), oxygen (monteponite) and selenium (cadmoselite), or mixed minerals with Hg and sulfide (cadmian metacinnabar) or carbonate (otavite), among others (Cullen and Maldonado, 2013). In non-polluted rivers and seas, the concentration of Cd ranges <0.01-0.1 ppb (Wedepohl, 2008) and the annual world consumption of Cd was estimated in 20,000 tons (Wedepohl, 2008). The massive industrial use of Cd is relatively recent, starting in the 1940s. Cd is currently used in the manufacturing of Ni-Cd batteries, pigments, plastics, metal coatings and some metal alloys (ATSDR, 1998). Due to these anthropogenic activities, Cd is mobilized to the environment. Relatively high Cd concentrations can be found in the atmosphere, fresh and marine waters, and soils in the proximities of urban and industrialized regions (Crea et al., 2013). As a result, this metal can be incorporated into the food chain and accumulate in living organisms. When present in low amounts, the gastrointestinal absorption of Cd from foods is minimal. In contrast, the inhalation of Cd-containing airborne particles or fumes causes its accumulation in the lungs where it is absorbed and distributed through the bloodstream to the other organs. This constitutes the main occupational-related route of intoxication in exposed workers. Similarly, non-occupationally exposed people may inhale Cd from cigarette smoke (Stohs et al., 1997), as tobacco leaves contain 0.3-2 µg Cd/g (Lugon-Moulin et al., 2006) which passes to the smoke upon burning (Lewis et al., 1972). For a complete and recent revision of Cd entry, trafficking and excretion pathways in humans, see Thévenod and Lee (2013).

b. Effects on Human Health

Cd acute intoxication in humans is rare, although there are reports about patients that upon inhalation of industrial fumes experienced respiratory distress syndrome, which in some cases progressed to death within 3 to 7 days (Yates and Goldman, 1990). On the other hand, since Cd has prolonged half-life in humans (10 to 30 years) (Goyer and Cherian, 1995), this metal accumulates in tissues and organs. Consequently, chronic Cd accumulation leads to kidney and liver failure, followed by endocrine, respiratory, cardiovascular, nervous and reproductive systems damage (Johri et al., 2010; Thévenod and Lee, 2013). Although Cd causes teratogenicity in animal models (Ferm and Carpenter, 1967; Chernoff, 1973; Carmichael et al., 1982; Schmid et al., 1985; Webb et al., 1988), there is no strong evidence demonstrating that Cd may be teratogenic in humans. Despite of this, several epidemiological studies relate Cd exposure to diverse kinds of human cancer (reviewed by Liu et al., 2009; Thévenod and Lee, 2013).

c. Cd and Oxidative Stress

Cd intoxication causes oxidative stress in diverse experimental models and in exposed humans (Stohs and Bagchi, 1995; Bertin and Averbeck, 2006; Thevenod, 2009; Cuypers et al., 2010; Ognjanovic et al., 2010; Matovic et al., 2011). Being a non-redox metal, Cd cannot generate ROS per se, as it has been confirmed by ESR in cell-free systems (O'Brien and Salacinski, 1998). Therefore, the oxidative damage to lipids and proteins observed upon Cd intoxication must be indirect (Stohs and Bagchi, 1995).

Working with isolated hepatocytes, Koizumi et al. (1996) demonstrated that Cd rapidly induces H_2O_2 production, an effect that reaches a maximum after 15 min of cell exposure to Cd. In addition, Cd causes cell acidification which affects the integrity of cell plasma membrane as evidenced by nuclear staining with the vital dye propidium iodide and by the release of lactate dehydrogenase (LDH) to the culture media (Koizumi et al., 1996). In these cells, the increase in ROS production was prevented by uncouplers of the respiratory chain, suggesting that mitochondria are targets of Cd toxicity (Pourahmad et al., 2003). In addition to mitochondria, Cd also accumulates in the lysosomes and causes their destabilization, with the subsequent release of free iron and the enhancement of ROS production (Pourahmad et al., 2003; Fotakis et al., 2005). On the other hand, Thevenod and Friedmann (1999) exposed an immortalized cell line obtained from the S1 segment of the proximal tubule of normotensive Wistar-Kyoto rats (WKPT-0293 Cl.2 cells) to micromolar concentrations of Cd and observed that the production of ROS occurred at much prolonged times of incubation (> 4 h) than in hepatocytes. A 2.9-fold increase in H_2O_2 content was also observed in normal human lung fibroblasts (MRC-5 cells) after 3 h of exposure to 100 µM Cd (Shih et al., 2004). In addition to H_2O_2, Cd induced in renal tubular epithelial (LLC-PK1) cells the generation of $O_2^{\cdot-}$ and $ONOO^{\cdot-}$, two oxidant species involved in Cd-mediated endoplasmic reticulum stress and cell apoptosis (Yokouchi et al., 2008). Using ESR, Liu et al. (2008) demonstrated the generation of $HO^{\cdot-}$ and carbon-centered radicals in the bile of rats 60 min after a single administration of Cd (40 (g/kg). In addition, these authors were able to identify the source of this oxidant species, and proposed that Cd induces the respiratory burst of Kupffer cells –the resident macrophages in liver–, which results in $HO^{\cdot-}$ production (Liu et al., 2008).

The mobilization of intracellular pools of iron is another mechanism that may explain the generation of ROS in Cd-exposed cells. In a study performed in vitro, Price and Joshi (1983) reported that ferritin has two binding sites for Cd, with Kd of 1.56 x 10^{-6} M and 6.11 x 10^{-6} M, respectively. On this basis, it is feasible that Cd may displace Fe^{3+} from its binding sites in ferritin. Supporting this, Casalino et al. (1997) demonstrated that ferritin incubation in the presence of 75 µM Cd resulted in a time-dependent release of iron. Similar results were obtained upon the incubation of rat liver mitochondria in the presence of 5 µM Cd (Dorta et al., 2003). The main source of iron in these organelles is the iron-containing proteins that compose the electron transfer chain. The relevance of this effect of Cd is two-fold. First, it causes the release of free iron able to trigger oxidative stress through the Haber-Weiss and Fenton reactions. Second, by losing the iron atoms from its proteins, the respiratory chain becomes less effective. Therefore, there is a displacement of electrons towards ROS production instead of ATP generation. By these two mechanisms, Cd induces ROS generation, which ultimately leads to lipid and protein oxidation.

NADPH oxidases are multicomponent enzymes located at cell plasma membrane (Kleniewska et al., 2012). This family is comprised by seven members (NOX1 to 5, Duox 1 and 2). Whereas NOX1, 2, 3 and 5 use an electron from NADPH to reduce O_2 to $O_2^{\cdot-}$ (Miller et al., 2006), NOX4, Duox 1 and Duox 2 do not generate $O_2^{\cdot-}$ but H_2O_2 instead (Chen et al., 2008). Interestingly, Thijssen et al. (2007) found that a 23-weeks exposure to low Cd doses administered to mice via the drinking water resulted in increased activity of NOX4 in kidney cells, together with the enzymes of the antioxidant defense system (CAT, GPx4, and HO-1). It is well accepted that, depending on the amount generated in cells, H_2O_2 plays a biphasic role in cell survival. At high concentrations, H_2O_2 causes cell death (apoptosis or necrosis), whereas at low doses H_2O_2 promotes cell survival and growth (Gough and Cotter, 2011). Therefore, the increased activity of NOX4 in Cd-intoxicated mice may be an adaptive response that, by enhancing the expression of the antioxidant enzymes, promotes cell survival. On the other hand, the increased production of ROS in mouse hippocampal (HT4) cells incubated with Cd was partially prevented by diphenyleniodonium (DPI), an inhibitor of NADPH oxidase-like flavoproteins (Rockwell et al., 2004). Consequently, the induction of JNK and p38 –two redox-sensitive MAPK associated with ROS-induced cell apoptosis– was prevented, and the viability of cells was maintained (Rockwell et al., 2004). Although further studies are required to characterize the role of NADPH oxidases in Cd toxicity in animals, these enzymes seem to constitute another source of ROS that will decide cell fate. Worth noticing, the increased production of ROS in humans chronically exposed to Cd was associated with increased blood pressure (Lassegue and Clempus, 2003). Recently, Nwokocha et al. (2013) demonstrated that the administration of apocynin (a specific inhibitor of NADPH oxidases) significantly decreased blood pressure in Cd-intoxicated rats, an effect that resulted from the enhanced expression and activity of endothelial nitric oxide synthase (eNOS). These results support the relationship between high blood pressure and high ROS production, and point to vascular NADPH oxidase as a potential therapeutic target to ameliorate the clinical symptoms of patients intoxicated with Cd.

It has been proposed that GSH plays a key role in modulating the oxidative stress induced by Cd. It is worth pointing out that low Cd concentrations induced a slight increase in GSH content in human lung (A549) cells (Gaubin et al., 2000), whereas high Cd concentrations depleted GSH in diverse experimental models (Bagchi et al., 1996; Fortuniak et al., 1996; Nigam et al., 1999; Gaubin et al., 2000; Xu et al., 2003; Lopez et al., 2006). The pro-oxidant effect of Cd in WKPT-0293 Cl.2 cells was prevented by cell treatment with NAC (Thevenod and Friedmann, 1999). Conversely, GSH depletion upon cell treatment with L-buthionine-[S,R]-sulfoximine (BSO) increased 2-fold the production of ROS in promonocytic leukemia (U-937) cells exposed to 200 μM Cd (Galan et al., 2001). Similar observations were reported in LLC-PK1 cells by Prozialeck and Lamar (1995). These results can be interpreted from two different points of view. First, being a substrate for GSH synthesis, NAC enhances the capacity of cells to counterbalance Cd-mediated ROS production. Second, both NAC and GSH have sulfhydryl groups capable of binding Cd with high affinity (Leverrier et al., 2007), and thus these compounds may chelate Cd and decrease the amount of free metal available to promote ROS generation. In fact, Perrin and Watt (1971) characterized the complexes that Cd forms with GSH at physiological pH, and concluded that the predominant species are $[Cd(HGSH)_2]^{2-} \gg [CdH(GSH)_2]^{3-}$, $[CdGSH]^-$. On the basis of the high concentration of intracellular GSH (~10 mM), it possible to speculate that most of the Cd will be complexed with GSH. In fact, a direct exit of Cd-GSH complexes through CFTR channels –an anion transporter– was demonstrated in primary cultures of mouse proximal collector tubule cells (L'Hoste et al., 2009), a mechanism that contributes to Cd detoxification.

Finally, Cd affects the functionality of the antioxidant enzymes. The consensus is that the activity of SOD is reduced after a short-term exposure to Cd (Jurczuk et al., 2004; Lopez et al., 2006; Yalin et al., 2006; Ognjanovic et al., 2010), whereas the activity of this enzyme is increased upon a long-term exposure (Jurczuk et al., 2004; Thijssen et al., 2007). Similar observations have been reported regarding CAT activity, with decreased activities found after acute exposures to Cd (Yang et al., 1996; Casalino et al., 2002; Ognjanovic et al., 2010) and increased activities after prolonged exposures (Kostic et al., 1993; Tandon et al., 2003; Gong et al., 2008). Casalino et al. (2002) proposed that Cd may directly interact with both SOD and CAT inhibiting their activities. These authors concluded that Cd could replace Mn in the active site of MnSOD, given that the activity was fully recovered when mitochondria were supplemented with Mn (Casalino et al., 2002). On the other hand, the inhibition of CuZnSOD activity could not be ascribed to Cu and/or Zn displacement by Cd, but to an alteration of enzyme topology of the channel that contains the active site of the enzyme, thus impeding the accessibility of the substrate (Casalino et al., 2002). In the long term, cells stimulate the expression of CAT, CuZnSOD and MnSOD in an attempt to compensate the oxidative stress status caused by Cd.

In addition to CAT, H_2O_2 is also metabolized by GPx using GSH as co-substrate. This enzyme belongs to a family of selenoproteins, and bears a selenol moiety in its active site with reducing power (Brigelius-Flohe, 2006). The reaction catalyzed by GPx can be summarized as:

$$H_2O_2 + 2\ GSH \xrightarrow{\text{GPx}} H_2O + GSSG$$

In turn, glutathione disulfide produced is reduced back to GSH by the enzyme GR, as follows:

$$GSSG + NADPH \xrightarrow{\text{GR}} 2\ GSH + NADP^+$$

The pattern of alterations in GPx activity upon Cd exposure is not as clear as that observed for CAT and SOD. For example, a short-term exposure of pneumocyte II (2 h) and CHO-K1 cells (4 h) to micromolar concentrations of Cd caused a marked decrease in GPx and GR activities (Yang et al., 1996; Tatrai et al., 2001), although the mechanisms underlying such inhibition are still not elucidated. Twenty-four h after receiving a single dose of 2.5 mg/kg Cd, the activity of GPx was increased in rat liver (+41%) and kidneys (+28%) (Casalino et al., 1997). Supporting the role of GPx in H_2O_2 detoxification in this model, GR was also increased (liver: +25%, kidneys: +30%) (Casalino et al., 1997). Ognjanovic et al. (2003) also reported increased activities of GPx and GR in rats exposed to Cd for 24 h (0.4 mg/kg b.w.). Similarly to what was observed for SOD and CAT, chronic exposure to Cd (15 mg $CdCl_2$/kg b.w./d for 30 d) lead to increased activities of GPx and GR (Kostic et al., 1993). As a whole, the experimental evidence suggests that Cd causes a rapid inhibition of the enzymes responsible for H_2O_2 and $O_2^{\cdot-}$ detoxification, thus enhancing the oxidative stress status. If the dose of Cd is relatively low, a prolonged exposure to this metal can be compensated by the modulation of the expression and/or the activity of the antioxidant enzymes, thus restoring the intracellular redox status. However, prolonged exposures to Cd causes the accumulation of the metal which cannot be compensated and leads to chronic pathologies, such as cardiovascular disease and cancer (Waisberg et al., 2003).

MERCURY

a. Chemical Properties and Uses

Mercury (Hg, atomic number 80, atomic weight 200.59) is a silvery-white, shiny heavy metal that belongs to element group 12. Metallic Hg is the only one that is liquid at room temperature. The oxidation states of Hg are 0, +1 and +2 (Drasch et al., 2008).

The average concentration of Hg in the Earth's crust is 0.056 ppm with significant local variations (Wedepohl, 1995). It can be rarely found as a native metal or forming minerals such as cinnabar (HgS), corderoite ($Hg_3S_2Cl_2$), livingstonite ($HgSb_4S_8$), and others. The annual world consumption of Hg was estimated in 5,800 tons (Wedepohl, 2008). Among others, Hg is used for artisanal gold-silver mining, the fabrication of batteries, discharge lamps, explosives and fireworks, electric and electronic switches, etc. (Drasch et al., 2008). It is also used for medical purposes as a constituent of metal amalgams for dentistry, in cosmetic and pharmaceutical industries as biocides and preservatives in vaccines, eye drops, eye cosmetics, and also as pesticides (Drasch et al., 2008). Anthropogenic activities constitute the main route of Hg^0 accumulation in the atmosphere, calculated in 13 $Mmol.y^{-1}$ (Lamborg et al., 2002). Once in the atmosphere, Hg can deposit in soils and water, and the net flux of Hg^0 into the ocean was calculated in 6 $Mmol.y^{-1}$ (Lamborg et al., 2002). In water, Hg^0 can be oxidized into Hg^+ and Hg^{2+}, and also Hg particles can precipitate and deposit on the ocean floor (Lamborg et al., 2002). The concentration of Hg in river and sea water was estimated in 0.07 and <0.0002 ppb, respectively (Wedepohl, 2008). In oceanic waters, mercury mainly exists as $HgCl_4^{2-}$ and $HgCl_3^-$ but it can be also found as dimethylmercury (Me_2Hg) which is the dominant species in deep ocean waters (Drasch et al., 2008). Environmental Hg is subject to inter-conversions via oxidation/reduction and methylathion/demethylation in what Clarkson (1997) denominated "the mercury cycle".

Fish can absorb Hg from contaminated waters and accumulate it in their tissues. The average Hg (as Me_2Hg) concentration in marine finfish ranges 0.009 to 1.32 mg Hg/kg b.w. (Drasch et al., 2008 and references therein). Thus, Hg can be incorporated in the food chain, including wildlife and humans. Once ingested, Me_2Hg is efficiently absorbed and distributed to the organs via the bloodstream. Even dough Hg can be excreted through urine, this process is not complete and Hg accumulates mainly in kidneys and other organs (Drasch et al., 2008). In humans, most of the absorption of Hg vapors occurs at the respiratory tract and was estimated in 70-85% of the inhaled dose (Sandborgh-Englund et al., 1998). Absorbed Hg vapor is converted into inorganic Hg which is recovered in ~98% in the kidneys (Valko et al., 2005).

b. Effects on Human Health

Humans that were exposed for a short-term to air containing approximately 1-2 mg $Hg.m^3$ vapor presented the following clinical symptoms: metallic taste, nausea, abdominal pain, vomiting, headache, diarrhea, bronchitis and bronchiolitis, lung emphysema and disturbances of the central nervous system such as tremor and irritability (Drasch et al., 2008). Similar clinical symptoms were reported upon the ingestion of soluble salts of Hg^{2+} and organic Hg compounds. Because of its lipophilicity, absorbed Hg vapor can freely cross the blood-brain barrier (Aschner and Aschner, 1990) and the placenta (Yang et al., 1997). In addition, Hg can be transported by the olfactory neurons and reach the brain (Henriksson and Tjalve, 1998). After some days, patients presented colitis mucomembranacea, stomatitis and bleeding gums (Schwartz et al., 1992), and in the long term, they presented renal symptoms. Chronic exposure to Hg affects the central nervous system, causing characteristic emotional and psychological disturbances. In addition, alterations in the immune system, genotoxicity, carcinogenicity, and disturbances in child development have been associated with Hg poisoning, although these findings are still controversial (Valko et al., 2005). In addition, the chronic exposure to Hg has been associated with vascular-related disorders, such as hypertension, generalized atherosclerosis, coronary heart disease, myocardial infarction, cardiac arrhythmias, heart rate variability, sudden death, cerebrovascular accidents, and carotid artery disease (Houston, 2011). The impact of environmental Hg on human health has been reviewed by Tchounwou et al. (2003) and Holmes et al. (2009).

c. Hg and Oxidative Stress

Several in vitro and in vivo reports relate the exposure to either inorganic or organic Hg with the induction of an oxidative stress status. In a study performed in mice exposed to either low (0.8 µg/kg b.w.) or mid (8 µg/kg b.w.) doses of $HgCl_2$ administered orally twice a week for two weeks, Mahboob et al. (2001) observed markedly increased (> 50%) levels of lipid peroxidation products in the kidneys, testis and epididymus, and only slight increases in the brain and liver. Similar results were reported by El-Demerdash (2001) who, after the administration of five consecutive oral doses of $HgCl_2$ (2 mg/kg b.w.) to rats, observed a 43% increase in the content of lipid peroxidation products in the liver, accompanied by an 18% increase in the brain. Interestingly, the oxidative damage to the liver in this experimental model was partially prevented by the simultaneous administration of selenium (Se, 2 mg/kg b.w.) (El-Demerdash, 2001). The importance of Se and Se-compounds in the toxicity of Hg will be discussed later in this chapter. In a pancreatic β-cell line (HIT-T15 cells) exposed to $HgCl_2$, a time- and concentration-dependent increase in ROS production was evidenced by the oxidation of the fluorescent probe DCF, which was in turn prevented by cell treatment with NAC (Chen et al., 2010). In addition, in an in vitro study using rat proximal tubular (NRK-52E) cells, Stacchiotti et al. (2009) found that 20 µM $HgCl_2$ caused a time- and concentration-dependent increase in ROS content, which was accompanied by mitochondrial damage and necrosis.

Until the present, no evidence has been found that Hg^+ or Hg^{2+} can generate per se oxidant species via Haber-Weiss or Fenton-like reactions and, thus, no generation of $HO^{\bullet-}$ or other ROS is expected upon Hg exposure. Supporting this, the incubation of LDL with 16 µM $HgCl_2$ −in the absence of further oxidants− did not affect LDL content of unsaturated fatty acids that are prone to be oxidized by ROS (Seppanen et al., 2004). In spite of this, there are reports suggesting that $HO^{\bullet-}$ is generated in experimental models of Hg^{2+} intoxication. For example, in human bronchial epithelial (BEAS-2B) cells incubated for only 10 min in the presence of 100 µM $HgCl_2$ significant amounts of $HO^{\bullet-}$ were evidenced by the appearance of an ESR signal corresponding to the DMPO-$^{\bullet}$OH adduct (Han et al., 2007), although the generation of this adduct was partially prevented by the $HO^{\bullet-}$ scavenger sodium formate (Han et al., 2007). In another study where rats were fed Hg-containing rice, increased levels of DMPO-$^{\bullet}$OH adduct were detected in their brains (Ji et al., 2006). In support of these findings, the potent $HO^{\bullet-}$ scavenger melatonin prevented the oxidative damage to kidneys from rats that received a single subcutaneous injection of $HgCl_2$ (2.5 mg/kg b.w.) (Nava et al., 2000). Finally, the exposure of human glioma (A172) cells to 20 µM $HgCl_2$ resulted in a marked decrease in cell viability after 60 min of incubation, an effect that was prevented by $HO^{\bullet-}$ scavengers but not by H_2O_2, $O_2^{\bullet-}$ or $ONOO^{\bullet-}$ scavengers (Lee et al., 2001). However, this finding does not necessarily indicate that $HO^{\cdot\cdot}$ was generated in this experimental model, because the $HO^{\cdot\cdot}$ scavengers assessed were dimethilthiourea and thiourea, and these two molecules are capable of forming stable complexes with Hg^{2+} (Paller, 1985). Therefore, the action of these compounds preventing Hg^{2+} oxidative damage could be mediated by the complexation of the metal rather than by the scavenging of the $HO^{\cdot\cdot}$ generated in the system.

On the basis of the above, the generation of $HO^{\cdot\cdot}$ –if any– must occur through a different mechanism. A plausible explanation involves an increase in total content and/or the mobilization of the physiological redox metals, iron and copper. In rats, the administration $HgCl_2$ (20 mg/l) with drinking water caused after 44 days either no changes or a tendency toward lower iron content in the kidneys, brain, spleen and liver (Bogden et al., 1980). In contrast, a marked increase in copper content was observed in the kidneys and brain, while no changes were found in the spleen and liver (Bogden et al., 1980). Also in rats, a single dose of $HgCl$ (1, 3 or 5 mg/kg b.w.) produced no alterations in iron content in the liver, kidney, lung, spleen, testis or muscle (Huang and Lin, 1997). However, the content of copper was increased 2-fold in the kidneys but it was unaffected in the other organs investigated (Huang and Lin, 1997). In a pioneer work, Van Campen (1966) reported that $HgCl_2$ caused a moderate decrease in the absorption of ^{64}Cu administered orally, and that ^{64}Cu was accumulated mostly in the kidneys instead of the liver. Consequently, it is possible that copper accumulation in the kidneys will participate in Haber-Weiss and Fenton reactions, thus enhancing the local production of $HO^{\cdot\cdot}$ and other ROS.

Another ROS that participates in Hg-mediated oxidative stress is $O_2^{\cdot\cdot}$. This particular species can be generated either by mitochondrial complexes I and III of the electron transport chain, or by the enzyme NADPH oxidase located at the plasma membrane. Regardless of its source, $O_2^{\cdot\cdot}$ will be rapidly metabolized by the corresponding SOD –MnSOD in mitochondria, CuZnSOD in cytosol– rendering H_2O_2. Using a fluorescent probe specific for $O_2^{\cdot\cdot}$, Shanker et al. (2004) observed that the mitochondria were the primary source of this ROS upon the exposure of cultured astrocytes to methylmercury ($MeHg^+$). In addition, Mori et al. (2007) observed increased $O_2^{\cdot\cdot}$ production in liver mitochondria isolated from rats that were previously intoxicated with $MeHg^+$. Supporting the role of mitochondria production of $O_2^{\cdot\cdot}$ upon $MeHg^+$ intoxication, Naganuma et al. (1998) observed in cultured HeLa cells that the overexpression of MnSOD but not of CuZnSOD, CAT, or GPx, limited the oxidative damage induced by $MeHg^+$. On the other hand, Aguado et al. (2013) observed that $HgCl_2$ increased the activity of NADPH oxidase in primary cultures of vascular smooth muscle cells. This effect depended on both the concentration of $HgCl_2$ and the time of exposure, and it was accompanied by an increase in $O_2^{\cdot\cdot}$ production (Aguado et al., 2013). Supporting this finding, the simultaneous administration of $HgCl_2$ and the specific inhibitor of NADPH oxidase apocynin to rats prevented the vascular effects caused by the chronic administration of $HgCl_2$ (Rizzetti et al., 2013).

The generation of H_2O_2 also has been demonstrated in several experimental models of $MeHg^+$ or $HgCl_2$ intoxication. In fact, it has been suggested that the electron transport chain is the earliest target of $MeHg^+$ toxicity leading to enhanced production of H_2O_2 (Yee and Choi, 1996). Supporting that, Lund et al. (1991) observed that $HgCl_2$ markedly increased H_2O_2 production in isolated mitochondria with impaired electron transport chain. Similarly, increased H_2O_2 and $O_2^{\cdot\cdot}$ production were observed in primary cultures of astrocytes exposed to 10 μM $MeHg^+$ for 30 min (Shanker et al., 2005). Working with isolated mouse brain mitochondria Franco et al. (2007) reported that both $HgCl_2$ and $MeHg^+$ increased by 80% the generation of H_2O_2 and by 50% the content of lipid peroxidation products. Also, cerebellar mitochondria isolated from rats that received $MeHg^+$ orally (10 mg/kg b.w.) for 5 days had increased oxygen consumption associated with high H_2O_2 production (Mori et al., 2007). The increased levels of H_2O_2 found upon $MeHg^+$ or $HgCl_2$ exposure may be caused not only by a direct effect of Hg with the components of the electron transport chain, but also by the inhibition of GPx. Thus, Hg may directly interact with GSH and/or GPx itself and impair the detoxification of H_2O_2 and other organic peroxides.

The possibility that oxidative stress caused by $HgCl_2$ and $MeHg^+$ may be related to decreased levels of GSH has been tested in a variety of experimental models. For example, working with isolated rat kidney mitochondria, Lund et al. (1991) observed that $HgCl_2$ caused an almost complete depletion of mitochondrial GSH after 30 min of incubation. Similarly, both $HgCl_2$ and $MeHg^+$ caused a concentration-dependent depletion of mouse brain mitochondrial GSH, equivalent to an 80% decrease at the highest concentration of Hg assessed (100 μM) (Franco et al., 2007). This effect was accompanied by impaired capacity of the mitochondrial enzyme succinate dehydrogenase –the complex II of the electron transport chain– to metabolize MTT dye, and by increased levels of H_2O_2 (Franco et al., 2007). Kaur et al. (2006) demonstrated that GSH plays a key role in the extent of the oxidative stress induced by $MeHg^+$ in primary cultures of cerebellar astrocytes and neurons. In these cells, $MeHg^+$ (5 μM) caused a 4-fold increase in ROS production. When cells were partially depleted in GSH with diethyl maleate, ROS content increased up to 5-fold the control value (Kaur et al., 2006). Conversely, cell supplementation with GSH precursor NAC prevented the effect of $MeHg^+$ on ROS production completely (in astrocytes) or partially (in neurons) (Kaur et al., 2006). The effect of GSH on the extent of $MeHg^+$-mediated oxidative damage to cells is two-fold. First, it provides antioxidant protection against the increased production of oxidant species, and second, it limits the accumulation of the metal within cells (Kaur et al., 2006). The latter is related to the fact that GSH-Hg conjugates, by virtue of their negative charge and size, can be extruded via the organic anion transporters thus helping cells to eliminate accumulated Hg (Valko et al., 2005). However, since the intracellular concentration of GSH largely exceeds the concentration of Hg, it should be enough to compensate the production of ROS. On the other hand, taking into consideration that upon Hg intoxication there is an oxidative stress status, the enhanced production of ROS must be the result of the action of Hg on other component/s of the antioxidant defense system.

$MeHg^+$ is a soft electrophile and, as a consequence it preferentially reacts with soft bases (nucleophiles). Selenol-containing molecules, such as the enzyme GPx, are softer bases than thiol-containing molecules and thus, $MeHg^+$ will bind to molecules having selenol groups rather than to those having thiols (Farina et al., 2011). In support of this finding, the activity of GPx was impaired in a large number of experimental models of Hg^{2+} intoxication (Nava et al., 2000; Mahboob et al., 2001; Manfroi et al., 2004; Mori et al., 2007; Farina et al., 2009; Franco et al., 2009; Branco et al., 2012a; Harisa et al., 2013), and the benefits of the administration of Se (Branco et al., 2012a) or seleno-compounds (Meinerz et al., 2011) to prevent $MeHg^+$-mediated neurotoxicity have been reported. In addition to GPx, $HgCl_2$ and $MeHg^+$ inhibit the thioredoxin (Trx)-dependent antioxidant system, which participates in the detoxification of H_2O_2 and other organic peroxides (Mustacich and Powis, 2000). Similar to the GSH-dependent antioxidant system, this one involves the coordinated action of the enzymes thioredoxin peroxidase also known as peroxiredoxin (Prx) and thioredoxin reductase (TrxR), in a sequence of reactions that can be summarized as follows:

$$H_2O_2 + Trx(SH)_2 \longrightarrow H_2O + Trx(S)_2$$

$$Trx(S)_2 + NADPH \xrightarrow{\ \ TrxR\ \ } Trx(SH)_2 + NADP^+$$

TrxR contains a total of 14 Cys residues, three of them located at the active site of the enzyme together with a selenocysteine (Mustacich and Powis, 2000). In vitro, the incubation of homogenates obtained from liver, brain or kidneys with $MeHg^+$ (0.025-1 µM) caused the inactivation of TrxR, with half-inhibitory concentrations (IC_{50}) of 0.071, 0.158 and 0.078 µM, respectively (Wagner et al., 2010). Worthy of notice, when rats were acutely exposed to a single dose of 1, 5 or 10 mg $MeHg^+$/kg b.w. administered by oral gavage, the activity of TrxR was only inhibited in the liver and kidneys, while no significant changes were observed in the brain (Wagner et al., 2010). On the other hand, in a chronic model of $MeHg^+$ intoxication in rats (5 mg/kg b.w./d, intragastrically), the activity of TrxR was decreased in the liver (-38%), brain (-64.3%) and kidneys (-73.8%) (Dalla Corte et al., 2013). Similarly, the exposure of juvenile zebra seabreams (*Diplodus cervinus*) for 28 days to water containing either $MeHg^+$ or $HgCl_2$ (2 µg/l) resulted in a time-dependent accumulation of Hg in the brain, liver, kidneys and muscle accompanied by a decreased activity of TrxR (Branco et al., 2012a). These authors observed that even when $HgCl_2$ accumulated less than $MeHg^+$ in the organs, the inhibitory effects of both mercurial molecules on TrxR were similar (Branco et al., 2012a). Moreover, the extent of $MeHg^+$- and $HgCl_2$-dependent inhibition of TrxR activity correlated with the histopathological alterations found in these organs, making the measurement of TrxR activity a potential biomarker of Hg toxicity (Branco et al., 2012b).

CONCLUSION

The occupational or environmental exposure to heavy metals, such as Co, Ni, Cd and Hg constitutes a hazard for human health. Among the many biochemical and cell signaling pathways that these metals may affect –whose analysis escapes the scope of this chapter–a common mechanism emerges, i.e., the alteration of intracellular redox status. The first reason of such alteration is the increased generation of ROS ($O_2^{\cdot-}$, $HO^{\cdot}$ and H_2O_2, Figure 1), which will oxidize the intracellular components. In addition, these oxidant species activate certain signaling cascades that will ultimately decide cell fate.

The second reason is the harmful effect of the metals on the antioxidant defense system (summarized in Figure 1), which comprises a group of molecules and enzymes devoted to neutralize the deleterious effects of ROS. Co, Ni, Cd and Hg bind to –SH groups with high affinity, and this kind of binding negatively affects the functionality of the glutathione- and thioredoxin-dependent antioxidant defense systems. GSH being the most abundant soluble antioxidant, its consumption and/or oxidation decreases cell efficiency to sustain the reduced environment required to the proper functioning of most enzymes, channels and receptors. Besides the increased ROS content due to GSH consumption, the binding of the metals to the active site of antioxidant enzymes affects their functionality. They can also interact with aminoacids in the proximities of the active site and induce conformational alterations that affect the catalytic properties and/or limit the accessibility of the substrates to the active site. On the other hand, the possibility that these metals affect the Trx-dependent antioxidant defense system is an only partially characterized aspect of heavy metals toxicology, and deserves further investigations.

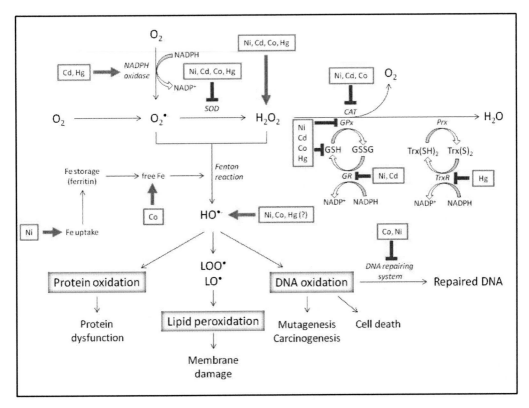

Figure 1. Proposed sites of action of Ni, Co, Cd and Hg that lead to enhanced oxidative damage to intracellular components.
Green arrows denote stimulation; blunted red lines indicate inhibition. For details, see text.

Through the exacerbated generation of ROS, these and other heavy metals indirectly induce the damage to lipids, proteins and DNA. In particular, the oxidative modifications to DNA bases, together with the inhibition of the DNA repairing system, are both pro-mutagenic effects, and support the linkage between metal-mediated oxidative stress and carcinogenicity.

REFERENCES

Aguado, A., Galan, M., Zhenyukh, O., Wiggers, G.A., Roque, F.R., Redondo, S., Pecanha, F., Martin, A., Fortuno, A., Cachofeiro, V., Tejerina, T., Salaices, M., Briones, A.M., 2013. Mercury induces proliferation and reduces cell size in vascular smooth muscle cells through MAPK, oxidative stress and cyclooxygenase-2 pathways. *Toxicol Appl Pharmacol* 268, 188-200.

Anard, D., Kirsch-Volders, M., Elhajouji, A., Belpaeme, K., Lison, D., 1997. In vitro genotoxic effects of hard metal particles assessed by alkaline single cell gel and elution assays. *Carcinogenesis* 18, 177-184.

Aschner, M., Aschner, J.L., 1990. Mercury neurotoxicity: mechanisms of blood-brain barrier transport. *Neurosci Biobehav Rev* 14, 169-176.

Athar, M., Hasan, S.K., Srivastava, R.C., 1987. Evidence for the involvement of hydroxyl radicals in nickel mediated enhancement of lipid peroxidation: implications for nickel carcinogenesis. *Biochem Biophys Res Commun* 147, 1276-1281.

ATSDR, 1998. Toxicological Profile for Cadmium. *ATSDR* (Agency for Toxic Substances and Disease Registry). Atlanta, GA.

ATSDR, 2004. Toxicological profile for Cobalt. *ATSDR* (Agency for Toxic Substances and Disease Registry). Atlanta, GA.

ATSDR, 2005. Toxicological profile for Nickel. *ATSDR* (Agency for Toxic Substances and Disease Registry). Atlanta, GA.

Bagchi, D., Bagchi, M., Hassoun, E.A., Stohs, S.J., 1996. Cadmium-induced excretion of urinary lipid metabolites, DNA damage, glutathione depletion, and hepatic lipid peroxidation in Sprague-Dawley rats. *Biol Trace Elem Res* 52, 143-154.

Bal, W., Jezowska-Bojczuk, M., Kasprzak, K.S., 1997a. Binding of nickel(II) and copper(II) to the N-terminal sequence of human protamine HP2. *Chem Res Toxicol* 10, 906-914.

Bal, W., Lukszo, J., Kasprzak, K.S., 1997b. Mediation of oxidative DNA damage by nickel(II) and copper(II) complexes with the N-terminal sequence of human protamine HP2. *Chem Res Toxicol* 10, 915-921.

Battaglia, V., Compagnone, A., Bandino, A., Bragadin, M., Rossi, C.A., Zanetti, F., Colombatto, S., Grillo, M.A., Toninello, A., 2009. Cobalt induces oxidative stress in isolated liver mitochondria responsible for permeability transition and intrinsic apoptosis in hepatocyte primary cultures. *Int J Biochem Cell Biol* 41, 586-594.

Bertin, G., Averbeck, D., 2006. Cadmium: cellular effects, modifications of biomolecules, modulation of DNA repair and genotoxic consequences (a review). *Biochimie* 88, 1549-1559.

Beyersmann, D., Hartwig, A., 2008. Carcinogenic metal compounds: recent insight into molecular and cellular mechanisms. *Arch Toxicol* 82, 493-512.

Bogden, J.D., Kemp, F.W., Troiano, R.A., Jortner, B.S., Timpone, C., Giuliani, D., 1980. Effect of mercuric chloride and methylmercury chloride exposure on tissue concentrations of six essential minerals. *Environ Res* 21, 350-359.

Branco, V., Canario, J., Lu, J., Holmgren, A., Carvalho, C., 2012a. Mercury and selenium interaction in vivo: effects on thioredoxin reductase and glutathione peroxidase. *Free Radic Biol Med* 52, 781-793.

Branco, V., Ramos, P., Canario, J., Lu, J., Holmgren, A., Carvalho, C., 2012b. Biomarkers of adverse response to mercury: histopathology versus thioredoxin reductase activity. *J Biomed Biotechnol* 2012, 359879.

Brigelius-Flohe, R., 2006. Glutathione peroxidases and redox-regulated transcription factors. *Biol Chem* 387, 1329-1335.

Bunick, D., Balhorn, R., Stanker, L.H., Hecht, N.B., 1990. Expression of the rat protamine 2 gene is suppressed at the level of transcription and translation. *Exp Cell Res* 188, 147-152.

Cameron, K.S., Buchner, V., Tchounwou, P.B., 2011. Exploring the molecular mechanisms of nickel-induced genotoxicity and carcinogenicity: a literature review. *Rev Environ Health* 26, 81-92.

Carmichael, N.G., Backhouse, B.L., Winder, C., Lewis, P.D., 1982. Teratogenicity, toxicity and perinatal effects of cadmium. *Hum Toxicol* 1, 159-186.

Cartañà, J., Romeu, A., Arola, L., 1992. Effects of copper, cadmium and nickel on liver and kidney glutathione redox cycle of rats (Rattus sp.). *Comp Biochem Physiol* C 101, 209-213.

Caruso, R.V., O'Connor, R.J., Stephens, W.E., Cummings, K.M., Fong, G.T., 2014. Toxic metal concentrations in cigarettes obtained from U.S. smokers in 2009: results from the International Tobacco Control (ITC) United States survey cohort. *Int J Environ Res Public Health* 11, 202-217.

Casalino, E., Calzaretti, G., Sblano, C., Landriscina, C., 2002. Molecular inhibitory mechanisms of antioxidant enzymes in rat liver and kidney by cadmium. *Toxicology* 179, 37-50.

Casalino, E., Sblano, C., Landriscina, C., 1997. Enzyme activity alteration by cadmium administration to rats: the possibility of iron involvement in lipid peroxidation. *Arch Biochem Biophys* 346, 171-179.

Cempel, M., Nikel, G., 2006. Nickel: A review of its sources and environmental toxicology. *Polish J of Environ Stud* 15, 375-382.

Ciccarelli, R.B., Wetterhahn, K.E., 1982. Nickel distribution and DNA lesions induced in rat tissues by the carcinogen nickel carbonate. *Cancer Res* 42, 3544-3549.

Clarkson, T.W., 1997. The toxicology of mercury. *Crit Rev Clin Lab Sci* 34, 369-403.

Costa, M., Heck, J.D., 1984. Perspectives on the mechanism of nickel carcinogenesis. *Adv Inorg Biochem* 6, 285-309.

Cotelle, N., Tremolieres, E., Bernier, J.L., Catteau, J.P., Henichart, J.P., 1992. Redox chemistry of complexes of nickel(II) with some biologically important peptides in the presence of reduced oxygen species: an ESR study. *J Inorg Biochem* 46, 7-15.

Crea, F., Foti, C., Milea, D., Sammartano, S., 2013. Speciation of Cadmium in the Environment, in: A. Sigel, H. Sigel, R.K.O. Sigel (Eds.), *Cadmium: From Toxicity to Essentiality*. Springer Netherlands, pp. 63-83.

Cullen, J., Maldonado, M., 2013. Biogeochemistry of Cadmium and Its Release to the Environment, in: A. Sigel, H. Sigel, R.K.O. Sigel (Eds.), *Cadmium: From Toxicity to Essentiality*. Springer Netherlands, pp. 31-62.

Cuypers, A., Plusquin, M., Remans, T., Jozefczak, M., Keunen, E., Gielen, H., Opdenakker, K., Nair, A.R., Munters, E., Artois, T.J., Nawrot, T., Vangronsveld, J., Smeets, K., 2010. Cadmium stress: an oxidative challenge. *Biometals* 23, 927-940.

Chen, C.Y., Huang, Y.L., Lin, T.H., 1998. Lipid peroxidation in liver of mice administrated with nickel chloride: with special reference to trace elements and antioxidants. *Biol Trace Elem Res* 61, 193-205.

Chen, K., Kirber, M.T., Xiao, H., Yang, Y., Keaney, J.F., Jr., 2008. Regulation of ROS signal transduction by NADPH oxidase 4 localization. *J Cell Biol* 181, 1129-1139.

Chen, Y.W., Huang, C.F., Yang, C.Y., Yen, C.C., Tsai, K.S., Liu, S.H., 2010. Inorganic mercury causes pancreatic beta-cell death via the oxidative stress-induced apoptotic and necrotic pathways. *Toxicol Appl Pharmacol* 243, 323-331.

Chernoff, N., 1973. Teratogenic effects of cadmium in rats. *Teratology* 8, 29-32.

Choi, J., Corder, N.L., Koduru, B., Wang, Y., 2014. Oxidative stress and hepatic Nox proteins in chronic hepatitis C and hepatocellular carcinoma. *Free Radic Biol Med* 72C, 267-284.

Christova, T., Duridanova, D., Braykova, A., Setchenska, M., Bolton, T., 2001. Heme oxygenase is the main protective enzyme in rat liver upon 6-day administration of cobalt chloride. *Arch Toxicol* 75, 445-451.

Dalla Corte, C.L., Wagner, C., Sudati, J.H., Comparsi, B., Leite, G.O., Busanello, A., Soares, F.A., Aschner, M., Rocha, J.B., 2013. Effects of diphenyl diselenide on methylmercury toxicity in rats. *Biomed Res Int* 2013, 983821.

Dally, H., Hartwig, A., 1997. Induction and repair inhibition of oxidative DNA damage by nickel(II) and cadmium(II) in mammalian cells. *Carcinogenesis* 18, 1021-1026.

Das, K.K., Dasgupta, S., 2000. Effect of nickel on testicular nucleic acid concentrations of rats on protein restriction. *Biol Trace Elem Res* 73, 175-180.

Das, K.K., Gupta, A.D., Dhundasi, S.A., Patil, A.M., Das, S.N., Ambekar, J.G., 2007. Protective role of L-ascorbic acid on antioxidant defense system in erythrocytes of albino rats exposed to nickel sulfate. *Biometals* 20, 177-184.

De Luca, G., Gugliotta, T., Parisi, G., Romano, P., Geraci, A., Romano, O., Scuteri, A., Romano, L., 2007. Effects of nickel on human and fish red blood cells. *Biosci Rep* 27, 265-273.

Denkhaus, E., Salnikow, K., 2002. Nickel essentiality, toxicity, and carcinogenicity. *Crit Rev Oncol Hematol* 42, 35-56.

Dorta, D.J., Leite, S., DeMarco, K.C., Prado, I.M., Rodrigues, T., Mingatto, F.E., Uyemura, S.A., Santos, A.C., Curti, C., 2003. A proposed sequence of events for cadmium-induced mitochondrial impairment. *J Inorg Biochem* 97, 251-257.

Drasch, G., Horvat, M., Stoeppler, M., 2008. *Mercury, Elements and Their Compounds in the Environment*. Wiley-VCH Verlag GmbH, pp. 931-1005.

Duffus, J.H., 2002. Heavy metals" a meaningless term. *Pure Appl Chem* 74, 793–807.

Eichhorn, G.L., Shin, Y.A., 1968. Interaction of metal ions with polynucleotides and related compounds. XII. The relative effect of various metal ions on DNA helicity. J Am Chem Soc 90, 7323-7328.

El-Demerdash, F.M., 2001. Effects of selenium and mercury on the enzymatic activities and lipid peroxidation in brain, liver, and blood of rats. *J Environ Sci Health* B 36, 489-499.

Farina, M., Aschner, M., Rocha, J.B., 2011. Oxidative stress in MeHg-induced neurotoxicity. *Toxicol Appl Pharmacol* 256, 405-417.

Farina, M., Campos, F., Vendrell, I., Berenguer, J., Barzi, M., Pons, S., Sunol, C., 2009. Probucol increases glutathione peroxidase-1 activity and displays long-lasting protection against methylmercury toxicity in cerebellar granule cells. *Toxicol Sci* 112, 416-426.

Ferm, V.H., Carpenter, S.J., 1967. Teratogenic effect of cadmium and its inhibition by zinc. *Nature* 216, 1123.

Fleury, C., Petit, A., Mwale, F., Antoniou, J., Zukor, D.J., Tabrizian, M., Huk, O.L., 2006. Effect of cobalt and chromium ions on human MG-63 osteoblasts in vitro: morphology, cytotoxicity, and oxidative stress. *Biomaterials* 27, 3351-3360.

Fortuniak, A., Zadzinski, R., Bilinski, T., Bartosz, G., 1996. Glutathione depletion in the yeast Saccharomyces cerevisiae. *Biochem Mol Biol Int* 38, 901-910.

Fotakis, G., Cemeli, E., Anderson, D., Timbrell, J.A., 2005. Cadmium chloride-induced DNA and lysosomal damage in a hepatoma cell line. *Toxicol In Vitro* 19, 481-489.

Franco, J.L., Braga, H.C., Stringari, J., Missau, F.C., Posser, T., Mendes, B.G., Leal, R.B., Santos, A.R.S., Dafre, A.L., Pizzolatti, M.G., Farina, M., 2007. Mercurial-Induced

Hydrogen Peroxide Generation in Mouse Brain Mitochondria: Protective Effects of Quercetin. *Chem Res Toxicol* 20, 1919-1926.

Franco, J.L., Posser, T., Dunkley, P.R., Dickson, P.W., Mattos, J.J., Martins, R., Bainy, A.C., Marques, M.R., Dafre, A.L., Farina, M., 2009. Methylmercury neurotoxicity is associated with inhibition of the antioxidant enzyme glutathione peroxidase. *Free Radic Biol Med* 47, 449-457.

Galan, A., Garcia-Bermejo, L., Troyano, A., Vilaboa, N.E., Fernandez, C., de Blas, E., Aller, P., 2001. The role of intracellular oxidation in death induction (apoptosis and necrosis) in human promonocytic cells treated with stress inducers (cadmium, heat, X-rays). *Eur J Cell Biol* 80, 312-320.

Gaubin, Y., Vaissade, F., Croute, F., Beau, B., Soleilhavoup, J., Murat, J., 2000. Implication of free radicals and glutathione in the mechanism of cadmium-induced expression of stress proteins in the A549 human lung cell-line. *Biochim Biophys Acta* 1495, 4-13.

Gong, P., Chen, F.X., Ma, G.F., Feng, Y., Zhao, Q., Wang, R., 2008. Endomorphin 1 effectively protects cadmium chloride-induced hepatic damage in mice. *Toxicology* 251, 35-44.

Gough, D.R., Cotter, T.G., 2011. Hydrogen peroxide: a Jekyll and Hyde signalling molecule. *Cell Death Dis* 2, e213.

Goyer, R., Cherian, M., 1995. Renal effects of metals. *Metal Toxicology,* 389-412.

Gupta, A.D., Dhundasi, S.A., Ambekar, J.G., Das, K.K., 2007. Effect of l-ascorbic acid on antioxidant defense system in testes of albino rats exposed to nickel sulfate. *J Basic Clin Physiol Pharmacol* 18, 255-266.

Gupta, A.D., Patil, A.M., Ambekar, J.G., Das, S.N., Dhundasi, S.A., Das, K.K., 2006. L-ascorbic acid protects the antioxidant defense system in nickel-exposed albino rat lung tissue. *J Basic Clin Physiol Pharmacol* 17, 87-100.

Han, S.G., Castranova, V., Vallyathan, V., 2007. Comparative cytotoxicity of cadmium and mercury in a human bronchial epithelial cell line (BEAS-2B) and its role in oxidative stress and induction of heat shock protein 70. *J Toxicol Environ Health A* 70, 852-860.

Hanna, P.M., Kadiiska, M.B., Mason, R.P., 1992. Oxygen-derived free radical and active oxygen complex formation from cobalt(II) chelates in vitro. *Chem Res Toxicol* 5, 109-115.

Hansen, J.M., Zhang, H., Jones, D.P., 2006. Differential oxidation of thioredoxin-1, thioredoxin-2, and glutathione by metal ions. *Free Radic Biol Med* 40, 138-145.

Harisa, G.I., Mariee, A.D., Abo-Salem, O.M., Attiaa, S.M., 2013. Erythrocyte nitric oxide synthase as a surrogate marker for mercury-induced vascular damage: The modulatory effects of naringin. *Environ Toxicol* (in press).

Hasan, M., Ali, S.F., 1981. Effects of thallium, nickel, and cobalt administration of the lipid peroxidation in different regions of the rat brain. *Toxicol Appl Pharmacol* 57, 8-13.

Henriksson, J., Tjalve, H., 1998. Uptake of inorganic mercury in the olfactory bulbs via olfactory pathways in rats. *Environ Res* 77, 130-140.

Hoekstra, K.A., Godin, D.V., Cheng, K.M., 2004. Protective role of heme oxygenase in the blood vessel wall during atherogenesis. *Biochem Cell Biol* 82, 351-359.

Holmes, P., James, K.A., Levy, L.S., 2009. Is low-level environmental mercury exposure of concern to human health? *Sci Total Environ* 408, 171-182.

Houston, M.C., 2011. Role of mercury toxicity in hypertension, cardiovascular disease, and stroke. *J Clin Hypertens (Greenwich)* 13, 621-627.

Huang, Y.-L., Lin, T.-H., 1997. Effect of acute administration of mercuric chloride on the disposition of copper, zinc, and iron in the rat. *Biol Trace Elem Res* 58, 159-168.

Ivancsits, S., Diem, E., Pilger, A., Rudiger, H.W., 2002. Induction of 8-hydroxy-2'-deoxyguanosine by cobalt(II) and hydrogen peroxide in vitro. *J Toxicol Environ Health A* 65, 665-676.

Ivanova, D., Bakalova, R., Lazarova, D., Gadjeva, V., Zhelev, Z., 2013. The impact of reactive oxygen species on anticancer therapeutic strategies. *Adv Clin Exp Med* 22, 899-908.

Ji, X.L., Cheng, J.P., Wang, W.H., Qu, L.Y., Zhao, X.X., Zhuang, H.S., 2006. Induction of free radicals after dietary exposure by mercury contaminated rice and protective effect of coexisting selenium. *Huan Jing Ke Xue* 27, 2087-2090.

Johri, N., Jacquillet, G., Unwin, R., 2010. Heavy metal poisoning: the effects of cadmium on the kidney. *Biometals* 23, 783-792.

Jomova, K., Valko, M., 2011. Advances in metal-induced oxidative stress and human disease. *Toxicology* 283, 65-87.

Joshi, S., Husain, M.M., Chandra, R., Hasan, S.K., Srivastava, R.C., 2005. Hydroxyl radical formation resulting from the interaction of nickel complexes of L-histidine, glutathione or L-cysteine and hydrogen peroxide. *Hum Exp Toxicol* 24, 13-17.

Jozefczak, M., Remans, T., Vangronsveld, J., Cuypers, A., 2012. Glutathione is a key player in metal-induced oxidative stress defenses. *Int J Mol Sci* 13, 3145-3175.

Jurczuk, M., Brzoska, M.M., Moniuszko-Jakoniuk, J., Galazyn-Sidorczuk, M., Kulikowska-Karpinska, E., 2004. Antioxidant enzymes activity and lipid peroxidation in liver and kidney of rats exposed to cadmium and ethanol. *Food Chem Toxicol* 42, 429-438.

Kalahasthi, R.B., Hirehal Raghavendra Rao, R., Bagalur Krishna Murthy, R., 2006. Plasma lipid peroxidation and erythrocyte antioxidants status in workers exposed to nickel. *Biomarkers* 11, 241-249.

Kasprzak, K.S., Sunderman, F.W., Jr., Salnikow, K., 2003. Nickel carcinogenesis. *Mutat Res* 533, 67-97.

Kauppinen, A., Suuronen, T., Ojala, J., Kaarniranta, K., Salminen, A., 2013. Antagonistic crosstalk between NF-kappaB and SIRT1 in the regulation of inflammation and metabolic disorders. *Cell Signal* 25, 1939-1948.

Kaur, P., Aschner, M., Syversen, T., 2006. Glutathione modulation influences methyl mercury induced neurotoxicity in primary cell cultures of neurons and astrocytes. *NeuroToxicology* 27, 492-500.

Kawanishi, S., Inoue, S., Yamamoto, K., 1989. Site-specific DNA damage induced by nickel(II) ion in the presence of hydrogen peroxide. *Carcinogenesis* 10, 2231-2235.

Kleniewska, P., Piechota, A., Skibska, B., Goraca, A., 2012. The NADPH oxidase family and its inhibitors. *Arch Immunol Ther Exp (Warsz)* 60, 277-294.

Koizumi, T., Shirakura, H., Kumagai, H., Tatsumoto, H., Suzuki, K.T., 1996. Mechanism of cadmium-induced cytotoxicity in rat hepatocytes: cadmium-induced active oxygen-related permeability changes of the plasma membrane. *Toxicology* 114, 125-134.

Kostic, M.M., Ognjanovic, B., Dimitrijevic, S., Zikic, R.V., Stajn, A., Rosic, G.L., Zivkovic, R.V., 1993. Cadmium-induced changes of antioxidant and metabolic status in red blood cells of rats: in vivo effects. *Eur J Haematol* 51, 86-92.

Krezel, A., Bal, W., 2004. Studies of zinc(II) and nickel(II) complexes of GSH, GSSG and their analogs shed more light on their biological relevance. *Bioinorg Chem Appl,* 293-305.

Kubrak, O.I., Husak, V.V., Rovenko, B.M., Storey, J.M., Storey, K.B., Lushchak, V.I., 2011. Cobalt-induced oxidative stress in brain, liver and kidney of goldfish Carassius auratus. *Chemosphere* 85, 983-989.

L'Hoste, S., Chargui, A., Belfodil, R., Duranton, C., Rubera, I., Mograbi, B., Poujeol, C., Tauc, M., Poujeol, P., 2009. CFTR mediates cadmium-induced apoptosis through modulation of ROS level in mouse proximal tubule cells. *Free Radic Biol Med* 46, 1017-1031.

Lamborg, C.H., Fitzgerald, W.F., O'Donnell, J., Torgersen, T., 2002. A non-steady-state compartmental model of global-scale mercury biogeochemistry with interhemispheric atmospheric gradients. *Geochimica et Cosmochimica Acta* 66, 1105-1118.

Lassegue, B., Clempus, R.E., 2003. Vascular NAD(P)H oxidases: specific features, expression, and regulation. *Am J Physiol Regul Integr Comp Physiol* 285, R277-297.

Lee, Y., Ha, M., Kim, Y., 2001. Role of Reactive Oxygen Species and Glutathione in Inorganic Mercury-Induced Injury in Human Glioma Cells. *Neurochemical Research* 26, 1187-1193.

Leonard, S., M. Gannett, P., Rojanasakul, Y., Schwegler-Berry, D., Castranova, V., Vallyathan, V., Shi, X., 1998. Cobalt-mediated generation of reactive oxygen species and its possible mechanism. *J Inorg Biochem* 70, 239-244.

Leverrier, P., Montigny, C., Garrigos, M., Champeil, P., 2007. Metal binding to ligands: cadmium complexes with glutathione revisited. *Anal Biochem* 371, 215-228.

Lewis, G., Coughlin, L., Jusko, W., Hartz, S., 1972. Contribution of cigarette smoking to cadmium accumulation in man. *The Lancet* 299, 291-292.

Liang, R., Senturker, S., Shi, X., Bal, W., Dizdaroglu, M., Kasprzak, K.S., 1999. Effects of Ni(II) and Cu(II) on DNA interaction with the N-terminal sequence of human protamine P2: enhancement of binding and mediation of oxidative DNA strand scission and base damage. *Carcinogenesis* 20, 893-898.

Liu, J., Qian, S.Y., Guo, Q., Jiang, J., Waalkes, M.P., Mason, R.P., Kadiiska, M.B., 2008. Cadmium generates reactive oxygen- and carbon-centered radical species in rats: insights from in vivo spin-trapping studies. *Free Radic Biol Med* 45, 475-481.

Liu, J., Qu, W., Kadiiska, M.B., 2009. Role of oxidative stress in cadmium toxicity and carcinogenesis. *Toxicol Appl Pharmacol* 238, 209-214.

Lopez, E., Arce, C., Oset-Gasque, M.J., Canadas, S., Gonzalez, M.P., 2006. Cadmium induces reactive oxygen species generation and lipid peroxidation in cortical neurons in culture. *Free Radic Biol Med* 40, 940-951.

Lugon-Moulin, N., Martin, F., Krauss, M.R., Ramey, P.B., Rossi, L., 2006. Cadmium concentration in tobacco (Nicotiana tabacum L.) from different countries and its relationship with other elements. *Chemosphere* 63, 1074-1086.

Lund, B.O., Miller, D.M., Woods, J.S., 1991. Mercury-induced H2O2 production and lipid peroxidation in vitro in rat kidney mitochondria. *Biochem Pharmacol* 42 Suppl, S181-187.

Lynn, S., Yew, F.H., Chen, K.S., Jan, K.Y., 1997. Reactive oxygen species are involved in nickel inhibition of DNA repair. *Environ Mol Mutagen* 29, 208-216.

Lloyd, D.R., Phillips, D.H., 1999. Oxidative DNA damage mediated by copper(II), iron(II) and nickel(II) fenton reactions: evidence for site-specific mechanisms in the formation of double-strand breaks, 8-hydroxydeoxyguanosine and putative intrastrand cross-links. *Mutat Res* 424, 23-36.

Magaye, R., Zhao, J., 2012. Recent progress in studies of metallic nickel and nickel-based nanoparticles' genotoxicity and carcinogenicity. *Environ Toxicol Pharmacol* 34, 644-650.

Magnus, K., Andersen, A., Hogetveit, A.C., 1982. Cancer of respiratory organs among workers at a nickel refinery in Norway. *Int J Cancer* 30, 681-685.

Mahboob, M., Shireen, K.F., Atkinson, A., Khan, A.T., 2001. Lipid peroxidation and antioxidant enzyme activity in different organs of mice exposed to low level of mercury. *J Environ Sci Health* B 36, 687-697.

Manfroi, C.B., Schwalm, F.D., Cereser, V., Abreu, F., Oliveira, A., Bizarro, L., Rocha, J.B.T., Frizzo, M.E.S., Souza, D.O., Farina, M., 2004. Maternal Milk as Methylmercury Source for Suckling Mice: Neurotoxic Effects Involved with the Cerebellar Glutamatergic System. *Toxicological Sciences* 81, 172-178.

Mao, Y., Liu, K.J., Jiang, J.J., Shi, X., 1996. Generation of reactive oxygen species by Co(II) from H2O2 in the presence of chelators in relation to DNA damage and 2'-deoxyguanosine hydroxylation. *J Toxicol Environ Health* 47, 61-75.

Matovic, V., Buha, A., Bulat, Z., Dukic-Cosic, D., 2011. Cadmium toxicity revisited: focus on oxidative stress induction and interactions with zinc and magnesium. *Arh Hig Rada Toksikol* 62, 65-76.

Meinerz, D.F., de Paula, M.T., Comparsi, B., Silva, M.U., Schmitz, A.E., Braga, H.C., Taube, P.S., Braga, A.L., Rocha, J.B., Dafre, A.L., Farina, M., Franco, J.L., Posser, T., 2011. Protective effects of organoselenium compounds against methylmercury-induced oxidative stress in mouse brain mitochondrial-enriched fractions. *Braz J Med Biol Res* 44, 1156-1163.

Miller, A.A., Drummond, G.R., Sobey, C.G., 2006. Novel isoforms of NADPH-oxidase in cerebral vascular control. *Pharmacol Ther* 111, 928-948.

Misra, M., Rodriguez, R.E., Kasprzak, K.S., 1990. Nickel induced lipid peroxidation in the rat: correlation with nickel effect on antioxidant defense systems. *Toxicology* 64, 1-17.

Moennich, J.N., Zirwas, M., Jacob, S.E., 2009. Nickel-induced facial dermatitis: adolescents beware of the cell phone. *Cutis* 84, 199-200.

Morgan, M.J., Liu, Z.G., 2011. Crosstalk of reactive oxygen species and NF-kappaB signaling. *Cell Res* 21, 103-115.

Mori, N., Yasutake, A., Hirayama, K., 2007. Comparative study of activities in reactive oxygen species production/defense system in mitochondria of rat brain and liver, and their susceptibility to methylmercury toxicity. *Arch Toxicol* 81, 769-776.

Murawska-Cialowicz, E., Bal, W., Januszewska, L., Zawadzki, M., Rychel, J., Zuwala-Jagiello, J., 2012. Oxidative stress level in the testes of mice and rats during nickel intoxication. *ScientificWorldJournal* 2012, 395741.

Mustacich, D., Powis, G., 2000. Thioredoxin reductase. *Biochem J* 346 Pt 1, 1-8.

Nackerdien, Z., Kasprzak, K.S., Rao, G., Halliwell, B., Dizdaroglu, M., 1991. Nickel(II)- and cobalt(II)-dependent damage by hydrogen peroxide to the DNA bases in isolated human chromatin. *Cancer Res* 51, 5837-5842.

Naganuma, A., Miura, K., Tanaka-Kagawa, T., Kitahara, J., Seko, Y., Toyoda, H., Imura, N., 1998. Overexpression of manganese-superoxide dismutase prevents methylmercury toxicity in HeLa cells. *Life Sci* 62, PL157-161.

Nava, M., Romero, F., Quiroz, Y., Parra, G., Bonet, L., Rodriguez-Iturbe, B., 2000. Melatonin attenuates acute renal failure and oxidative stress induced by mercuric chloride in rats. *Am J Physiol Renal Physiol* 279, F910-918.

Nigam, D., Shukla, G.S., Agarwal, A.K., 1999. Glutathione depletion and oxidative damage in mitochondria following exposure to cadmium in rat liver and kidney. *Toxicol Lett* 106, 151-157.

Nwokocha, C.R., Baker, A., Douglas, D., McCalla, G., Nwokocha, M., Brown, P.D., 2013. Apocynin ameliorates cadmium-induced hypertension through elevation of endothelium nitric oxide synthase. *Cardiovasc Toxicol* 13, 357-363.

O'Brien, P., Salacinski, H.J., 1998. Evidence that the reactions of cadmium in the presence of metallothionein can produce hydroxyl radicals. *Arch Toxicol* 72, 690-700.

Ognjanovic, B.I., Markovic, S.D., Ethordevic, N.Z., Trbojevic, I.S., Stajn, A.S., Saicic, Z.S., 2010. Cadmium-induced lipid peroxidation and changes in antioxidant defense system in the rat testes: protective role of coenzyme Q(10) and vitamin E. *Reprod Toxicol* 29, 191-197.

Ognjanovic, B.I., Pavlovic, S.Z., Maletic, S.D., Zikic, R.V., Stajn, A.S., Radojicic, R.M., Saicic, Z.S., Petrovic, V.M., 2003. Protective influence of vitamin E on antioxidant defense system in the blood of rats treated with cadmium. *Physiol Res* 52, 563-570.

Paller, M.S., 1985. Free radical scavengers in mercuric chloride-induced acute renal failure in the rat. *J Lab Clin Med* 105, 459-463.

Patel, E., Lynch, C., Ruff, V., Reynolds, M., 2012. Co-exposure to nickel and cobalt chloride enhances cytotoxicity and oxidative stress in human lung epithelial cells. *Toxicol Appl Pharmacol* 258, 367-375.

Paustenbach, D.J., Tvermoes, B.E., Unice, K.M., Finley, B.L., Kerger, B.D., 2013. A review of the health hazards posed by cobalt. *Crit Rev Toxicol* 43, 316-362.

Perrin, D.D., Watt, A.E., 1971. Complex formation of zinc and cadmium with glutathione. *Biochim Biophys Acta* 230, 96-104.

Phillips, J.I., Green, F.Y., Davies, J.C., Murray, J., 2010. Pulmonary and systemic toxicity following exposure to nickel nanoparticles. *Am J Ind Med* 53, 763-767.

Pourahmad, J., O'Brien, P.J., Jokar, F., Daraei, B., 2003. Carcinogenic metal induced sites of reactive oxygen species formation in hepatocytes. *Toxicol In Vitro* 17, 803-810.

Price, D.J., Joshi, J.G., 1983. Ferritin. Binding of beryllium and other divalent metal ions. *J Biol Chem* 258, 10873-10880.

Prozialeck, W.C., Lamar, P.C., 1995. Effects of glutathione depletion on the cytotoxic actions of cadmium in LLC-PK1 cells. *Toxicol Appl Pharmacol* 134, 285-295.

Rizzetti, D.A., Torres, J.G., Escobar, A.G., Pecanha, F.M., Santos, F.W., Puntel, R.L., Alonso, M.J., Briones, A.M., Salaices, M., Vassallo, D.V., Wiggers, G.A., 2013. Apocynin prevents vascular effects caused by chronic exposure to low concentrations of mercury. *PLoS One* 8, e55806.

Rockwell, P., Martinez, J., Papa, L., Gomes, E., 2004. Redox regulates COX-2 upregulation and cell death in the neuronal response to cadmium. *Cell Signal* 16, 343-353.

Saeidnia, S., Abdollahi, M., 2013. Toxicological and pharmacological concerns on oxidative stress and related diseases. *Toxicol Appl Pharmacol* 273, 442-455.

Salnikow, K., Gao, M., Voitkun, V., Huang, X., Costa, M., 1994. Altered oxidative stress responses in nickel-resistant mammalian cells. *Cancer Res* 54, 6407-6412.

Sandborgh-Englund, G., Elinder, C.G., Johanson, G., Lind, B., Skare, I., Ekstrand, J., 1998. The absorption, blood levels, and excretion of mercury after a single dose of mercury vapor in humans. *Toxicol Appl Pharmacol* 150, 146-153.

Schmid, B.P., Kao, J., Goulding, E., 1985. Evidence for reopening of the cranial neural tube in mouse embryos treated with cadmium chloride. *Experientia* 41, 271-272.

Schrauzer, G.N., 2008. Cobalt, Elements and Their Compounds in the Environment. *Wiley-VCH Verlag GmbH,* pp. 825-839.

Schwartz, J.G., Snider, T.E., Montiel, M.M., 1992. Toxicity of a family from vacuumed mercury. *Am J Emerg Med* 10, 258-261.

Sen, P., Costa, M., 1986. Pathway of nickel uptake influences its interaction with heterochromatic DNA. *Toxicol Appl Pharmacol* 84, 278-285.

Seppanen, K., Soininen, P., Salonen, J.T., Lotjonen, S., Laatikainen, R., 2004. Does mercury promote lipid peroxidation? An in vitro study concerning mercury, copper, and iron in peroxidation of low-density lipoprotein. *Biol Trace Elem Res* 101, 117-132.

Shanker, G., Aschner, J.L., Syversen, T., Aschner, M., 2004. Free radical formation in cerebral cortical astrocytes in culture induced by methylmercury. *Brain Res Mol Brain Res* 128, 48-57.

Shanker, G., Syversen, T., Aschner, J.L., Aschner, M., 2005. Modulatory effect of glutathione status and antioxidants on methylmercury-induced free radical formation in primary cultures of cerebral astrocytes. *Brain Res Mol Brain Res* 137, 11-22.

Shih, C.M., Ko, W.C., Wu, J.S., Wei, Y.H., Wang, L.F., Chang, E.E., Lo, T.Y., Cheng, H.H., Chen, C.T., 2004. Mediating of caspase-independent apoptosis by cadmium through the mitochondria-ROS pathway in MRC-5 fibroblasts. *J Cell Biochem* 91, 384-397.

Sies, H., 2014. Role of metabolic H2O2 generation: redox signaling and oxidative stress. *J Biol Chem* 289, 8735-8741.

Simonsen, L.O., Harbak, H., Bennekou, P., 2012. Cobalt metabolism and toxicology--a brief update. *Sci Total Environ* 432, 210-215.

Singh, B.K., Mishra, P., Garg, B.S., 2007. Nickel(II) complexes of biologically active glutathione: spectroscopic, kinetics of thermal decomposition and XRPD studies. *Spectrochim Acta A Mol Biomol Spectrosc* 67, 719-729.

Song, B.C., Joo, N.S., Aldini, G., Yeum, K.J., 2014. Biological functions of histidine-dipeptides and metabolic syndrome. *Nutr Res Pract* 8, 3-10.

Stacchiotti, A., Morandini, F., Bettoni, F., Schena, I., Lavazza, A., Grigolato, P.G., Apostoli, P., Rezzani, R., Aleo, M.F., 2009. Stress proteins and oxidative damage in a renal derived cell line exposed to inorganic mercury and lead. *Toxicology* 264, 215-224.

Stohs, S.J., Bagchi, D., 1995. Oxidative mechanisms in the toxicity of metal ions. *Free Radic Biol Med* 18, 321-336.

Stohs, S.J., Bagchi, D., Bagchi, M., 1997. Toxicity of trace elements in tobacco smoke. *Inh Toxicol* 9, 867-890.

Stojanovic, D., Nikic, D., Lazarevic, K., 2004. The level of nickel in smoker's blood and urine. *Cent Eur J Public Health* 12, 187-189.

Sunderman, F.W., 2008. Nickel, Elements and Their Compounds in the Environment. *Wiley-VCH Verlag GmbH,* pp. 841-865.

Sunderman, F.W., Jr., Selin, C.E., 1968. The metabolism of nickel-63 carbonyl. *Toxicol Appl Pharmacol* 12, 207-218.

Sunderman Jr, F.W., 1987. Lipid peroxidation as a mechanism of acute nickel toxicity. *Toxicol Environm Chem* 15, 59-69.

Tandon, S.K., Singh, S., Prasad, S., Khandekar, K., Dwivedi, V.K., Chatterjee, M., Mathur, N., 2003. Reversal of cadmium induced oxidative stress by chelating agent, antioxidant or their combination in rat. *Toxicol Lett* 145, 211-217.

Tatrai, E., Kovacikova, Z., Hudak, A., Adamis, Z., Ungvary, G., 2001. Comparative in vitro toxicity of cadmium and lead on redox cycling in type II pneumocytes. *J Appl Toxicol* 21, 479-483.

Tchounwou, P.B., Ayensu, W.K., Ninashvili, N., Sutton, D., 2003. Review: Environmental exposure to mercury and its toxicopathologic implications for public health. *Environmental Toxicology* 18, 149-175.

Thevenod, F., 2009. Cadmium and cellular signaling cascades: to be or not to be? *Toxicol Appl Pharmacol* 238, 221-239.

Thevenod, F., Friedmann, J.M., 1999. Cadmium-mediated oxidative stress in kidney proximal tubule cells induces degradation of Na+/K(+)-ATPase through proteasomal and endo-/lysosomal proteolytic pathways. *FASEB J* 13, 1751-1761.

Thévenod, F., Lee, W.-K., 2013. Toxicology of Cadmium and Its Damage to Mammalian Organs, in: A. Sigel, H. Sigel, R.K.O. Sigel (Eds.), *Cadmium: From Toxicity to Essentiality*. Springer Netherlands, pp. 415-490.

Thijssen, S., Cuypers, A., Maringwa, J., Smeets, K., Horemans, N., Lambrichts, I., Van Kerkhove, E., 2007. Low cadmium exposure triggers a biphasic oxidative stress response in mice kidneys. *Toxicology* 236, 29-41.

Valko, M., Morris, H., Cronin, M.T., 2005. Metals, toxicity and oxidative stress. *Curr Med Chem* 12, 1161-1208.

Van Campen, D.R., 1966. Effects of zinc, cadmium, silver and mercury on the absorption and distribution of copper-64 in rats. *J Nutr* 88, 125-130.

Wagner, C., Sudati, J.H., Nogueira, C.W., Rocha, J.B., 2010. In vivo and in vitro inhibition of mice thioredoxin reductase by methylmercury. *Biometals* 23, 1171-1177.

Waisberg, M., Joseph, P., Hale, B., Beyersmann, D., 2003. Molecular and cellular mechanisms of cadmium carcinogenesis. *Toxicology* 192, 95-117.

Wang, S., Shi, X., 2001. Molecular mechanisms of metal toxicity and carcinogenesis. *Mol Cell Biochem* 222, 3-9.

Wang, X.Y., Yokoi, I., Liu, J.K., Mori, A., 1993. Cobalt(II) and Nickel(II) Ions as Promoters of Free Radicals in Vivo: Detected Directly Using Electron Spin Resonance Spectrometry in Circulating Blood in Rats. *Arch Biochem Biophys* 306, 402-406.

Webb, M., Holt, D., Brown, N., Hard, G.C., 1988. The teratogenicity of cadmium-metallothionein in the rat. *Arch Toxicol* 61, 457-467.

Wedepohl, K.H., 1995. The composition of the continental crust. *Geochim Cosmochim Acta* 59, 1217-1232.

Wedepohl, K.H., 2008. The Composition of Earth's Upper Crust, Natural Cycles of Elements, Natural Resources, *Elements and Their Compounds in the Environment*. Wiley-VCH Verlag GmbH, pp. 2-16.

Wohrl, S., 2007. Mobile telephone as new source for nickel dermatitis. *Contact Dermatitis* 56, 113.

Xu, J., Maki, D., Stapleton, S.R., 2003. Mediation of cadmium-induced oxidative damage and glucose-6-phosphate dehydrogenase expression through glutathione depletion. *J Biochem Mol Toxicol* 17, 67-75.

Yalin, S., Comelekoglu, U., Bagis, S., Sahin, N.O., Ogenler, O., Hatungil, R., 2006. Acute effect of single-dose cadmium treatment on lipid peroxidation and antioxidant enzymes in ovariectomized rats. *Ecotoxicol Environ Saf* 65, 140-144.

Yang, J., Jiang, Z., Wang, Y., Qureshi, I.A., Wu, X.D., 1997. Maternal-fetal transfer of metallic mercury via the placenta and milk. *Ann Clin Lab Sci* 27, 135-141.

Yang, J.L., Chao, J.I., Lin, J.G., 1996. Reactive oxygen species may participate in the mutagenicity and mutational spectrum of cadmium in Chinese hamster ovary-K1 cells. *Chem Res Toxicol* 9, 1360-1367.

Yates, D.H., Goldman, K.P., 1990. Acute cadmium poisoning in a foreman plater welder. *Br J Ind Med* 47, 429-431.

Yee, S., Choi, B.H., 1996. Oxidative stress in neurotoxic effects of methylmercury poisoning. *NeuroToxicology* 17, 17-26.

Yokouchi, M., Hiramatsu, N., Hayakawa, K., Okamura, M., Du, S., Kasai, A., Takano, Y., Shitamura, A., Shimada, T., Yao, J., Kitamura, M., 2008. Involvement of selective reactive oxygen species upstream of proapoptotic branches of unfolded protein response. *J Biol Chem* 283, 4252-4260.

Zambelli, B., Ciurli, S., 2013. Nickel and human health. *Met Ions Life Sci* 13, 321-357.

Zou, W., Yan, M., Xu, W., Huo, H., Sun, L., Zheng, Z., Liu, X., 2001. Cobalt chloride induces PC12 cells apoptosis through reactive oxygen species and accompanied by AP-1 activation. *J Neurosci Res* 64, 646-653.

In: Reactive Oxygen Species, Lipid Peroxidation …
Editor: Angel Catalá

ISBN: 978-1-63321-886-4
© 2015 Nova Science Publishers, Inc.

Chapter 6

BIODEGRADATION OF METALLIC BIOMATERIALS: ITS RELATION WITH THE GENERATION OF REACTIVE OXYGEN SPECIES

Natalia S. Fagali[1]*, Claudia A. Grillo[1],
Susana Puntarulo[2] and Mónica A. Fernández Lorenzo[1,3]

[1]Instituto de Investigaciones Fisicoquímicas Teóricas y Aplicadas (INIFTA),
CONICET - Dpto. de Química, Fac. de Cs. Exactas,
La Plata, Buenos Aires, Argentina
[2]Physical Chemistry-IBIMOL, School of Pharmacy and Biochemistry,
UBA-CONICET, Buenos Aires, Argentina
[3]Facultad de Ingeniería, UNLP, La Plata,
Buenos Aires, Argentina

ABSTRACT

Some specific clinical problems, particularly those related to orthopedic trauma and some cardiovascular diseases need only temporary support for healing. This support can be provided by biodegradable metallic materials such as, Fe-, Mg- based alloys that avoid some of the side effects of traditional biomaterials. They are expected to support the healing process of a diseased tissue or organ with slowly degrading after fulfilling their function. However, the excess of metal ions may catalyze the formation of reactive oxygen and nitrogen species (ROS and RNS). An increase in the intracellular levels of free metal ions affects the normal balance ROS-antioxidant. ROS could cause lipid peroxidation with changes in the composition and fluidity of cell membrane and alterations in other macromolecules as proteins and DNA. Considering that the concentration of metal ions can reach high values in the biomaterial-tissue interface inducing ROS generation it is important to evaluate the possible adverse effects of the degradation products of biodegradable biomaterials.

* E-mail: nfagali@inifta.unlp.edu.ar, nfagali@gmail.com.

INTRODUCTION

Biomaterials can be defined as "materials (synthetic and natural) that are used in contact with biological systems" [1]. This general definition does not take into account the concept of biocompatibility defined by Williams [2] as "ability of a biomaterial to perform its desired function with respect to a medical therapy, without eliciting any undesirable local or systemic effects in the recipient or beneficiary of that therapy, but generating the most appropriate beneficial cellular or tissue response to that specific situation, and optimizing the clinically relevant performance of that therapy". This last definition implies that the body reacts against the foreign material while simultaneously the biomaterial is modified by its interaction with the environment. The interface material-biological medium is dynamic and this interaction depends on many factors, such as the kind of tissue where the interface is created, the composition of the biological medium, surface roughness and topography of the biomaterial, patient health status, technique used, etc. Therefore, the presence of a biomaterial within the body induces reactions from the surrounding tissues that are known as "host responses". A biocompatible biomaterial is expected to show minimum inflammatory and toxicity reactions both locally and systematically [3].

Before William´s definition, the prevailing view was that successful materials played largely "inert" roles in the body, as in the case of joint replacements (hip, knee), heart valves, bone plates, dental implants, intraocular lens, etc. Those devices are intended to remain a long time within the body. To achieve this goal, the materials employed are commonly metals (Co, Cr, Ti, Ni alloys, and stainless steels), ceramics, polymers, glasses, among others. However, the biological environment can lead to gradual breakdown of many biomaterials; thus, many materials are exposed to continuous or cyclic stress and abrasion and flexure may also take place and lead to failures. Biological environment interacts with degradation products since proteins adsorb to the material and enhance or delay the corrosion rate of metals. Additionally, cells secrete powerful oxidizing agents and enzymes that can digest the material. Degradative agents usually concentrate in the interface between the cells and the material and sometimes, adverse effects may be detected.

For decades, the concept of metallic biomaterials has been thought as materials resistant to corrosion once implanted in the human body. Recently, degradable metallic biomaterials (DMB) have been proposed for some specific applications, including orthopaedic and cardio-vascular applications. These materials are expected to disappear after providing structural support for an appropriate period that ensures the healing process. Once the tolerance of surrounding tissues and organs to the presence of degradation products is evaluated, the improvement of degradation rate and host response may be possible [4] and a biodegradable material becomes a reality.

Metals are mechanically interesting for load-bearing degradable implants such as, internal bone fixation screws and plates and coronary stents. When biodegradable metallic materials are necessary, two groups of metals have been proposed: Mg- and Fe-based alloys [4].

Mg-based biomaterials are one of the promising biodegradable metals for orthopedic applications because they exhibit low density and mechanical properties close to those of cortical bone and consequently are suitable for fracture repair of weight bearing bone [5]. Their degradability allows avoiding a second surgery intervention for implant removal, which is necessary for other non-degradable implants. However, one of the main limitations of using these materials is its high degradation rate that leads to changes in physical and mechanical properties [6]. The high susceptibility to corrosion can be mitigated using techniques such as, surface coatings, anodizing and with incorporation of alloying elements [7]. Diverse Mg alloys have been explored in an effort to increase its applicability, such as the ZEK100, AX30 and also Mg-Mn, Mg-Al-Zn alloys [8-10]. In the last years, other different systems such as Mg-Zn-Se and Mg-Zn-Cu [11] have been developed. Different corrosion mechanisms detected in Mg alloys could locally induce time-dependent concentration gradients for the alloying elements (Zn, Al, Cu, etc). This alteration in the local concentration may contribute differentially to the generation of adverse effects on the nearest cells.

Among biodegradable materials, Cu, main component of intrauterine devices (IUD), should also be considered. Cu-based IUDs are commonly used as a reversible contraception method by over 150 million women (about 15% of the world's women in reproductive age). They based its contraceptive action on the release of Cu ions from a Cu wire [12]. The biological response depends on the concentration of ions released and the exposure time, among other factors. In this sense, during insertion Cu-IUD probably represents a dangerous combination of variables since the metallic device is in intimate proximity with local tissue for a long period and a high amount of Cu ions is released, particularly in the first period after insertion (burst release). In fact, cellular and biochemical changes occurring in the endometrium and uterine fluid after Cu-IUD insertion [13, 14], as well as inflammatory response enhancement by cupric ions together with an increase of Cu ions in plasma, were reported [15-17]. On the other hand, it is worth mentioning that several hundreds of Cu alloys are also employed in odontology for prosthodontic restorations [18]. Biocompatibility analysis shows some apparent inconsistencies between several authors [19-20]. Some of them found that cellular functions were not altered in response to ions released from the alloys and to their salts. They highlighted that salt solutions are not adequate to represent alloy cytotoxicity because ions release from these alloys is a complex process and when salts or extracts are used to simulate the effect of ion release in cell cultures, the concentration is uniform without the concentration gradients characteristic of the *in vivo* situation. Whereas, when the evaluation of the alloy is made *in situ*, within the culture, cytotoxic effects were observed [21].

Otherwise, nanotechnology has provided new materials for medical and dental applications. They show interesting properties due to their large surface area to volume ratios. However, are also involved in adverse effects. Some of them are effective growth inhibitors against various microorganisms and thereby are applicable to diverse medical devices such as catheters, bandages for burn healing, and dressing materials for wound repair [22]. They are also used as active antibacterial ingredient for dental materials and as topically applied agents in the control of oral infections [23]. Ag nanoparticles are effective biocides that are biodegradable in the biological fluid and release Ag ions and/or are internalized by the bacteria or cells. It has been reported that they cause ROS formation in the cells, a reduction in their cell viability and mitochondrial membrane potential (MMP), an increase in the proportion of cells in the sub-G1 (apoptosis) population, S phase arrest and down-regulation of the cell cycle associated proliferating cell nuclear antigen (PCNA) protein, in a concentration time-dependent manner [24]. Overall, biodegradable metallic materials in the macro or nano-scale may provide interesting properties as biomaterials but may also cause adverse effects, frequently associated to ROS generation.

BIODEGRADABLE STENTS

In the last decade, the study of degradable biomaterials has become one of the most revolutionary topics in the field of biomaterials. So-called *biodegradable stents* provide support for the temporary opening of the blood vessel permitting tissue remodeling with the simultaneous gradual dissolution of the stent. Degradability avoids the problems of traditional permanent stents: restenosis [25, 26], thrombosis [27, 28] and the need for prolonged antiplatelet therapy [29], besides they are specially intended for children during growth.

Stent degradation should ideally start at a low speed in order to maintain the mechanical integrity required for tissue remodeling process. Tissue remodeling requires an estimated period of 6 to 12 months[30, 31]. As mechanical integrity decreases as a consequence of the degradation process, corrosion should take place at controlled rate without causing excessive accumulation of degradation products in the area close to the site of implantation. It is considered that a period of 12 to 24 months after implantation is adequate to achieve complete degradation of the stent. The effects of changes during stent dissolution on the cells in contact with the implant are described in Figure 1.

FE IONS RELEASE IN RELATION WITH THE MASS AND SURFACE OF THE STENT

When experiments related to Fe-based biodegradable materials are designed one of the first steps is to estimate the rate of the ions release and the probable local concentrations at the biomaterial surroundings to evaluate cytotoxicity and oxidative damage by Fe ions and pH changes.

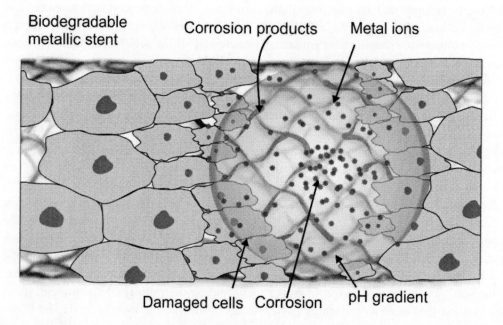

Figure 1. Schematic representation of biological and physicochemical changes during stent dissolution and its possible effects on cells in contact with the implant.

For this purpose one may assume that the amounts of Fe released from implanted coronary or femoral stents were related with their weights (weight: 41 mg for a 4 mm diameter x 20 mm long stent, weight: 750 mg for a 7 mm diameter x 200 mm long stent, respectively). Thus, 41-750 mg of degradation products should be released by the stent in c.a. 12 months. This means that the amount released per day (assuming a constant dissolution rate) is between 0.11 and 2 mg day^{-1}. A fraction of this material is removed by blood but some may diffuse and be retained in the endothelium-stent interface. It is not easy to know the fluid volume present at the interface in which Fe ions dissolve to calculate a real local concentration. If 0.5 ml of biological fluid are considered as a rough estimation of the volume of biological medium in contact with the stent, concentrations between 3.9 and 71.0 mM could be reached in the interface. Moravej et al. [32] evaluated the degradation rate of pure Fe in simulated biological fluids under static conditions and found a corrosion rate of c.a. 0.4 mm year$^{-1} \cong 3.44$ mg day^{-1}. Corrosion rates close to 1.8 mg day^{-1} were found by Zhu et al. [33] in simulated body fluids, with 2 cm^2 samples. However, it must be taken into account that the corrosion rate of the metal is strongly dependent on the electrolyte and on the environmental properties and, frequently, *in vivo* results are lower than the results obtained by *in vitro* assays [34]. Anyway, an increasing accumulation of Fe degradation products in the vessel wall adjacent to the stent strut over time was found *in vivo* by Peuster et al. [35].

DEGRADATION OF IRON: DIFFERENT SPECIES INVOLVED

It was previously mentioned that both, degradation rate and mechanical integrity, depend not only on the characteristics of the biomaterial but on the conditions of the implantation site. Consequently, it is necessary to investigate the interaction of degradation products with the surrounding tissue [36]. It is well known that toxicity of elements depends on their physicochemical forms and their excess may have serious implications in living organisms. Among degradable materials for stent applications, pure Fe is a good option due to its moderate degradation rate, mechanical properties comparable with those of stainless steel as well as probably, good biocompatibility because of the role of Fe as essential element for human body [32, 37]. The study of Fe is particularly interesting because its ions (Fe^{2+} and Fe^{3+}) and its several oxidation products represent an additional complexity. Degradation of Fe in a chloride medium such as simulated biological fluids occurs through the following reactions that, in most cases, are pH dependent.

$$Fe \rightarrow Fe^{2+} + 2\ e- \tag{1}$$

Some of Fe^{2+} can be oxidized to Fe^{3+} under neutral conditions and oxygen environment and Fe(OH)$_3$ is produced

$$\frac{1}{2}\ O_2 + H_2O + 2e- \rightarrow 2OH^- \tag{2}$$

$$Fe^{2+} + 2\ OH^- \rightarrow Fe(OH)_2 \tag{3}$$

$$Fe^{2+} \rightarrow Fe^{3+} + e^- \tag{4}$$

$$Fe^{3+} + 3\,OH^- \rightarrow Fe(OH)_3 \qquad (5)$$

In the presence of O_2 and chloride ions, $Fe(OH)_3$ is hydrolyzed and goethite (α-FeO(OH)) precipitates according to

$$2\,Fe(OH)_3 + H_2O \rightarrow 2\,FeO(OH)_{(s)} + 2\,H+ \qquad (6)$$

Whereas Fe^{2+} is extremely water soluble, Fe^{3+} is quite insoluble in water (at pH 7, $[Fe^{3+}]=10^{-18}$ M) and significant concentrations of water-soluble Fe^{3+} species can be attained only by strong complex formation [38]. Since the maximal coordination number of Fe is six, a chelator molecule that binds to all six sites of the Fe ion completely deactivates the "free Fe". Such chelators are termed "hexidentate" [38]. Free metal ions which are released during degradation could bind to various metal chelators such as adenosine 5′-diphosphate (ADP), histidine, ethylenediaminetetraacetic acid (EDTA), citrate, etc. These chelators form complexes which catalyze the formation of ROS with different efficiency through the Fenton reaction [39].

TRANSPORT OF THE RELEASED METAL IONS WITH EMPHASIS IN FE

An important issue to be considered when the toxicity of degradation products is analyzed is the variation of local levels of metal ions concentrations [40,41] because high concentration of corrosion by-products could become trapped at the stent/tissue interface leading to cytotoxicity and migration of the ions through the *tunica intima*. On this respect, mass transport theory developed for drug eluting stents may provide some information about the movement of degradable mass of metals. The elution of the drug is the key issue in the drug-eluting stents but metal ions release is critical for biodegradable stents. Mass transport within the human vasculature can be broken up into two types. One of them is blood side mass transport, related to species transport within the vessel lumen which is subject of haemodynamics.

The second, and most important mode in relation to toxicity studies of bioabsorbable stents, is the transport within the wall of the artery, frequently referred as wall side mass transport (WSMT). The situation is complex because coronary arteries are usually heavily diseased and even a thin layer of plaque between the stent strut and the wall can inhibit WSMT. Simulations of the drug concentrations through the depth of the artery wall showed that concentrations can vary in one order with respect to the bulk within 0.04 mm depth. Moreover, after implantation, a clot will immediately develop once the strut becomes covered by the plasma proteins, altering the diffusion of ions. Thus, concentration distribution along the stent is heterogeneous, with important accumulation of ions in some places which may lead to cytotoxic effects.

In the bloodstream, serum transferrin has the specific role of transporting Fe from sites of absorption and haem degradation to sites of utilization and storage. This protein is able to bind tightly (affinity constant= 10^{19} - 10^{20} M^{-1}), but reversibly, two Fe^{3+} ions with concomitant binding of two carbonate anions. *In vitro*, Fe can be released from serum transferrin by acidification. Great number of other metals can bind to transferrins in addition to Fe^{3+}, including Al^{3+}, Ga^{3+}, Cr^{3+}, Cu^{2+}, Mn^{3+}, Co^{3+}, Cd^{2+}, Zn^{2+}, among others. Apotransferrin binds Fe rapidly and seems to be quite able to oxidize Fe^{2+} and incorporate it in the Fe^{3+} form. Fe cellular cycle involves the endocytosis of diferric transferrin bound to its receptor, which leads to Fe release within the endosome at pH values below 6, followed by recycling of apotransferrin and the transferrin receptor. In essentially all proliferating (both normal and malignant), differentiating and haemoglobin synthesizing mammalian cells, Fe uptake is mediated by transferrin receptors [38].

Another potential source of Fe for cells is a receptor-independent uptake of Fe from transferrin. Furthermore, evidence indicates the existence of a transferrin-independent cellular Fe-uptake system and a tissue-distribution pattern that depends on the presence or absence of transferrin.

Non-transferrin bound iron (NTBI) are found in serum mainly complexed to citrate. Strictly speaking, NTBI corresponds to Fe which is not only unbound to transferrin but also does not correspond to heme or ferritin Fe. This Fe is thought to be much more reactive and available than transferrin-bound Fe, and to pose a greater potential toxicity. NTBI uptake may involve more than one transport system [38].

Thus, Fe enters the cell, via de transferrin receptor 1 pathway, through endocytotic vesicles and is released into de cytosol. Ferritin- bound Fe represents the major form of storage Fe, with each molecule of ferritin being capable of storing up to 4500 Fe atoms. Another form of intracellular Fe is the the transit iron pool or labile iron pool (LIP). It corresponds to the Fe species exerting a pivotal role between the vesicular storage, and functional Fe compartments. This pool of Fe consists of chemical forms of Fe that can participate in redox cycling and are associated with oxidative stress [42].

METAL IONS- MEDIATED ADVERSE REACTIONS

Specific differences between the toxicity of the components of metallic biomaterials may be related to differences in solubility, adsorbability, transport, chemical reactivity and the complexes that are formed in the biological medium [43]. Fe, Cu, Cr, V and Co undergo redox-cycling reactions. A second group of metals, Hg, Cd and Ni, the primary route for toxicity is depletion of glutathione and bonding to sulfhydryl groups of proteins. Arsenic (As) is thought to bind directly to critical thiols. However, the unifying factor in determining toxicity and carcinogenicity for all these elements is the generation of ROS and RNS. Common mechanisms involving the Fenton reaction, generation of the superoxide radical ($O_2^{\bullet-}$) and the hydroxyl radical ($HO^{\bullet}$), appear to be involved for Fe, Cu, Cr, V and Co primarily associated with mitochondria, microsomes and peroxisomes [44].

Metal-mediated formation of free radicals causes various modifications to DNA bases and proteins, enhances lipid peroxidation, and alteres calcium and sulfhydryl homeostasis. Lipid peroxides, formed by the attack of radicals on polyunsaturated fatty acid residues of phospholipids, can further react with redox metals finally producing mutagenic and carcinogenic malondialdehyde, 4-hydroxynonenal and other exocyclic DNA adduct.

Reactive radical species include a wide range of oxygen-, carbon-, sulfur- radicals, originated from $O_2^{\bullet-}$ radical, H_2O_2 and lipid peroxides but also from chelates of amino-acids, peptides, and proteins complexed with the toxic metals.

METAL IONS AND ROS GENERATION

Fe ions

It is well known that Fe is an important component of proteins such as hemoglobin, myoglobin and cytochrome and also participates in the exchange of oxygen and carbon dioxide and promotes the transport of lipids in blood [45, 46]. As we mentioned above, major portion of Fe in circulation is associated with transferrin which prevent the existence of free Fe. Almost all forms of life require Fe but this element, under certain conditions, has unfavorable chemical properties that lead to the formation of insoluble ferri-hydroxide polymers and toxic free radicals. Molecules having one or more unpaired electrons are termed free radicals: they are generally very reactive, and will act as chain carriers in chemical reactions. Thus, the hydrogen atom, with one unpaired electron, is a free radical, as are most transition metals and the oxygen molecule itself [38]. When a single electron is accepted by the ground-state O_2 molecule, it must enter one of the p* antibonding orbitals, to form the $O_2^{\bullet-}$. Addition of a second electron to $O_2^{\bullet-}$ gives the peroxide ion (O_2^{2-}) with no unpaired electrons. At physiological pH, O_2^{2-} will immediately protonate to give H_2O_2. The third reactive oxygen species found in biological systems is $HO^{\bullet}$. Two $HO^{\bullet}$ can be formed by homolytic fission of the O–O bond in H_2O_2, either by heating or by irradiation. However, as Fenton first observed in 1894 [47], a simple mixture of H_2O_2 and Fe^{2+} salt also produces the $HO^{\bullet}$ radical (equation 7):

$$Fe^{2+} + H_2O_2 \rightarrow Fe^{3+} + HO^{\bullet} + OH^- \tag{7}$$

In the presence of trace amounts of Fe, $O_2^{\bullet-}$ can then reduce Fe^{3+} to molecular oxygen and Fe^{2+}.

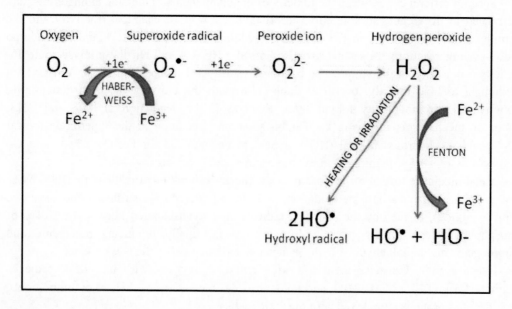

Figure 2. Reactive species formation.

The sum of this reaction (equation 8) plus the Fenton reaction (equation 7) produces O_2 plus $HO^{\bullet}$, plus OH^{-} from $O_2^{\bullet-}$ and H_2O_2, in the presence of catalytic amounts of Fe, the so-called Haber–Weiss reaction [48] (equation 9).

$$Fe^{3+} + O_2^{\bullet-} \rightarrow Fe^{2+} + O_2 \tag{8}$$

$$O_2^{\bullet-} + H_2O_2 \rightarrow O_2 + HO^{\bullet} + OH^{-} \tag{9}$$

The generation of the mentioned reactive species and the role of Fe in these reactions is schematized in Figure 2.

It should be noted that this proposed sequence requires that the reaction would occur under standard conditions reaching equilibrium state, which is rarely the case for biological systems. A simple example will illustrate the problem, whereas under standard conditions, reaction 8 has a redox potential of -330 mV (at an O_2 pressure$= 1$ atm), *in vivo* with $[O_2] = 3.5 \times 10^{-5}$ M and $[O_2^{\bullet-}] = 10^{-11}$ M the redox potential is $+230$ mV [38].

Thus, "free" Fe^{2+} may catalyze a variety of free radical oxidative reactions which in turn lead to various degenerative changes (lipid peroxidation, changes in the composition and fluidity of cell membrane proteins and DNA alterations) [49]. Accordingly, when toxicity of metal ions from bioadsorbable materials is assessed, degradation rate, ion transport and possible accumulation in human vasculature should be taken into account. However, it is worth noting, that the biological damage is not only owed to the presence of ions but also to other parameters such as pH changes.

Other Biodegradable Metals

As previously mentioned, one of the attractive features of biodegradable metal materials is their ability to serve as a temporary scaffold for biological tissue growth and degrade thereafter [50]. Several metallic materials have emerged as a potential alternative to permanent metal devices, because they possess the ability of degrading at physiological environment. In addition to Fe, extensively described previously, Mg-based materials are other of the promising biodegradable metals [7]. Diverse Mg alloys have been explored in an effort to control their degradation rate to increase their applicability [8-10], but in some cases chemical and biological effects at biomaterial-tissue interface, were observed.

Al and Cu are some of the alloying elements frequently present in different Mg alloys. However, they may induce cellular damage by direct or indirect generation of free radicals through various mechanisms. Among these mechanisms, Fenton– and Haber–Weiss type reactions are the most common, leading to generation of the $O_2^{\bullet-}$ and $HO^{\bullet}$ radicals. Even though Al is in principle a non-redox metal, it is well known [51] that it can exert a significant pro-oxidant activity. An early hypothesis by Exley [52] established that central to this ability was the possibility of stabilization by Al^{3+} of $O_2^{\bullet-}$. This could eventually lead to the formation of various ROS either by a direct pathway with formation of the $\bullet$OOH radical, either indirectly by influencing the redox equilibrium in the Fenton reaction.

Cu, the main component of Cu-based IUD, can induce oxidative stress by two mechanisms depending on its concentration level. It can directly catalyze the formation of

ROS via a Fenton-like reaction [53, 54] for low concentrations or can significantly decrease glutathione levels at higher levels [55].

Cu ions (cupric and cuprous) can act in both oxidation and reduction reactions. Cu^{2+} in the presence of $O_2^{\bullet-}$ (reaction 11) or biological reductants, such as ascorbic acid or reduced glutathione (GSH), can be reduced to Cu^+ which is capable of catalyzing the formation of reactive $OH^\bullet$ through the decomposition of H_2O_2 via the Fenton reaction (reaction 10) [56-58].

$$Cu^+ + H_2O_2 \rightarrow Cu^{2+} + OH^\bullet + OH^- \tag{10}$$

$$Cu^{2+} + O_2^{\bullet-} \rightarrow Cu^+ + O_2 \tag{11}$$

The $OH^\bullet$ is extremely reactive and can further react with practically any biological molecules in the near vicinity. Cu is also capable of causing DNA strand breaks and oxidation of bases via ROS. Cu in both oxidation states (cupric or cuprous) was more active than Fe in enhancing DNA breakage induced by the genotoxic benzene metabolite 1,2,4-benzenetriol. DNA damage occurred mainly by a site-specific Fenton reaction [59].

GSH is a substrate for several enzymes that removes ROS and is also a powerful cellular antioxidant present in the cells in millimolar concentration. It has multiple functions in intracellular Cu metabolism and detoxification. GSH can suppress Cu toxicity by directly chelating the metal [60] and maintaining it in a reduced state making it unavailable for redox cycling. Disruption of Cu homeostasis resulting in elevated pools of Cu may contribute to a shift in redox balance towards more oxidizing environment by depleting GSH levels [61]. The depletion of GSH may enhance the cytotoxic effect of ROS and allow the metal to be more catalytically active, thus producing higher levels of ROS. The large increase in Cu toxicity following GSH depletion clearly demonstrates that GSH, is an important cellular antioxidant acting against Cu toxicity [62].

A new generation of biomaterials in the nanoscale has been developed in the last years. Inorganic nanomaterials from metals and derivatives are also potentially degradable biomaterials for biomedical applications. However, cyto- and genotoxicity have been detected for these nanoparticles, the origin of nanotoxicity have been frequently attributed to ROS generation and oxidative stress [63]. He et al. [64] provide direct evidence of ROS generation during decomposition of H_2O_2 assisted by Ag nanoparticles. Additionaly, Setyawati et al. [65] showed than ZnO nanoparticles induced cytotoxicity on several cellular systems by ROS way. Interesting, at low concentrations these nanoparticles induce ROS and p53 triggers expression of antioxidant genes to restore oxidative homeostasis while at higher concentrations apoptosis of cells due to the elevated level of intracellular ROS was found.

CONCLUSION

- Biodegradation of metals induces the accumulation of ions at the metal/tissue interface.
- Released ions are involved in conformational changes of biomolecules.

- Trace amounts of metals may catalyze the production of ROS by Fenton or Haber-Weiss reactions
- ROS, in turn, induce peroxidation of lipids, proteins and DNA. This situation is associated to alteration of membranes, enzymes and proteins that can result in cell injury and death.

Importantly, metal-induced and metal-enhanced formation of free radicals and other reactive species may be a common factor in determining metal-induced toxicity and carcinogenicity.

REFERENCES

[1] Ratner B. D., Hoffman A. S., Schoen F. J., Lemons J. E. Biomaterials Science: An Introduction to Materials in Medicine, 2nd Ed. 1555 (Eds. Elsevier Academic Press). 2004.

[2] Williams D. F. On the mechanisms of biocompatibility. *Biomaterials,* 29 (20):2941-2953. 2008.

[3] Black J. Biological Performance of Materials: Fundamentals of Biocompatibility, 4th Ed. (CRC Press). 2006.

[4] Purnama A., Hermawan H., Couet J., Mantovani D. Assessing the biocompatibility of degradable metallic materials: state-of-the-art and focus on the potential of genetic regulation. *Acta. Biomater.*, 6(5):1800-1807. 2010.

[5] Witte F. The history of biodegradable magnesium implants: A review. *Acta Biomater.*, 6(5):1680-1692. 2010.

[6] Persaud-Sharma D., McGoron A. Biodegradable Magnesium Alloys: A Review of Material Development and Applications. *J. Biomim. Biomater. Tissue Eng.*, 12:25-39. 2012.

[7] Poinern G. E., Brundavanam S., Fawcett D. Biomedical magnesium alloys: A review of material properties, surface modifications, and potential as a biodegradable orthopedic implant. *Am. J. Biomed. Eng.*, 2:218-240. 2012.

[8] Huehnerschulte T. A., Reifenrath J., von Rechenberg B., Dziuba D., Seitz J. M., Bormann D., Windhagen H., Meyer-Lindenberg A. In vivo assessment of the host reactions to the biodegradation of the two novel magnesium alloys ZEK100 and AX30 in an animal model. *Biomed. Eng. Online*, 20;11:14. 2012.

[9] Gu X. N., Zheng Y. F., Chen L. J. Influence of artificial biological fluid composition on the biocorrosion of potential orthopedic Mg-Ca, AZ31, AZ91 alloys. *Biomed. Mater.*, 4(6):065011. 2009.

[10] Liu C., Yang H., Wan P., Wang K., Tan L., Yang K. Study on biodegradation of the second phase Mg17Al12 in Mg-Al-Zn alloys: in vitro experiment and thermodynamic calculation. *Mater. Sci. Eng. C Mater. Biol. Appl.*, 35:1-7. 2014.

[11] Persaud-Sharma D. N., Budiansky N., McGoron A. J. Biocompatibility Assessment of Novel Bioresorbable Alloys Mg-Zn-Se and Mg-Zn-Cu for Endovascular Applications: In- Vitro Studies. *J. Biomim. Biomater. Tissue Eng.*, 17: 25-44. 2013.

[12] Zipper J. A., Tatum H. J., Medel M., Pastene L., Rivera M. Contraception through the use of intrauterine metals. I. Copper as an adjunct to the T device. *Am. J. Obstet. Gynecol.*, 109:771-774. 1979.

[13] Beltran-García M. J., Espinosa A., Herrera N., Rerez-Zapata A. J., Beltrán-García C., Ogura T. Formation of copper oxychloride and reactive oxygen species as causes of uterine injury during copper oxidation of Cu-IUD. *Contraception*, 61:99-103. 2000.

[14] Arancibia V., Peña C., Allen H. E., Lagos G. Characterization of copper in uterine fluids of patients who use the copper T-380A intrauterine device. *Clinica Chim. Acta.*, 332:69-78. 2003.

[15] Mansour D. Copper IUD and LNG IUD compared with tubal occlusion. *Contraception*, 75:144-151. 2007.

[16] Okerete T., Strenlib I., Morell A., Sheinberg I. Systemic absorption of intrauterine copper, *Science,* 177:358-361. 1972.

[17] Fahmy K., Ghoneim M., Eisa I., el-Gazzar A., Afifi A. Serum and endometrial copper, zinc, iron and cobalt with inert and copper-containing IUCD's. *Contraception,* 47:483. 1993.

[18] Roach M. Base metal alloys used for dental restorations and implants. *Dent. Clin. North Am.*, 51(3):603-627. 2007.

[19] Messer R. L. W., Lucas L. C. Evaluations of metabolic activities as biocompatibility tools: a study of individual ions' effects on fibroblasts. *Dent. Mater.,* 15(1):1-6. 1999.

[20] Locci P., Marinucci L., Lilli C., Belcastro S., Staffolani N., Bellocchio S., Damiani F., Becchetti E. Biocompatibility of alloys used in orthodontics evaluated by cell culture tests. *J. Biomed. Mater Res.,* 51(4):561-568. 2000.

[21] Grillo C. A., Morales M. L., Mirífico M. V., Fernández Lorenzo de Mele M. Synergistic cytotoxic effects of ions released by zinc-aluminum bronze and the metallics salts on osteoblastic cells. *J. Biomed. Mater Res. (Part A),* 7:2129-2140. 2013.

[22] Flores C. Y., Diaz C., Rubert A., Benítez G. A., Moreno M. S., Fernández Lorenzo de Mele M. A., Salvarezza R. C., Schilardi P. L., Vericat C. Spontaneous adsorption of silver nanoparticles on Ti/TiO2 surfaces. Antibacterial effect on Pseudomonas aeruginosa. *J. Colloid Interface Sci.,* 15; 350(2):402-408. 2010.

[23] Mohamed Hamouda I. Current perspectives of nanoparticles in medical and dental biomaterials. J Biomed Res. 26(3):143-151. 2012.

[24] Chairuangkitti P., Lawanprasert S., Roytrakul S., Aueviriyavit S., Phummiratch D., Kulthong K., Chanvorachote P., Maniratanachote R. Silver nanoparticles induce toxicity in A549 cells via ROS-dependent and ROS-independent pathways. *Toxicol. In Vitro*, 27(1):330-338. 2013.

[25] Virmani R., Farb A., Guagliumi G., Kolodgie F. D. Drug-eluting stents: caution and concerns for long-term outcome. *Coron. Artery Dis.*, 15:313-318. 2004.

[26] Mitra A. K., Agrawal D. K. In stent restenosis: bane of the stent era. *J. Clin. Pathol.*, 59: 232-239. 2006.

[27] Hoffmann R., Mintz G. S., Dussaillant G. R., et al. Patterns and Mechanisms of In-Stent Restenosis: A Serial Intravascular Ultrasound Study. *Circulation*, 94(6):1247. 1996.

[28] Ong A. T., McFadden E. P., Regar E., de Jaegere P. P., van Domburg R. T., Serruys P. W. Late angiographic stent thrombosis (LAST) events with drug-eluting stents. *J. Am. Coll. Cardiol.,* 45:2088-2092. 2005.

[29] Waksman R. Update on bioabsorbable stents: from bench to clinical. *J. Interv. Cardiol.*, 19:414-421. 2006.

[30] El-Omar M. M., Dangas G., Iakovou I., Mehran R. Update on in-stent restenosis. *Curr. Interv. Cardiol. Rep.*, 3:296-305. 2001.

[31] Schömig A., Kastrati A., Mudra H., Blasini R., Schühlen H., Klauss V., Richardt G., Neumann F. J. Four-year experience with Palmaz-Schatz stenting in coronary angioplasty complicated by dissection with threatened or present vessel closure. *Circulation*, 90: 2716-2724. 1994.

[32] Moravej M., Purnama A., Fiset M., Couet J., Mantovani D. Electroformed pure iron as a new biomaterial for degradable stents: in vitro degradation and preliminary cell viability studies. *Acta Biomater.*, 6:1843-1851. 2010.

[33] Zhu S., Huang N., Xu L., Zhang Y., Liu H., Lei Y., Sun H., Yao Y. Biocompatibility of Fe–O films synthesized by plasma immersion ion implantation and deposition. *Surf. Coat Tech.*, 203(10-11):1523-1529. 2009.

[34] Zartner P., Cesnjevar R., Singer H., Weyand M. First successful implantation of a biodegradable metal stent into the left pulmonary artery of a preterm baby. *Catheter Cardiovasc. Interv.*, 66:590-594. 2005.

[35] Peuster M., Hesse C., Schloo T., Fink C., Beerbaum P., von Schnakenburg C. Long-term biocompatibility of a corrodible peripheral iron stent in the porcine descending aorta. *Biomaterials*, 27:4955-4962. 2006.

[36] Hermawan H., Dubé D., Mantovani D. Developments in metallic biodegradable stents. *Acta Biomater.*, 6:1693-1697. 2010.

[37] Peuster M., Wohlsein P., Brügmann M., Ehlerding M., Seidler K., Fink C., Brauer H., Fischer A., Hausdorf G. A novel approach to temporary stenting: degradable cardiovascular stents produced from corrodible metal-results 6-18 months after implantation into New Zealand white rabbits. *Heart*, 563-569. 2001.

[38] Crichton R. Inorganic Biochemistry of Iron Metabolism: From Molecular Mechanisms to Clinical Consequences. 2 ed. 336. (Wiley ed). 2001.

[39] Puntarulo S. Cederbaum A. I. Comparison of the Ability of the Ferric Complexes to Catalyze Microsomal Chemiluminescence, Lipid Peroxidation and Hydroxyl Radical Generation. *Arch. Biochem. Biophys.*, 264:482-491. 1988.

[40] O'Connell B. M., Walsh M. T. Arterial Mass Transport Behaviour of Drugs from Drug Eluting Stents, Biomedical Science, Engineering and Technology. (Prof. Dhanjoo N. Ghista Ed. InTech). 2012.

[41] Pereda M. D.; Reigosa M.; Fernández Lorenzo de Mele M. Relationship between radial difusión of copper ions from a metal disk and cytotoxic effects. Comparison with results using extracts. *Bioelectrochemistry*, 72:94-101. 2008.

[42] Patel M., Ramavataram D. V. S. S. Non Transferrin Bound Iron: Nature, Manifestations and Analytical Approaches for Estimation. *Indian J. Clin. Biochem.*, 27:322-332. 2012.

[43] Stohs S., Bagchi D. Oxidative mechanisms in the toxicity of metal ions. *Free Radic. Biol. Med.*, 18: 321-336. 1995.

[44] Valko M., Morris H., Cronin M. T. D. Metals, Toxicity and Oxidative Stress. *Curr. Med. Chem.*, 12:1161-1208. 2005.

[45] Anderson G. J., Frazer D. M., McLaren G. D. Iron absorption and metabolism. *Curr. Opin. Gastroenterol.*, 25 (2):129-135. 2009.

[46] Stangl G. I., Kirchgessner M., Different degrees of moderate iron deficiency modulate lipid metabolism of rats. *Lipids*, 33 (9):889-895. 1998.

[47] Fenton H. J. H. Oxidation of tartaric acid in presence of iron. *J. Chem. Soc. Trans.*, 65 (65):899-911. 1894.

[48] Haber F., Weiss J. Über die Katalyse des Hydroperoxydes (On the catalysis of hydroperoxide). *Naturwissenschaften*, 20 (51):948-950. 1932.

[49] Jomova K., Valko M. Advances in metal-induced oxidative stress and human disease. *Toxicology*, 283(2–3):65-87. 2011.

[50] Moravej M., Mantovani D. Biodegradable metals for cardiovascular stent application: interest and new opportunities. *Int. J. Mol. Sci.*, 12:4250- 4270. 2011.

[51] Kong S., Liochev S., Fridovich I. Aluminum (III) facilitates the oxidation of NADH by the superoxide anion. *Free Radical. Biol. Med.*, 13:79-81. 1992.

[52] Exley C. The pro-oxidant activity of aluminum. *Free Radical. Biol. Med.*, 36:380-387. 2004.

[53] Prousek J. Fenton chemistry in biology and medicine. *Pure Appl. Chem.*, 79:2325-2338. 2007.

[54] Liochev S. I., Fridovich I. The Haber–Weiss cycle—70 years later: an alternative view. *Redox. Rep.*, 7:55-57. 2002.

[55] Speisky H., Gómez M., Burgos-Bravo F., López-Alarcón C., Jullian C., Olea-Azar C., Aliaga M. E. Generation of superoxide radicals by copper-glutathione complexes: redox-consequences associated with their interaction with reduced glutathione. *Bioorg. Med. Chem.*, 17:1803-1810. 2009.

[56] Aruoma O. I., Halliwell B., Gajewski E., Dizdaroglu M. Copper-ion-dependent damage to the bases in DNA in the presence of hydrogen peroxide. *Biochem. J.*, 1; 273(3):601-604. 1991.

[57] Prousek J. Fenton reaction after a century. *Chem. Listy*, 89:11-21. 1995.

[58] Barbusinski K. Fenton reaction—controversy concerning the chemistry. *Ecol. Chem. Eng.*, 16:347-358. 2009.

[59] Moriwaki H., Osborne M. R., Phillips D. H. Effects of mixing metal ions on oxidative DNA damage mediated by a Fenton-type reduction. *Toxicol. In Vitro*, 22:36-44. 2008.

[60] Mattie M. D., Freedman J. H. Copper-inducible transcription: regulation by metal- and oxidative stress-responsive pathways. *Am. J. Physiol. Cell Physiol.*, 286:293-301. 2004.

[61] Linder M. C. Biochemistry of Copper. Plenum Press, New York. 1991.

[62] Steinebach O. M., Wolterbeek H. T. Role of cytosolic copper, metallothionein and glutathione in copper toxicity in rat hepatoma tissue culture cells. *Toxicology*, 92:75-90. 1994.

[63] Li J., Chang X., Chen X., Gu Z., Zhao F., Chai Z., Zhao Y. Toxicity of inorganic nanomaterials in biomedical imaging. *Biotechnol. Adv.*, 32(4):727-743. 2014.

[64] He W., Zhou Y. T., Wamer W. G., Boudreau M. D., Yin J. J. Mechanisms of the pH dependent generation of hydroxyl radicals and oxygen induced by Ag nanoparticles. *Biomaterials*, 33(30):7547-7555. 2012.

[65] Setyawati M. I., Tay C. Y., Leong D. T. Effect of zinc oxide nanomaterials-induced oxidative stress on the p53 pathway. *Biomaterials*, 34(38):10133-10142. 2013.

In: Reactive Oxygen Species, Lipid Peroxidation …
Editor: Angel Catalá

ISBN: 978-1-63321-886-4
© 2015 Nova Science Publishers, Inc.

Chapter 7

OXIDATIVE MODIFICATIONS OF PROTEINS IN THE AGING HEART

Peter Kaplan[1],[*], Zuzana Tatarkova[1], Veronika Ilovska[1], Jan Lehotsky[1], Peter Racay[1] and Dusan Dobrota[1]

[1]Department of Medical Biochemistry, Comenius University in Bratislava, Jessenius Faculty of Medicine, Martin, Slovak Republic

ABSTRACT

Aging is a major risk factor for cardiovascular diseases. The aging heart is characterized by a variety of structural and functional changes, including contractile dysfunction, ultimately leading to increased morbidity and mortality in the elderly. Although the molecular mechanisms underlying cardiac decay are not fully elucidated, the increase in formation of reactive oxygen species (ROS) and a result, increased oxidative stress, has been proposed to be an important factor in the aging process. Besides DNA mutations and changes in gene expression, the post-translational modifications of proteins by ROS appear to be a principal mechanism of age-related oxidative injury. The mitochondrial electron transport chain (ETC) is the major intracellular site of ROS and non-uniform decline in activities of ETC complexes may cause increased ROS leakage during aging. As a primary source of ROS the mitochondria are also the main target of their damaging effects. Mitochondrial proteins undergo complex modifications during aging; however, growing evidence suggests that structural alterations do not correlate with protein functions. Aging also affects the function of sarcoplasmic reticulum (SR), the major intracellular store of Ca^{2+} ions, regulating cardiac contraction-relaxation. The results suggest that both irreversible and reversible oxidation/nitration of SR Ca^{2+}-ATPase (SERCA2a) and other Ca^{2+} handling proteins may contribute to the loss of their transporting activities and impaired ventricular relaxation during aging. Cross-talk between mitochondria and SR is an important factor in cell redox signaling and dysregulation in Ca^{2+}-ROS interplay is likely involved in heart aging. Aging is also associated with loss in total antioxidant capacity and altered levels/activities of redox balance regulating proteins. Overall, the present results suggest that ROS-related

[*] Tel.: +421-43-2633 442, E-mail: kaplan@jfmed.uniba.sk.

alterations in mitochondrial bioenergetics, intracellular Ca^{2+} handling and redox regulatory components may contribute to age-associated decline in the heart function.

Keywords: Aging, heart, reactive oxygen species, protein oxidative damage, mitochondria, sarcoplasmic reticulum, redox state

INTRODUCTION

Aging is a major risk factor for cardiovascular diseases. More than three quarters of patients with heart failure are older than 65 years and among the elderly cardiovascular diseases are the leading cause of morbidity and mortality. The aging heart is characterized by progressive degeneration and impairment of normal functions, such as decline in cardiac functional reserve, diastolic dysfunction, and increased arrhythmias and risk of sudden cardiac death. Several cellular and molecular mechanisms are thought to be involved in the process of aging, including alterations in energy production, Ca^{2+} homeostasis, cell signaling and gene expression. In this article, we focused on cardiomyocytes but structural and functional alterations of proteins in other cells, including fibroblasts, endothelial cells and smooth muscle cells, are also involved in cardiovascular aging.

MITOCHONDRIA AND ROS PRODUCTION DURING AGING

Among numerous theories of aging, the free radical theory of aging is one of the most recognized and has been extensively examined during the last decades. According to this theory, originally proposed by Harman in 1956 (Harman 1956), aging results from the accumulation of cellular oxidative damage caused by free radicals produced as by-products of normal metabolism. Later, Harman (Harman 1972) redefined his theory, including the principal role of mitochondria in the production of free radicals and other reactive oxygen species (ROS). The bulk of mitochondrial ROS is produced during oxidative phosphorylation when electrons escape from the electron transport chain (ETC) directly to O_2, producing a superoxide anion radical $\cdot O_2^-$. Over time the mitochondrial free radical theory has been further modified to the oxidative stress theory of aging, which postulates that age-related accumulation of oxidative damage is caused by an imbalance between pro-oxidants and antioxidants in favor of the former (see Salmon et al. 2010). The heart is especially vulnerable to oxidative damage since it is an obligate aerobic organ utilizing at resting-state significantly more O_2 than other organs. During vigorous exercise O_2 consumption still increases several times more (Giordano 2005). Oxygen serves as a final acceptor of electrons during mitochondrial oxidative phosphorylation – major mechanism of cellular ATP production. The electron flow from NADH or $FADH_2$ toward O_2 is mediated by four ETC complexes embedded in the inner mitochondrial membrane (Figure 1). It has been frequently but erroneously stated that about 1-3% of O_2 consumed in mitochondrial ETC forms $\cdot O_2^-$, which is subsequently converted to H_2O_2. This value is overestimated since it was determined in experiments with isolated mitochondria in air-saturated solutions containing approximately 200 µM O_2 (Boveris and Chance, 1973, Murphy, 2009).

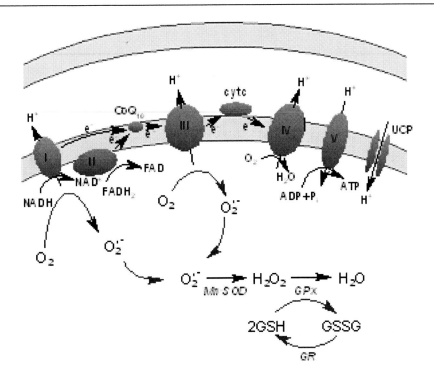

Figure 1. Mitochondrial electron transport chain, oxidative phosphorylation and ROS metabolism. Oxidation of NADH and $FADH_2$ is associated with transfer of electrons (e[-]) from complex I (I) or complex II (II) to ubiquinone (CoQ_{10}), complex III (III), cytochrome c (cyt c), complex IV (IV), and final acceptor O_2. During electron flow, structural alterations in complexes I, III and IV lead to extrusion of protons (H^+) from matrix into intermembrane space creating an electrochemical gradient. This gradient enables F_1F_0-ATP synthase/complex V (V) to drive phosphorylation of ADP to ATP. Superoxide radical is formed by one electron reduction of O_2 at complexes I and III. $\cdot O_2^-$ is rapidly dismutated to H_2O_2 by Mn-SOD. H_2O_2 can be eliminated by glutathione peroxidase (Gpx) using glutathione (GSH) or thioredoxin (Thx). Oxidized glutathione (GSSG) is converted to GSH by glutathione reductase (GR). Mitochondrial membrane potential and consequently ATP synthesis and ROS production are regulated via uncoupling proteins (UCP).

ROS production *in vivo* could be much lower mainly because of significantly lower physiological O_2 concentration in the mitochondrial matrix. Also other factors, such as actual concentrations of substrates and mitochondrial membrane potential, make extrapolation of *in vitro* ROS production to the *in vivo* conditions impossible. Therefore only methods able to measure ROS production *in vivo* can provide plausible data. ROS productions in isolated mitochondria were detected mainly by utilization of redox-sensitive fluorescent probes, such as N-Acetyl-3,7-dihydroxyphenoxazine (Amplex red) or dichlorodihydrofluorescein (DCFH) (Fato et al. 2009). In the physiological state, the main site of ROS production is ETC complex I. It produces $\cdot O_2^-$ by two mechanisms. At a high NADH/NAD^+ ratio, when respiration supported by substrates like glutamate, malate or pyruvate is low, $\cdot O_2^-$ is generated at the flavin (FMN) group complex. In mitochondria oxidizing complex II substrate succinate, high membrane potential forces electrons back from reduced coenzyme Q into complex I. This rotenone-sensitive reverse electron transport (RET) is thought to be important source of ROS also at pathological states (for review see Murphy 2009). In addition to complex I, complex III can also produce ROS, however, under physiological conditions its $\cdot O_2^-$ formation is negligible. On the other hand, 2-oxoglutarate dehydrogenase, an enzyme of the citric acid cycle, may significantly contribute to mitochondrial ROS production at elevated concentrations of NADH. Several other mitochondrial enzymes can also produce ROS; however, their significance under physiological and pathological conditions is unclear.

Few studies have examined the effect of aging on ROS production in mitochondria isolated from rat heart. While some of them suggest that there is no age-dependent increase in ROS formation (Hansford et al. 1997, Hofer et al. 2009), others indicate that ROS production increases during aging (Sohal et al., 1994; Bejma et al., 2000; Moghaddas et al., 2003; Petrosilo et al., 2009, Kuka et al., 2013). We have investigated the role of aging in mitochondrial formation of ROS in cardiac mitochondria isolated from adult (6-month old), old (15-month old) and senescent (26-month old) male Wistar rats. Rate of ROS production was established using conversion of DCFH to oxidized fluorescent DCF. In presence of NADH-linked substrates, malate and glutamate, ROS production gradually increased with age (Figure 2A). Similar findings were obtained in mitochondria oxidizing succinate (Figure 2B). Very little is known about sites contributing to an enhanced ROS leak. In interfibrillar mitochondria, aging leads to increased production of ROS from the ubiquinol-binding site of complex III (Moghaddas et al. 2003). Our studies, using succinate as substrate and rotenone, suggest that complex I also contributes to an elevated ROS leak, but not through the RET mechanism, since rotenone-blocked ROS formation was similar in adult, old and senescent rat hearts (Kuka et al. 2013).

ELECTRON TRANSPORT CHAIN IN THE AGING HEART

Because mitochondria are a major site of ROS formation, it is likely that extremely short-lived ROS attack their components and affect function. Nevertheless, the relationship between age-dependent mitochondrial ROS production and functional alterations are only partially understood. Several studies have shown that mitochondrial function is impaired during aging, but the degree of this impairment is controversial. An age-related decrease in state 3 (ADP-stimulated) respiration appears to be associated mainly with a decrease in activities of ETC complexes I and IV (Navarro and Boveris 2007, Tatarkova et al. 2011). Our studies have shown a $24\pm1\%$ decrease of complex I activity in senescent rats, although activity in old rats was not significantly different from that of adult controls (Figure 3) (Tatarkova et al. 2011). The most pronounced changes occurred in complex IV (cytochrome c oxidase) activity, compared to adults where the activity decreased by $21\pm3\%$ and $37\pm4\%$ in old and senescent rats, respectively. In contrast, complex II and III activities were much less affected by aging. In senescent rats, the activity of complex II was decreased by $14\pm3\%$ and of complex III by $17\pm2\%$. It is likely that this non-uniform decline in activities of ETC complexes ultimately leads to impaired energy metabolism and an increased superoxide leak from ETC. The mechanism that accounts for age-dependent impairment of mitochondrial function is a multifactorial process. ETC complexes consist of multiple protein subunits. While all subunits of complex II are encoded by the nuclear DNA (nDNA), subunits of complexes I, III, IV and V (F_1F_0-ATP synthase) are encoded by both nDNA and mitochondrial DNA (mtDNA). Unlike the nuclear genome, histone proteins do not protect mtDNA and their repair mechanism is much less effective. These factors and close proximity to ETC make mtDNA a possible target of damaging ROS.

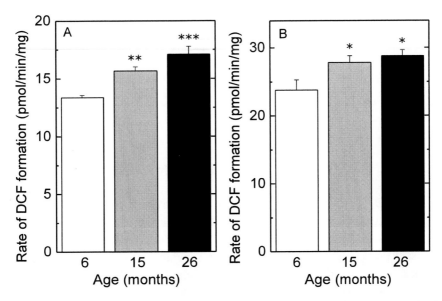

Figure 2. Effect of aging on ROS production in rat cardiac mitochondria. Rate of ROS production was measured by monitoring the fluorescence increase of oxidized DCF probe in isolated mitochondria supplemented with glutamate+malate (A) and succinate (B) as substrates. Values are given mean±SEM of 5 experiments. *p<0.05, ** $p < 0.01$; *** $p < 0.001$; significantly different when compared to 6-month-old rats. Adopted from Kuka et al., 2013 with permission.

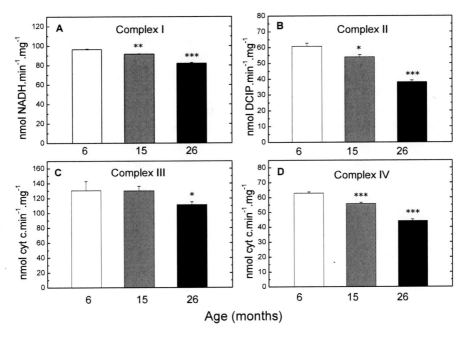

Figure 3. Effect of aging on activities of electron transport chain complex I (A), II (B), III (C) and IV (D) in rat cardiac mitochondria. Values are given as mean±SEM of 5 experiments. *p<0.05, **p<0.01, ***p<0.001; significantly different as compared to 6-month-old rats. Adopted from Tatarková et al., 2011 with permission.

Although mtDNA mutations accumulate with age the role of ROS in these lesions is unclear. It remains to be determined whether mtDNA mutations are generated by increased oxidative damage or by an accumulation of replication errors (Lagouge and Larsson 2013). Aging is also associated with changes at the level of transcription of genes encoding mitochondrial proteins. The expression (mRNA levels) of both nuclear and mitochondrial gene coding for several subunits of ETC complexes were down-regulated in hearts of senescent (24-months old) rats compared to adult (6-months old) (Preston et al. 2008). However, except for complex I these changes were not associated with a significant decline in activity.

OXIDATION OF MITOCHONDRIAL PROTEINS IN THE AGING HEART

Since alterations in mRNA levels often do not correlate well with protein contents; analysis of the heart proteome is essential for determining the role of protein expression in aging. The identification and quantification of expressed proteins in complex biological systems is possible due to recent progress in protein separation approaches coupled with high-throughput mass spectrometric (MS) techniques (Langley et al. 2013). Interestingly, analysis of mitochondrial proteome showed that only three proteins (0.4% of mitochondrial proteins) are differentially expressed in aged rat heart (24-25 vs. 6-7 months old rats) (Chang et al. 2007). Proteomic profiling of rat ventricular myocardium revealed progressive age-dependent changes in expression of numerous proteins related mainly to apoptosis, hypertrophy, fibrosis and diastolic dysfunction (Richardson et al. 2008). To evaluate the role of protein expression in age-dependent ETC inhibition we assess the level of cytochrome c oxidase subunit 1 (CO1). CO1 is one of three functional core subunits of complex IV, encoded by mtDNA. Although complex IV activity dramatically declined (see above), CO1 protein content was not changed with age as demonstrated by Western blot analysis with monoclonal anti-CO1 (Figure 4A). On the other hand, the content of succinate dehydrogenase subunit A (SDHA), a major catalytic subunit of complex II, decreased significantly with age (Figure 4B), still the activity was not altered. In interfibrillar mitochondria (IFM) of the rat heart, which seems to be more affected by aging than subsarcolemmal mitochondria, aging also does not result in changes in contents of any individual ETC. IFM dysfunction appears to be associated with destabilization of supracomplexes – large macromolecular assemblies of ETC (Gómez et al. 2009). In contrast to studies on rat heart, proteomic analysis of mouse heart indicate an altered expression of several mitochondrial proteins and enzymes involved in the energy metabolism, including several subunits of ETC complexes (Chakravarti et al. 2008). These results suggest that age-associated changes in the expression of mitochondrial proteins are species-dependent and at least in the rat heart they do not correlate with ETC dysfunction and impaired ATP production.

Another potential mechanism for mitochondrial dysfunction involves ROS-induced protein oxidative damage. Protein oxidative modifications could occur directly by ROS attack or indirectly by non-enzymatic reactions with by-products of lipid or carbohydrate oxidation. ROS-induced oxidation of proteins can cause cleavage of peptide bonds and modification of amino acid side chains. These oxidative lesions can result in various secondary processes such as fragmentation, cross-linking or unfolding of proteins.

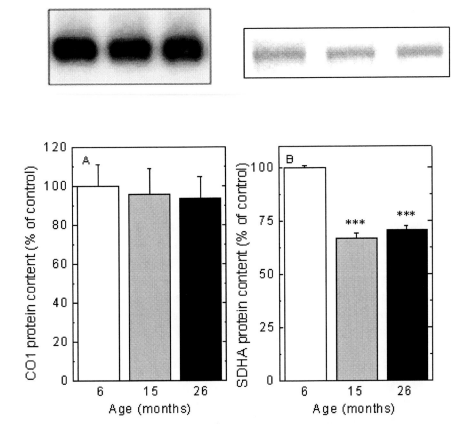

Figure 4. Effect of aging on cardiac proteins. Representative Western blots of cytochrome c oxidase (complex IV) subunit 1, CO1, (left) and succinate dehydrogenase (complex II) subunit A, SDHA, (right), and protein contents of CO1 (A) and SDHA (B) expressed as percentage of average value in 6-month-old rats. Values are given as mean±SEM of 4 experiments. *** $p<0.001$; significantly different as compared to 6-month-old rats.

While peptide bond cleavage is rarely used to investigate protein oxidation, various oxidative modifications of amino acids are examined as markers of oxidative damage. Oxidative reactions differ in their specificity, some are quite specific, altering the particular amino acid side-chain in a specific manner, others can occur on multiple side-chains leading to several products. Formation of protein carbonyl (PCO) groups can arise from direct attack of various ROS on Arg, Lys, Pro or Thr, or from secondary reactions with reactive aldehydes or ketones, such as molondialdehyde or 4-hydroxy-2-nonenal (HNE). Although carbonylation is a nonspecific modification it has been frequently used as a marker of protein oxidative damage because it is stable and its tissue content is much higher compared to more specific modifications. Formation of PCO derivatives is considered to be severe damage usually associated with loss of protein function. A number of studies has demonstrated accumulation of PCOs during aging and selective carbonylation of mitochondrial proteins was suggested several decades ago (Agarwal and Sohal 1995). Nevertheless, only improvements in proteomic technologies have allowed identification and characterization of protein posttranslational modifications (PTM) in a complex manner (Baraibar et al. 2013). Mass spectrometric analyses revealed age-dependent accumulation of numerous carbonylated proteins involved in metabolism, signal transduction, transport and oxidative phosphorylation, including several subunits of ETC complexes (Padrão et al. 2012). Intriguingly, studies on mouse heart showed decreases in carbonylation levels of ETC complex subunits with age, and these changes did not correlate with declines in complex activity (Choksi and Papaconstantinou 2008). Another recent proteomic study on long-living naked-mole rats suggest that elevated protein carbonylation might not cause structural and functional alterations in kidney proteins (De Waal et al. 2013).

Proteins could also be attacked by reactive nitrogen species (RNS). NO is an important regulator of cardiac contractions, but due to its free radical character, it can contribute to oxidative damage. NO reacts rapidly with superoxide radicals to produce a strong oxidizing and nitrating agent, peroxynitrite ONOO⁻. Peroxynitrite can react directly with protein thiols, leading to their S-nitrosylation, or after transformation to nitrogen dioxide ($\cdot NO_2$) with protein tyrosines, forming 3-nitrotyrosines. Protein 3-nitrotyrosine is widely used as a biomarker of oxidative/nitrative stress (Peluffo and Radi 2007). To evaluate the role of aging on protein nitration we measured the 3-nitrotyrosine content in rat hearts using the ELISA method. The content of 3-nitrotyrosines increased almost twice in old rats when compared with adult rats, but no significant differences were observed between senescent and adult rats. It remains to be elucidated whether unchanged 3-nitrotyrosine content in senescent rat is a consequence of decreased protein nitration or accelerated turnover of nitrated proteins. Identification of nitrotyrosine-containing proteins by mass spectrometry is very challenging due to their low abundance (Zhan et al. 2013). Nitration of cardiac proteins appears to be highly selective and independent on the protein relative abundance. Age-associated increase in nitration of several cardiac proteins was determined using electrophoresis and tandem mass spectrometry; however, only two of them were ETC complex subunits (Kanski et al. 2005, Choksi and Papaconstantinou 2008). Moreover, the 7- to 10-fold increase in their nitration was not accompanied by a decline in enzyme activity.

Reaction of protein tyrosines with peroxynitrite or other ROS/RNS can also lead to the formation of 3,3'-bityrosine. Although it is not as widely studied as 3-nitrotyrosines, bityrosine can also serve as specific biomarker of protein oxidative damage. It is easily detectable because of its specific and intense fluorescence at 380-440 nm. Our studies have shown progressive increase in bityrosine levels in cardiac mitochondria with age (Tatarkova et al. 2011) (Figure 5A); however, bityrosine cross-linked proteins remains to be identified. Formation of bityrosine cross-links may result in protein unfolding or misfolding associated with increased surface hydrophobicity. To evaluate conformational protein changes we measured the binding of the 1-anilino-8-naphthalenesulfonate (ANS) probe to cardiac mitochondria as an index of protein hydrophobicity. As shown in Figure 5B, ANS binding increases with age, suggesting that oxidative modifications of sterically large aromatic rings result in a derangement of structural protein.

Structural and functional properties of membrane proteins are critically dependent on their lipid environment. Cardiolipin (CL) is a phospholipid, which is almost exclusively located in the inner mitochondrial membrane and is required for optimal functioning of ETC complexes I, III, IV and V. Moreover, CL is required for assembly of ETC into super complexes, which appear to be important in regulation of mitochondrial energy metabolism. Alterations in CL content/composition have been shown to be associated with mitochondrial dysfunction at various diseases (see Paradies at al. 2009). Our results suggest that mitochondrial CL content is not altered during aging, cardiac CL concentration was 45.5±1.3 and 42.6±3.8 nmol per mg of protein in adult and senescent rats, respectively.

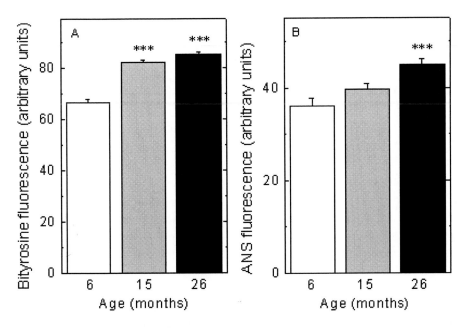

Figure 5. Age-associated changes in fluorescence intensities of bityrosines (A) and ANS probe (B) in rat cardiac mitochondria. Values are given as mean±SEM of 5 experiments. [***] p<0.001; significantly different as compared to 6-month-old rats. Adopted from Tatarková et al., 2011 with permission.

Similar findings were reported by Lesnefsky et al. (2009) but a 30% decrease in the mitochondria of aged rats was observed by Petrosillo et al. (2009). This decrease could result from CL oxidation by ROS. Due to its high content of unsaturated fatty acids (four linoleic acids) CL is particularly prone to peroxidation. Since CL represents about 25% of the total phospholipids in the inner mitochondrial membrane its oxidative modification would disrupt the lipid bilayer leading to alterations in ion permeability, ETC activity, ATP production and activation of cell death (Paradies et al. 2009). Future studies are needed to clarify the role of CL in the aging process.

Lipid peroxidation (LPO) can also mediate protein dysfunction through its products. LPO of n-6 polyunsaturated fatty acids, such as linoleic, linolenic or arachidonic acid, results in formation of highly reactive aldehydes, malonedialdehyde (MDA) and 4-hydroxynonenal (HNE). In contrast to ROS, these secondary end-products of LPO are relatively stable and can easily diffuse through membranes and react with biomolecules far from the site of their origin. Among LPO end-products, HNE is considered to be the most reactive one (Catalá 2009). HNE reacts with nucleophilic groups of DNA, proteins and phospholipids primarily forming adducts via the Michael addition and consecutively in a variety of cross-links. In proteins, HNE preferentially reacts with cysteine, histidine and lysine residues. There is a growing body of evidence that HNE acts as a signaling molecule, through the modifications of cellular signaling proteins affecting various physiological pathways including inflammation, apoptosis and heat shock response. However, increased LPO or impaired pathways of HNE detoxification may result in pathological events. Due to a very high content of unsaturated fatty acids in phospholipids (around half of the fatty acid chains) and the close proximity of ROS sources the inner mitochondrial membrane is highly vulnerable to LPO resulting in HNE production. Mitochondrial HNE-protein adduct formation result in protein dysfunction was documented following *in vitro* oxidative stress and in a variety of pathological conditions, targeted proteins include 2-oxoglutarate dehydrogenase, pyruvate dehydrogenase, succinate dehydrogenase, cytochrome c oxidase, ADP/ATP translocase, uncoupling proteins and mitochondrial permeability transition pore (see Catalá 2009, Anderson et al. 2012). Several studies have also investigated the role of reactive aldehydes in the aged heart. Our spectrophotometrical analysis of LPO shows increased formation of conjugated dienes upon aging paralleled by accumulation of MDA and HNE (Tatarkova et al. 2011) (Figure 6). In comparison to MDA content, the age-dependent increase in HNE was more pronounced, the level of HNE increased by 25±7% in aged rats and by 76±3% in senescent rats. MDA levels observed in our study are more than 3 orders lower than those inhibiting ETC complexes. *In vitro* studies on rat liver mitochondria have shown that complexes I and II are inhibited by exogenous MDA at concentrations ≥800 nmol/mg protein and complexes III and IV were not inhibited even at 6.4 μmol/mg protein (Long et al. 2006). On the other hand, several studies have demonstrated that HNE can inhibit ETC complexes or enzymes of the citric acid cycle at much lower concentrations. We observed a significant decrease in activity of cytochrome c oxidase (complex IV) already after a 10 min incubation of cardiac mitochondria with 1 μM HNE and half-maximally effective concentration, IC_{50}, was around 8 μM (Kaplan et al. 2007) (Figure 7). These concentrations are within the physiological range of HNE and 1 μM corresponds to 2 nmol HNE/mg protein, which is close to HNE levels determined in rat hearts (Figure 6). Immunoprecipitation-Western blot analysis showed a concentration dependent increase in formation of HNE adducts with cytochrome c oxidase subunit I.

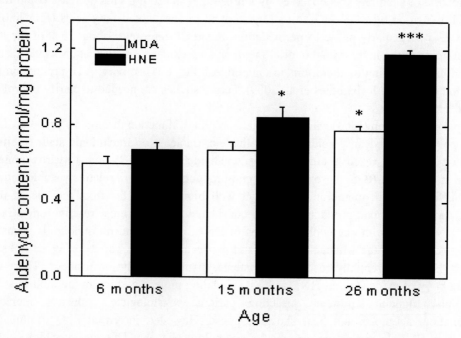

Figure 6. Age-associated changes in contents of malondialdehyde (MDA) (A) and 4-hydroxynonenal (HNE) (B) in rat heart homogenates. Values are given as mean±SEM of 4 experiments. * p<0.05, *** p<0.001; significantly different as compared to 6-month-old rats. Reprinted from Tatarková et al., 2011 with permission.

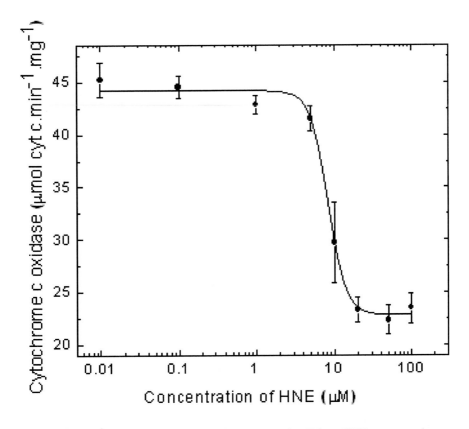

Figure 7. Dependence of cytochrome c oxidase activity (complex IV) on HNE concentration. Mitochondrial fractions were treated with various concentrations of HNE for 10 min at 25°C. Values are given as mean±SD of 6 experiments. Reprinted from Kaplan et al., 2007 with permission from Maney Publishing www.maneyonline.com/rer.

This subunit is one of three largest subunits of complex IV forming active core of the complex IV (Khalimonchuk and Rödel 2005). It contains redox centers and several histidine, cysteine and lysine residues, which play important roles in enzyme function and are potential targets for modification by HNE. Consistent with this prediction is decreased content of cysteine thiol groups and accumulation of HNE-lysine adducts after 20 min exposure of mitochondria to 10 and 20 μM HNE (Table 1). Our results suggest that similar modifications also occur in cardiac mitochondria during aging (Tatarkova et al. 2011). Oxidative rearrangement of HNE-lysine Michael adduct-Schiff base leads to formation of fluorescent cross-links. Figure 8 shows that formation of HNE-protein adducts, as detected by this fluorophore, progressively increased during aging, while thiol group content gradually decreased. Suh et al. (2003) were the first to show that age-related decline in complex IV activity is paralleled by an increase in HNE modification of this complex in rat heart. Proteomic analysis, not related to aging, has shown numerous adducts of LPO products with mitochondrial proteins (Chavez et al. 2011), but data related to aging are scarce. Study on the mouse heart has shown increased HNE modification only of two proteins, complex IV subunit 4 and β chain of F_1F_0-ATP synthase (Choksi and Papaconstantinou 2008). Furthermore, increased modification occurred only in middle age, in old age the levels of HNE modified proteins were not different from those in the younger age.

Table 1. Effect of HNE on thiol group content and HNE-protein adducts

Sample	SH group content (nmol/mg protein)	Fluorescence of HNE-protein adducts (arbitrary units)
Control	144±3	37.1±1.0
10 µM HNE	121±4***	40.4±0.5***
20 µM HNE	114±3***	51.9±1.4***

Values are expressed as means±SD of 5 experiments. *** $p<0.0001$;
significantly different when compared to control.

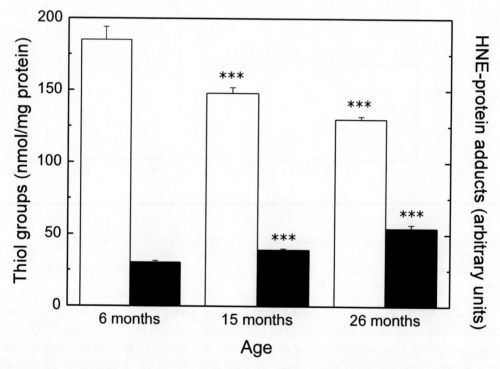

Figure 8. Age-associated changes in thiol group content and fluorescence of HNE-protein adducts in in rat cardiac mitochondria. Values are given as mean±SEM of 5 experiments. *** $p<0.001$; significantly different as compared to 6-month-old rats. Adopted from Tatarková et al., 2011 with permission.

Levels of other four HNE modified proteins were either not changed with age (subunit 1 of complex I and α chain of F_1F_0-ATP synthase) or surprisingly decreased in the middle age (complex II subunit A and complex III core1). We have examined age-related HNE-protein adduct in rat cardiac mitochondria and our studies also suggest that there is no consistent pattern of HNE modifications during aging. Using polyacrylamide gel electrophoresis and Western blot analysis with anti-HNE antibodies we recognized several spots with HNE-modified proteins. These spots were analyzed by MALDI-TOF mass spectral analysis. Following a database search eleven of these spots were successfully identified. Identified proteins included complex I subunits 1, 9 and 10, complex IV subunit 4, and α and β chains of F_1F_0-ATP synthase (complex V). Thus, in contrast to results on mouse heart (Choksi and Papaconstantinou 2008) we could not identify HNE modified subunits of complexes II and

IV, but we detected two additional modifications of complex I subunits, which were not observed in mouse heart. The levels of HNE-protein adducts did not increase progressively with age as illustrated for complex IV subunit 4 (Figure 9) and these changes did not correlate with an age-related decline in complex activity (see Figure 3).

Besides HNE and MDA, glucose is also an aldehyde, which can modify structure and function of proteins. A non-enzymatic reaction of glucose with protein lysine residue produces a Schiff base, which then undergoes a series of rearrangements, eliminations and oxidations (with contribution of ROS) resulting in formation of advanced glycation end-products (AGE) (see Simm 2013). AGEs are a chemically highly heterogenous group of compounds; the most well known examples are carboxymethyllysine (CML) and pentosidine. Accumulation of these compounds in the blood and various tissues occurs not only at a pathological glucose metabolism but also due to their ingestion in food, which was processed at elevated temperatures (e.g., deep-fraying, broiling, roasting or pasteurization). AGEs alter protein structure and function mainly via formation of macromolecular cross-links. Collagen and other extracellular proteins are thought to be the principal targets of glycation, but intracellular accumulation of AGE-modified proteins was also demonstrated. In the aging mouse heart, several intracellular proteins with molecular weights from 50 to 75 kDa displayed significantly higher AGE-modification than in young hearts (Li et al. 2005). Although accumulation of AGEs parallels impaired cardiac relaxation, a causal relationship between mechanical dysfunction and AGE cross-linking remains to be elucidated. Little is known about glycation of mitochondrial proteins in the aging heart. Proteomic analysis of glycation damage to liver mitochondrial matrix proteins showed selective AGE-modification of enzymes involved in the citric acid cycle, urea cycle and β-oxidation of fatty acids.

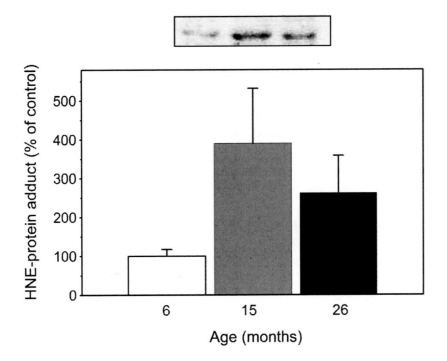

Figure 9. (Continued)

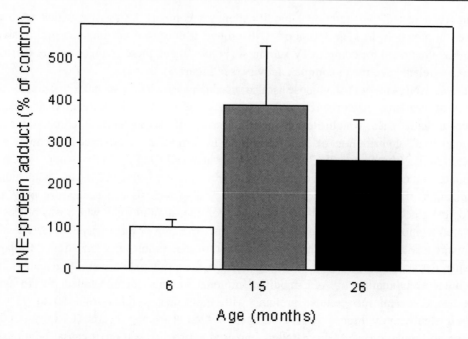

Figure 9. Effect of aging on HNE modification of complex IV subunit 4 in rat cardiac mitochondria. Representative Western blot of HNE-complex IV subunit 1 adduct (upper panel - upper panel is missing in the figure. Complete figure is above) and HNE-protein contents (lower panel) expressed as percentage of average value in 6-month-old rats. Values are given as mean±SEM of 3 experiments. Adopted from Tatarková et al., 2011 with permission.

Antioxidant enzyme catalase was one of the most strongly modified proteins, however, mitochondrial membrane proteins were not analyzed (Bakala et al. 2013).

The importance of mitochondrial oxidative stress in aging remains an area of extensive research. Rapid growth of proteomic technologies has increased our understanding of protein oxidative modifications. ROS can initiate a large number of structural and functional alterations by a variety of mechanisms. The results suggest that these changes are selective, indicating that some proteins are more vulnerable to oxidative modifications than others. It is also evident that some structural alterations do not correlate with protein functions. Thus, the key issue of whether there is a causal relationship between oxidation of mitochondrial proteins and a decline in cardiac function during aging, remains unanswered.

OXIDATION OF SARCOPLASMIC RETICULUM IN THE AGING HEART

Numerous proteomic studies have shown that the accumulation of protein oxidative damage is not limited to mitochondria, but also occurs in other cellular structures. There are several possible mechanisms for generation of extra mitochondrial oxidative stress. As mentioned above, some oxidants or end-products, like H_2O_2, peroxynitrite or HNE, have a long biological lifetime and can cross the mitochondrial membrane to spread oxidative stress in cytosol or other cellular organelles. Secondly, apart from mitochondria, a number of cellular enzymes, including NADPH oxidase, xanthine oxidase, NO synthase and lipoxygenase, can contribute to formation of ROS/RNS.

In the heart, the precise regulation of intracellular free Ca^{2+} concentration plays a key role in excitation-contraction coupling and in various other processes, including cellular metabolism, gene expression and apoptosis. The major intracellular store of Ca^{2+} in cardiac cells is sarcoplasmic reticulum (SR). SR is a closed membrane network which controls Ca^{2+} concentration through the release of Ca^{2+} via Ca^{2+} release channels and Ca^{2+} reuptake by ATP-driven Ca^{2+} pump (SR Ca^{2+}-ATPase or SERCA) during relaxation (Periasamy and Kalyanasundaram 2007). Thus, Ca^{2+}-ATPase plays a key role in cardiac relaxation and restoring Ca^{2+} in SR also determines the next contraction. The age-related relationship between impaired diastolic relaxation and decline in Ca^{2+}-ATPase activity was demonstrated in several studies, including ours (Kaplan et al. 2007, Babušíková et al. 2012). As illustrated in Figure 10, SR Ca^{2+}-ATPase activity of old and senescent rats was significantly lower at physiological free Ca^{2+} concentrations 0.02-5 µmol/l than in adult ones. Nonlinear regression analysis of data presented in Figure 11 showed that maximum velocity, V_{max}, decreased to 75±5% in old and to 64±3% in senescent rats when compared to V_{max} in adult rats. In contrast, the half-maximally activating Ca^{2+} concentration (K_{Ca}), which is a measure of Ca^{2+}-ATPase affinity to Ca^{2+} was only slightly decreased in senescent rats. The Hill coefficient (n_{Hill}), an index of the degree of cooperativity between Ca^{2+} binding sites in Ca^{2+}-ATPase, was unchanged upon aging (Table 2). These data suggest an age-dependent decrease in the number of active Ca^{2+}-ATPase molecules without a change in their catalytic properties. In some studies, depressed Ca^{2+}-ATPase activity has been attributed to an altered expression of SERCA protein, but others suggest that SERCA content is unchanged. Lack of the changes in SERCA expression was also demonstrated in our studies. In the heart, the predominantly expressed isoform is SERCA2a encoded by the SERCA2 gene transcript.

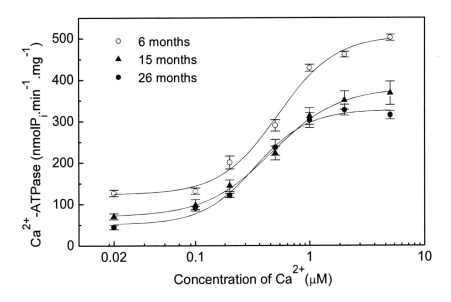

Figure 10. Calcium dependence of Ca^{2+}-ATPase activity in sarcoplasmic reticulum from hearts of adult (○), old (▲) and senescent (●) rats. Values are given as mean±SEM of 8 experiments. Adopted from Babušíková et al., 2012 with permission.

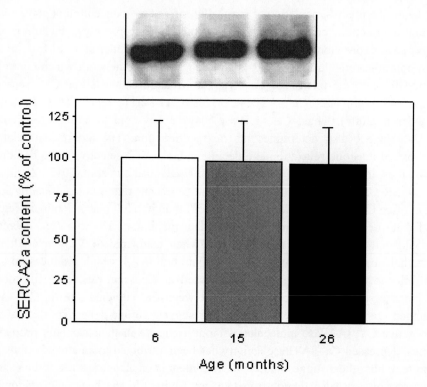

Figure 11. Effect of aging on cardiac proteins. Representative Western blot of SERCA2a (upper panel) and SERCA2a protein content (lower panel) expressed as percentage of average value in 6-month-old rats. Values are given as mean±SEM of 8 experiments. Adopted from Babušíková et al., 2012 with permission.

Table 2. Effect of age on the kinetic parameters of SR Ca^{2+}-ATPase

Age	V_{max} (nmol P_i.min^{-1}.mg^{-1})	K_{Ca} (μmol/l)	n_{Hill}
6 months	507.4 ± 13.13	0.62 ± 0.07	1.73 ± 0.22
15 months	$381.7 \pm 26.08^{**}$	0.63 ± 0.08	1.66 ± 0.46
26 months	$327.3 \pm 12.8^{***}$	0.50 ± 0.04	1.87 ± 0.37

V_{max} – maximum Ca^{2+}-ATPase activity; K_{Ca} – half-maximally activating free $[Ca^{2+}]$; n_{Hill} – the Hill coefficient. Values are expressed as means ± SEM of 8 experiments. ** $p < 0.01$; *** $p < 0.001$; significantly different as compared to 6 months animals.

Comparison of gene transcription and Western blot analysis did not reveal any changes in the levels of SERCA2 mRNA and the SERCA2a protein in the aged rat myocardium (Figure 11). Knyushko et al. (2005) have shown that loss of Ca^{2+}-ATPase activity in the aging heart can be only partially attributed to diminished SERCA2a content, additional loss in activity results from increased tyrosine nitration of SERCA2a protein. Mass spectral analysis identified an age-related increase in nitration of Tyr-294, Tyr-295 and Tyr-753. Nitration of two vicinal tyrosines Tyr-294 and Tyr-295 correlated with the loss of transport function of Ca^{2+}-ATPase. Since peroxynitrite has a relatively long half-life the site of its formation may be quite distant from Ca^{2+}-ATPase. However, two enzymes involved in $ONOO^-$ formation, NADPH oxidase and nitric oxide synthase are also localized in SR and are thought to play important roles in the regulation of Ca^{2+} channel activity. The decline in Ca^{2+}-ATPase activity and impaired myocyte relaxation during aging is associated also with oxidative sulfonation of Cys-647, which seems to be involved in regulating Ca^{2+} translocation (Qin et al. 2013). The important role of ROS in Ca^{2+}-ATPase dysfunction is supported by finding that both Cys-647 oxidation and pump inhibition are prevented by overexpression of catalase. Cysteine sulfonation or tyrosine nitration is thought to be a regulatory mechanism rather than protein oxidative damage (Bigelow 2009). Our studies also show age-related thiol oxidation: when compared to the adult heart the thiol group content decreased by 23±7 and 20±5% in the old and senescent heart, respectively. However, our data suggest that aging of the heart is also associated with accumulation of irreversible SR damage (Babušíková et al., 2012) as documented by the increased formation of bityrosine cross-links in old and senescent rat hearts (Figure 12A). In contrast, formation of adducts with a LPO end product may not contribute to protein modification in SR since their levels were not significantly changed with age (Figure 12B). Despite their almost identical primary structures, SERCA isoforms exhibit different sensitivity to oxidative/nitrative stress. Cardiac isoform SERCA2a seems to be more prone to oxidation/nitration than other isoforms and this difference could result from the unique association with its regulatory protein, phospholamban (Bigelow 2009). We previously showed that exposure to the Fe^{2+}/EDTA free radical generating system causes inhibition of cardiac Ca^{2+}-ATPase activity without change of K_{Ca} or the Hill coefficient. This inhibition was associated with accumulation of protein oxidative damage, including modification of cysteine, lysine, tyrosine and tryptophan residues (Kaplan et al. 2003). Our study has also suggested that oxidatively modified amino acid residues are localized in both hydrophobic and hydrophilic regions and that combination of various modifications, rather than oxidation of an amino acid of one kind, is responsible for inhibition of Ca^{2+}-ATPase activity.

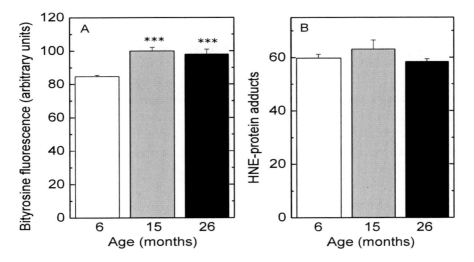

Figure 12. Age-associated changes in fluorescence intensities of bityrosines (A) and HNE-protein adducts (B) in rat cardiac sarcoplasmic reticulum. Values are given as mean±SEM of 8 experiments. *** p<0.001; significantly different as compared to 6-month-old rats. Adopted from Babušíková et al., 2012 with permission.

In the heart, Ca^{2+} release from SR during systole occurs mainly through Ca^{2+} release channels, ryanodine receptors (RyR). The majority of studies on aging hearts have shown unchanged contents of RyR. We also did not find any age-dependent changes in gene expression of type 2 RyR, which is a predominant isoform in the heart (Kaplan et al. 2007). On the other hand, mRNA and protein contents of type 1 IP_3R were almost 2-times and 3-times higher in 15- and 26-month-old rats, respectively, compared to 5- month-old rats. Studies on intracellular Ca^{2+} cycling in ventricular myocytes of old experimental animals have shown altered gating properties and accelerated leak of Ca^{2+} via of RyR (see Puzianowska-Kuznicka and Kuznicki 2009), which enhances the risk of life-threatening cardiac arrhythmias. The open probability of RyR is controlled mainly by cytosolic and SR luminal Ca^{2+} concentrations, but beside this regulatory mechanism many other factors, including post-translational modifications, may affect the RyR function. RyR tetramer contains numerous cysteine residues and their thiol groups can undergo reversible oxidation, S-nitrosylation or S-gluathionylation. Reactive thiols acts as redox sensors and moderate oxidative/nitrative stress increase channel activity, resulting in a positive inotropic effect on heart function. However, extensive exposure to ROS/RNS causes irreversible and sustained activation of RyRs resulting in depletion of SR Ca^{2+} stores, increased incidence of arrhythmia, decline in Ca^{2+} transient and contractile dysfunction (see Niggli et al. 2013). Age-associated oxidative modification of RyRs with concomitant increased SR Ca^{2+} leak and development of spontaneous Ca^{2+} waves were recently demonstrated in aging rabbit hearts (Cooper et al. 2013). Furthermore, this study has also demonstrated that increased RyR oxidation in SR is a consequence of increased ROS production in mitochondria of aged hearts. Yet another study has indicated that mitochondrial ROS are involved in SR Ca^{2+} handling in the heart. Increased ROS production induced by mitochondrial uncoupling has been shown to downregulate the expression of SR Ca^{2+} binding protein calsequestrin, leading to reduced SR Ca^{2+} content (Hänninen et al. 2010).

CROSS-TALK BETWEEN MITOCHONDRIA AND SARCOPLASMIC RETICULUM AND REDOX REGULATION

Cytochemical studies revealed that mitochondria and SR are in close contact and the cross-talk between these two organelles is essential for cell signaling (see e.g., Eisner et al., 2013). Close proximity to Ca^{2+} release channels allows Ca^{2+} entry into mitochondrial matrix resulting in activation of mitochondrial dehydrogenases and ATP production. Conversely, ATP produced by mitochondria is required not only for Ca^{2+} pumping activity of SERCA but also to potentiate the Ca^{2+} release through RyR and IP_3R Ca^{2+} release channels. A growing body of evidence suggests that ROS/RNS are other important mediators of mitochondrial SR cross-talk. Using photo stimulation of mitochondrial ROS production, it has been shown that mitochondrial ROS regulate Ca^{2+} sparks through the opening of RyRs. The ROS regulation of Ca^{2+} signaling can be both excitatory and inhibitory depending on the ROS level (Yan et al. 2008). However, the interaction between Ca^{2+} and ROS is mutual, local increases of cytosolic calcium concentration, due to Ca^{2+} release from the SR, initiates Ca^{2+} uptake into neighboring mitochondria, transient opening of mitochondrial permeability transition pores (mPTP) and increased ROS production (Odagiri et al. 2009). These findings suggest that cross-talk between mitochondria and SR is an important factor in physiological cell signaling. Recent data (see above) indicate that dysregulation in Ca^{2+}-ROS interplay is likely involved in the process of heart aging.

Although irreversible oxidative damage to proteins is thought to be an important mechanism of cellular dysfunction in aging and many pathological conditions, compelling evidence supports a view that physiological levels of ROS can induce reversible, site-specific modifications of proteins. Reversible and specific oxidative modifications of sulfur-containing amino acids methionine, and particularly cysteine, are important mechanisms for the regulation of protein structure and function. Thiol group (-SH) of cysteine residue can undergo a variety of oxidative/nitrative modifications (see Chung et al. 2013). Oxidation of thiols to sulfenic acid (-SOH) is reversible, but further oxidation leads to an irreversible conversion to sulfinic (-SO_2H) or sulfonic (-SO_3H) acid. The reaction between two thiols or thiol and sulfenic acid produces a dislulfide bond (-S-S-). Reversible conversion of thiol to disulfide can induce changes in protein structure and function. Some thiols can react with glutathione (GSH) causing reversible S-glutathionylation (-S-SG), which seems to have a protective role against irreversible damage. Furthermore, protein thiols can react with NO or other RNS forming reversible S-nitrosylation (-S-NO). Thus, depending on the degree of oxidative stress, protein thiols can be oxidized either reversibly or irreversibly. Numerous studies have shown that reversible modifications, such as formation of disulfide bonds or S-nitrosylation, are important regulatory mechanisms of protein function (see e.g., Burgoyne et al. 2012). In contrast, irreversible cysteine oxidations may result in aberrant protein function with pathological consequences.

Besides SR Ca^{2+}-ATPase and RyR discussed above, a wide variety of cardiac proteins can by regulated through modification of their cysteine thiols. Such proteins include ion channels and transporters, transcription factors, protein kinases, protein phosphatases and other enzymes.

A second type of SR Ca^{2+} release channel IP_3R also has numerous cysteine residues and their oxidation was shown to amplify IP_3-induced Ca^{2+} release. However, it remains to be elucidated whether aging is associated with an altered redox state of this Ca^{2+} release channel. In addition to direct regulation resulting from modification of their thiols, both SERCA and RyR also undergo indirect redox regulation. Phosphorylation of RyR is another important mechanism for regulation of channel activity. RyR is phosphorylated by variety of protein kinases, including protein kinase A (PKA) and Ca/calmodulin-dependent protein kinase II (CaMKII). RyR has several possible phosphorylation sites, but the functional and pathological consequences of phosphorylations are less clear. It was, however, shown that PKA-mediated hyperphosphorylation of RyR at serine 2808 increases open the probability of a channel resulting in elevated diastolic SR Ca^{2+} leak (Ulrich et al. 2012). Importantly, PKA and CaMKII are themselves targets of redox regulation and pro-oxidant conditions are associated with activation of their kinase activity via oxidation of their cysteine or methionine residues (see Burgoyne et al. 2012). Both PKA and CaMKII phosphorylate also phospholamban, SERCA2a regulatory protein and SERCA2a itself is phosphorylated by CaMK. Phosphorylation-related dysregulation of SR Ca^{2+} handling proteins in aged rat myocardium is known for a long time (Xu and Narayanan 1998), but the potential role of redox regulation of protein kinases in altered SR Ca^{2+} homeostasis and contractile dysfunction during aging remains to be elucidated.

Mitochondrial proteins are very rich in cysteine residues and redox regulation appears to be an important mechanism for control of mitochondrial function (Mailloux et al. 2014). Physiological regulators of mitochondrial membrane potential and consequently ATP synthesis are uncoupling proteins (UCPs). UCP1 and UCP2 are located in the inner mitochondrial membranes of various tissues and organs, including the heart, and dissipate energy of proton gradient to heat. UCP can also regulate ROS production. Uncoupling of ETC from ATP synthesis increases the rate of respiration leading to reduced partial pressure of oxygen and consequently reduced ROS production. Reversible S-glutathionylation of UCPs deactivates the proton leak but the increase in H_2O_2 reactivates it and reduces ROS production. In bovine heart mitochondria, S-glutathionylation of only two cysteine residues Cys-531 and Cys-704 of complex I was shown to reduce catalytic activity (Hurd et al. 2008). Reversible S-glutathionylation of cysteine residues may play a role in preventing ROS production and complex I oxidative damage. Redox modifications of cysteine thiols of other ETC complexes have also been demonstrated in *in vitro* studies not related to aging, but again their role in the aged heart is unknown.

Reversible oxidative modification of cysteines is also a key mechanism in regulation of several transcription factors, including Nrf2, NF-κB, AP-1, HIF and p53. Transcription factor Nrf2 (nuclear factor-erythroid 2-related factor 2) is thought to be a principal regulator of the antioxidant response under oxidative stress. Although activation of Nrf2 is not fully elucidated, ROS induced post-translational modification of Nrf2 and/or cytosolic repressor protein Keap1 seems to be responsible for release of Nrf2 from Keap1, translocation to the nucleus and binding to antioxidant response elements (AREs). Interaction of Nrf2 with AREs induces expression of various antioxidant enzymes such as NAD(P)H dehydrogenase, superoxide dismutases (SODs), heme oxygenase-1, glutathione peroxidase (GPx) and γ-glutamylcysteine synthetase, the rate-limiting enzyme for glutathione (GSH) synthesis (see Hybertson et al. 2011). It has been shown that aging is associated with reduced Nrf2 expression and activation. Studies on the mouse model of accelerated aging suggest that accelerated senescence of SAMP8 mice is associated with reduced translocation of Nrf2 into the nucleus inhibiting the expression of detoxifying and antioxidant enzymes in the liver (Tomobe et al. 2012).

ANTIOXIDANTS AND REDOX REGULATING COMPONENTS IN THE AGING HEART

Reduced expression of antioxidant enzymes and depletion of low-molecular-weight antioxidants can significantly affect redox balance and dysregulate redox-signaling pathways. The overall antioxidant potential is a relevant index of plasma/tissue ability to control ROS production and redox balance. We have determined antioxidant potential of rat blood plasma and heart homogenate by total peroxyl radical-trapping potential (TRAP) method (Sivoňová et al. 2007). TRAP is based on prevention afforded by plasma/tissue antioxidants against the decay of R-phycoerythrin fluorescence caused by controlled production of ROS. The results have shown a gradual decrease in both plasma and heart antioxidant capacity with aging (Figure 13).

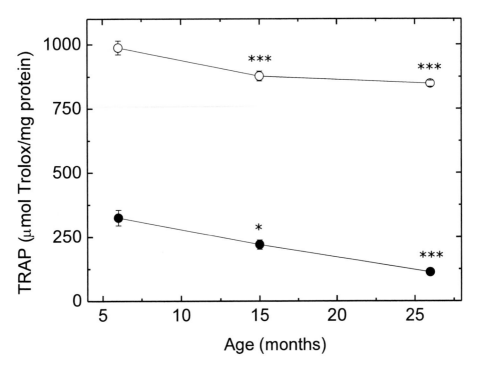

Figure 13. Age-dependent changes in antioxidant capacity - total peroxyl radical-trapping potential (TRAP) in the blood plasma (○) and heart homogenate (●) of rats. Values are given as mean±SEM of 7 experiments. [*] $p<0.05$, [***] $p<0.001$; significantly different as compared to 6-month-old rats. Adopted from Sivoňová et al., 2007 with permission.

The primary defense system consists of classical antioxidant enzymes such as superoxide dismutase, catalase and glutathione peroxidase. Mn-SOD is a primary antioxidant enzyme in the mitochondrial matrix, responsible for dismutation of superoxide radical to hydrogen peroxide and oxygen. Our results indicate that age-dependent loss of antioxidant potential is accompanied by a decline in activities of this enzyme. Intriguingly, Mn-SOD activity was reduced although Mn-SOD protein expression was not decreased. These results suggest that antioxidant enzymes may also undergo post-translational oxidative modifications during aging. In rat kidney, angiotensin II induced increase in superoxide radical production was accompanied by about 50% inhibition of Mn-SOD activity and extensive tyrosine nitration of Mn-SOD, without a change in protein content (Guo et al. 2003). It remains to be elucidated whether Mn-SOD also undergoes nitration or other oxidative modification in the aging heart. In addition to the aforementioned classical enzyme systems, cellular redox balance is regulated by several thiol/disulfide containing peptides and proteins such as glutathione, thioredoxins and peroxiredoxins. Our analysis of tissue contents of these redox regulators showed different patterns of age-dependent changes. The level of glutathione, the most abundant thiol group containing compound, was unchanged during aging. In contrast, the content of thioredoxin (Trx), which appears to be a more specific regulator of redox balance in the heart (see Berndt et al. 2007), decreased nearly 3-fold in old and senescent hearts (Figure 14). Peroxiredoxins (Prdx) are a family of ubiquitous Trx-dependent peroxidases, which also participate in redox state regulation. Their reaction rate with hydrogen peroxide is seven orders of magnitude higher than that of GSH or Trx (Winterbourn and Hampton 2008).

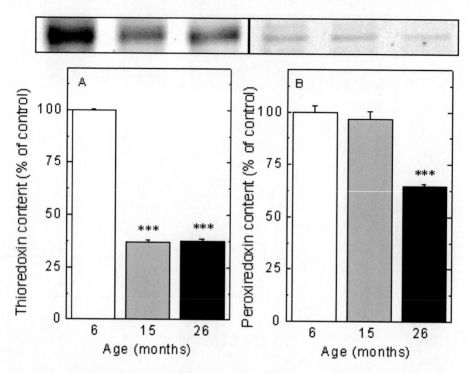

Figure 14. Effect of aging on cardiac proteins. Representative Western blots of thioredoxin (left) and peroxiredoxin 2 (right), and protein contents of Trx (A) and Prdx2 (B) expressed as percentage of average value in 6-month-old rats. Values are given as mean±SEM of 4 experiments. *** $p<0.001$; significantly different as compared to 6-month-old rats.

Our results suggest that Prdx2 content is unchanged in old rats (15 months) but is significantly reduced at the age of 24 months. Together, these data provide evidence that the antioxidant potential and regulatory components of the redox balance are altered in the aged heart and support the view of altered redox signaling during aging. Still, the research on redox signaling in aging is only beginning and further studies will be needed for more detailed understanding of its role in the process of aging.

CONCLUSION

Overall, presented findings suggest that aging of the heart is associated with increased mitochondrial production of ROS and oxidative stress. Depending on the degree of oxidative stress the proteins can be oxidized either irreversibly or reversibly. Proteomic studies suggest that irreversible oxidative modifications during aging are specific and selective. However, lack of causal relationships between age-related dysfunction and structural damage to ETC complexes questions the traditional mitochondrial free radical theory that accumulation of mitochondrial oxidative damage is a primary factor in the aging process (for review see e.g., Hekimi et al. 2011, Sohal and Orr 2012). Recent evidence suggests that reversible modifications of critical cysteine thiols are more important than accumulation of oxidative damage and could affect the function of many cellular proteins, including those controlling Ca^{2+} homeostasis and excitation-contraction coupling. Interactions between mitochondria and sarcoplasmic reticulum indicate that Ca^{2+} signaling may work in concert with redox signaling. An age-associated increase in ROS production together with an altered expression of antioxidants and redox state regulating proteins could change the redox balance to pro-oxidizing conditions. These conditions may result in increased reversible oxidative modifications of proteins leading to protein and cell dysfunctions. A progressive increase in ROS production and/or loss of redox regulating components with age may further result in irreversible macromolecular damage, which then can contribute to age-related pathologies.

ACKNOWLEDGMENT

This work was partially supported by grant VEGA 1/0129/14 from the Ministry of Education and Science of the Slovak Republic and project "Competence Center for research and development in the field of diagnostics and therapy of oncological diseases", ITMS: 26220220153, co-funded from EU sources and European Regional Development Fund.

REFERENCES

Agarwal S., Sohal R. S. (1995) Differential oxidative damage to mitochondrial proteins during aging. *Mech. Agein. Dev.,* 85: 55-63.

Anderson E. J., Katunga L. A., Willis M. S. (2012) Mitochondria as a source and target of lipid peroxidation products in healthy and diseased heart. *Clin. Exp. Pharmacol. Physiol.,* 39: 179–193.

Babušíková E., Lehotský J., Dobrota D., Račay P., Kaplán P. (2012) Age-associated changes in Ca2+-ATPase and oxidative damage in sarcoplasmic reticulum of rat heart. *Physiol. Res.,* 61: 453-460.

Bakala H., Ladouce R., Baraibar M. A., Friguet B. (2013) Differential expression and glycative damage affect specific mitochondrial proteins with aging in rat liver. *Biochim. Biophys. Acta.,* 1832: 2057-2067.

Baraibar M. A., Ladouce R., Friguet B. (2013) Proteomic quantification and identification of carbonylated proteins upon oxidative stress and during aging. *J. Proteomics,* 92: 63-70.

Bejma J., Ramires P., Ji L. L. (2000): Free radical generation and oxidative stress with ageing and exercise: differential effects in the myocardium and liver. *Acta. Physiol. Scand.,* 169: 343-351.

Berndt C., Lillig C. H., Holmgren A. (2007) Thiol-based mechanisms of the thioredoxin and glutaredoxin systems: implications for diseases in the cardiovascular system. *Am. J. Physiol. - Heart Circ. Physiol.,* 292: H1227-H1236.

Bigelow D. J. (2009) Nitrotyrosine–modified SERCA2: a cellular sensor of reactive nitrogen species. *Eur. J. Physiol.,* 457: 701-710.

Boveris A. and Chance B. (1973) The mitochondrial generation of hydrogen peroxide. General properties and effect of hyperbaric oxygen. *Biochem. J.,* 128: 617-630.

Burgoyne J. R., Mongue-Din H., Eaton P., Shah A. M. (2012) Redox regulation in cardiac physiology and pathology. *Circ. Res.,* 111: 1091-1106.

Catalá A. (2009) Lipid peroxidation of membrane phospholipids generates hydroxyl-alkenals and oxidized phospholipids active in physiological and/or pathological conditions. *Chem. Phys. Lipids,* 157: 1-11.

Chakravarti B., Oseguera M., Dalal N., Fathy P., Mallik B., Raval A., Chakravarti D. N. (2008) Proteomic profiling of aging in the mouse heart: altered expression of mitochondrial proteins. *Arch. Biochem. Biophys.,* 474: 22-31.

Chang J., Cornell J. E., Van Remmen H., Hakala K., Ward W. F., Richardson A. (2007) Effect of aging and caloric restriction on the mitochondrial proteome. *J. Gerontol.,* 62A: 223-234.

Chavez J. D., Wu J., Bisson W., Maier C. S. (2011) Site-specific proteomic analysis of lipoxidation adducts in cardiac mitochondria reveals chemical diversity of 2-alkenal adduction. *J. Proteomics,* 74: 2417-2429.

Choksi K. B., Papaconstantinou J. (2008) Age-related alterations in oxidatively damaged proteins of mouse heart mitochondrial electron transport chain complexes. *Free Radic. Biol. Med.,* 44:1795-1805.

Chung H. S., Wang S.-B., Venkatraman V., Murray C. I., Van Eyk J. E. (2013) Cysteine oxidative posttranslational modifications. Emerging regulation in the cardiovascular system. *Circ. Res.,* 112: 382-392.

Cooper L. L., Li W., Lu Y., Centracchio J., Terentyeva R., Koren G., Terentyev D. (2013) Redox modification of ryanodine receptors by mitochondria-derived reactive oxygen species contributes to aberrant Ca2+ handling in ageing rabbit hearts. *J. Physiol.,* 23: 5895-5911.

De Waal E. M., Liang H., Pierce A., Hamilton R. T., Buffenstein R., Chaudhuri A. R. (2013) Elevated protein carbonylation and oxidative stress do not affect protein structure and function in the long-living naked-mole rat: a proteomic approach. *Biochem. Biophys. Res. Commun.,* 434: 815-819.

Eisner V., Csordás G., Hajnóczky G. (2013) Interactions between sarco-endoplasmic reticulum and mitochondria in cardiac and skeletal muscle – pivotal roles in Ca2+ and reactive oxygen species signaling. *J. Cell Sci.,* 126: 2965-2978.

Fato R., Bergamini C., Bortolus M., Maniero A. L., Leoni S., Ohnishi T., Lenaz G. (2009) Differential effects of mitochondrial complex I inhibitors on production of reactive oxygen species. *Biochim. Biophys. Acta.,* 1787: 384-392.

Giordano F. J. (2005) Oxygen, oxidative stress, hypoxia, and heart failure. *J. Clin. Invest.,* 115:500-508.

Gómez L. A., Monette J. S., Chavez J. D., Maier C. S., Hagen T. M. (2009) Supracomplexes of the mitochondrial electron transport chain decline in the aging rat heart. *Arch. Biochem. Biophys.,* 490: 30-35.

Guo W., Adachi T., Matsui R., Xu S., Jiang B., Zou M.-H., Kirber M., Lieberthal W., Cohen R. A. (2003) Quantitative assessment of tyrosine nitration of manganese superoxide dismutase in angiotensin II-infused rat kidney. *Am. J. Physiol. - Heart Circ. Physiol.,* 285: H1396-H1403.

Hänninen S. L., Ronkainen J., Leskinen H., Tavi P. (2010) Mitochondrial uncoupling downregulates calsequestrin expression and reduces SR Ca2+ stores in cardiomyocytes. *Cardiovasc. Res.,* 88: 75-82.

Hansford R. G., Hogue B. A., Mildaziene V. (1997) Dependence of H2O2 formation by rat heart mitochondria on substrate availability and donor age. *J. Bioenerg. Biomembr.*, 29: 89-95.

Harman D. (1956) Aging: A theory based on free radical and radiation chemistry. *Gerontol.*, 11: 298-300.

Harman D. (1972) The biologic clock: the mitochondria? *J. Am. Geriatr. Soc.*, 20: 145-147.

Hekimi S., Lapointe J., Wen Y. (2011) Taking a "good" look at free radicals in the aging process. *Trends Cell. Biol.*, 21: 569-576.

Hofer T., Servais S., Seo A. Y., Marzetti E., Hiona A., Upadhyay S. J., Wohlgemuth S. E., Leeuwenburgh C. (2009) Bioenergetics and permeability transition pore opening in heart subsarcolemmal and interfibrillar mitochondria: Effects of aging and lifelong calorie restriction. *Mech. Ageing Dev.*, 130: 297-307.

Hurd T. R., Requejo R., Filipovska A., Brown S., Prime T. A., Robinson A. J., Fearnley I. M., Purphy M. P. (2008) Complex I within oxidatively stressed bovine heart mitochondria is glutathionylated on Cys-531 and Cys-704 of the 75-kDa subunit. Potential role of Cys residues in decreasing oxidative damage. *J. Biol. Chem.*, 283: 24801-24815.

Hybertson B. M., Gao B., Bose S. K., McCord J. M. (2011) Oxidative stress in health and disease: The therapeutic potential of Nrf2 activation. *Mol. Asp. Med.*, 32: 234-246.

Kanski J., Behring A., Pelling J., Schöneich C. (2005) Proteomic identification of 3-nitrotyrosine-containing rat cardiac proteins: effects of biological aging. *Am. J. Physiol. Heart Circ. Physiol.*, 288:H371-H381.

Kaplan P., Babusikova E., Lehotsky J., Dobrota D. (2003) Free radical-induced protein modification and inhibition Ca2+-ATPase of cardiac sarcoplasmic reticulum. *Mol. Cell. Biochem.*, 248: 41-47.

Kaplan P., Jurkovicova D., Babusikova E., Hudecova S., Racay P., Sirova M., Lehotsky J., Drgova A., Dobrota D., Krizanova O. (2007) Effect of aging on the expression of intracellular Ca2+ transport proteins in a rat heart. *Mol. Cell. Biochem.*, 301: 219-226.

Kaplan P., Tatarkova Z., Racay P., Lehotsky J., Pavlikova M., Dobrota D. (2007) Oxidative modifications of cardiac mitochondria and inhibition of cytochrome c oxidase activity by 4-hydroxynonenal. *Redox. Rep.*, 12: 211-218.

Khalimonchuk O., Rödel G. (2005) Biogenesis of cytochrome c oxidase. *Mitochondrion*, 5: 363-388.

Knyushko T. V., Sharov V. S., Williams T. D., Schoneich C., Bigelow D. J. (2005) 3-Nitrotyrosine modification of SERCA2a in the aging heart: a distinct signature of the cellular redox environment. *Biochemistry*, 44: 13071-13081.

Kuka S., Tatarkova Z., Racay P., Lehotsky J., Dobrota D. and Kaplan P. (2013) Effect of aging on formation of reactive oxygen species by mitochondria of rat heart. *Gen. Physiol. Biophys.*, 32: 415-420.

Lagouge M., Larsson N.G. (2013) The role of mitochondrial DNA mutations and free radicals in disease and ageing. *J. Intern. Med.*, 273: 529-543.

Langley S. R., Dwyer J., Drozdov I., Yin X., Mayr M. (2013) Proteomics: from single molecules to biological pathways. *Cardiovasc. Res.*, 97: 612-622.

Lesnefsky E. J., Minkler P., Hoppel C. L. (2009) Enhanced modification of cardiolipin during ischemia in the aged heart. *J. Mol. Cell. Cardiol.*, 46: 1008–1015.

Li S.-Y., Du M., Dolence E. K., Fang C. X., Mayer G. E., Ceylan-Isik A. F., LaCour K. H., Yang X., Wilbert C. J., Sreejayan N., Ren J. (2005) Aging induces cardiac diastolic dysfunction, oxidative stress, accumulation of advanced glycation end products and protein modification. *Aging Cell.*, 4: 57-64.

Long J., Wang X., Gao H., Liu Z., Liu C., Miao M., Liu J. (2006) Malonaldehyde acts as a mitochondrial toxin: inhibitory effects on respiratory function and enzyme activities in isolated rat liver mitochondria. *Life Sci.*, 79:1466-1472.

Mailloux R. J., Jin X., Willmore W. G. (2014) Redox regulation of mitochondrial function with emphasis on cysteine oxidation reactions. *Redox. Biol.*, 2: 123-139.

Moghaddas S., Hoppel C. L., Lesnefsky E. J. (2003): Aging defect at the Qo site of complex III augments oxyradical production in rat heart interfibrillar mitochondria. *Arch. Biochem. Biophys.*, 414: 59-66.

Murphy M. P. (2009) How mitochondria produce reactive oxygen species. *Biochem. J.*, 417: 1-13.

Navarro A., Boveris A. (2006) The mitochondrial energy transduction system and the aging process. *Am. J. Physiol. Cell. Physiol.*, 292: 670-686.

Niggli E., Ullrich N. D., Gutierrez D., Kyrychenko S., Poláková E., Shiroka N. (2013) Posttranslational modification of cardiac ryanodine receptors: Ca2+ signaling and EC-coupling. *Biochim. Biophys. Acta.*, 1833: 866-875.

Odagiri K., Katoh H., Kawashima H., Tanaka T., Ohtani H., Saotome M., Urushida T., Satoh H., Hayashi H. (2009) Local control of mitochondrial membrane potential, permeability transition pore and reactive oxygen species by calcium and calmodulin in rat ventricular myocytes. *J. Mol. Cell Cardiol.*, 46: 989–997.

Padrão A. I., Ferreira R., Vitorino R., Alves R. M. P., Figueiredo P., Duarte J. A., Amado F. (2012) Effect of lifestyle on age-related mitochondrial protein oxidation in mice cardiac muscle. *Eur. J. Appl. Physiol.*, 112: 1467-1474.

Paradies G., Petrosillo G., Paradies V., Ruggiero F. M. (2009) Role of cardiolipin peroxidation and Ca2+ in mitochondrial dysfunction and disease. *Cell Calcium*, 45: 643–650.

Peluffo G., Radi R. (2007) Biochemistry of protein tyrosine nitration in cardiovascular pathology. *Cardiovasc. Res.*, 75: 291-302.

Periasamy M., and Kalyanasundaram A. (2007) SERCA pump isoforms: Their role in calcium transport and disease. *Muscle Nerve*, 35: 430-442.

Petrosillo G., Matera M., Moro N., Ruggiero F. M., Paradies G. (2009): Mitochondrial complex I dysfunction in rat heart with aging: critical role of reactive oxygen species and cardiolipin. *Free Radic. Biol. Med.*, 46: 88-94.

Petrosillo G., Matera M., Moro N., Ruggiero F. M., Paradies G. (2009): Mitochondrial complex I dysfunction in rat heart with aging: critical role of reactive oxygen species and cardiolipin. *Free Radic. Biol. Med.*, 46: 88-94.

Preston C. C., Oberlin A. S., Holmuhamedov E. L., Gupta A., Sagar S., Syed R. H., Siddiqui S. A., Raghavakaimal S., Terzic A., Jahangir A. (2008) Aging-induced alterations in gene transcripts and functional activity of mitochondrial oxidative phosphorylation complexes in the heart. *Mech. Ageing Dev.*, 129:304-312.

Puzianowska-Kuznicka M., Kuznicki J. (2009) The ER and ageing II: Calcium homeostasis. *Ageing Res. Rev.*, 8: 160-172.

Qin F., Siwik D. A., Lancel S., Zhang J., Kuster G. M., Luptak I., Wang L., Tong X., Kang Y. J., Cohen R. A., Colucci W. S. (2013) Hydrogen peroxide-mediated SERCA cysteine

674 oxidation contributes to impaired cardiac myocyte relaxation in senescent mouse heart. *J. Am. Heart Assoc.*, 2: 1-9.

Salmon A. B., Richardson A., Pérez V. I. (2010) Update on the oxidative stress theory of aging: Does oxidative stress play a role in aging or healthy aging? *Free Radic. Biol. Med.*, 48: 642-655.

Sim A. (2013) Protein glycation during aging and in cardiovascular disease. *J. Proteomics,* 92: 248-259.

Sivoňová M., Tatarková Z., Ďuračková Z., Dobrota D., Lehotský J., Matáková T., Kaplán P. (2007) Relationship between antioxidant potential and oxidative damage to lipids, proteins and DNA in aged rats. *Physiol. Res.*, 56: 757-764.

Sohal R. S., Ku H.-H., Agarwal S., Forster M. J., Lal H. (1994): Oxidative damage, mitochondrial oxidant generation and antioxidant defenses during aging and in response to food restriction in the mouse. *Mech. Ageing Dev.*, 74: 121-133.

Sohal R. S., Orr W. C. (2012) The redox stress hypothesis of aging. *Free Radic. Biol. Med.,* 52: 539-555.

Suh J. H., Heath S. H., Hagen T. M. (2003) Two subpopulations of mitochondria in the aging rat heart display heterogenous levels of oxidative stress. *Free Radic. Biol. Med.*, 35:1064-1072.

Tatarkova Z., Kuka S., Racay P., Lehotsky J., Dobrota D., Mistuna D., Kaplan P. (2011) Effects of aging on activities of mitochondrial electron transport chain complexes and oxidative damage in rat heart. *Physiol. Res.,* 60: 281-289.

Tomobe K., Shinozuka T., Kuroiwa M., Nomura Y. (2012) Age-related changes of Nrf2 and phosphorylated GSK-3b in a mouse model of accelerated aging (SAMP8). *Arch. Gerontol. Geriat.,* 54: e1–e7.

Ullrich N. D., Valdivia H. H., Niggli E. (2012) PKA phosphorylation of cardiac ryanodine receptor modulates SR luminal Ca2+ sensitivity. *J. Mol. Cell Cardiol.*, 53: 33-42.

Winterbourn C., Hampton M. B. (2008) Thiol chemistry and specificity in redox signaling. *Free Radic. Biol. Med.*, 45: 549-561.

Xu A., Narayanan N. (1998) Effects of aging on sarcoplasmic reticulum Ca2+-cycling proteins and their phosphorylation in rat myocardium. *Am. J. Physiol.*, 275: H2087-H2094.

Yan Y., Liu J., Wei C., Li K., Xie W., Wang Y., Cheng H. (2008) Bidirectional regulation of Ca2+ sparks by mitochondria-derived reactive oxygen species in cardiac myocytes. *Cardiovasc. Res.*, 77: 432–441.

Zhan X., Wang X., Desiderio D. M. (2013) Mass spectrometry analysis of nitrotyrosine-containing proteins. *Mass Spec. Rev.*, 2013 doi: 10.1002/mas.21413.

Chapter 8

ROLE OF REACTIVE OXYGEN SPECIES AS SIGNALING MOLECULES IN THE REGULATION OF PHYSIOLOGICAL PROCESSES OF THE NERVOUS SYSTEM

Mauricio Olguín-Albuerne[1],*, Marco Antonio Zaragoza-Campillo[1],†
and Julio Morán[1],‡

[1]División de Neurociencias, Instituto de Fisiología Celular,
Universidad Nacional Autónoma de México,
México City, México

ABSTRACT

In the nervous system, reactive oxygen species (ROS) have been implicated in several physiological and pathological events. It has been suggested that the members of the family of the NADPH-oxidases (NOX) could be a source of ROS involved in many of these processes. In hippocampus, ROS produced by NOX are required for the NMDA receptor-dependent long-term potentiation (LTP), thereby regulating hippocampal synaptic plasticity and memory formation. In developing neurons, ROS regulate the dynamics of the axonal growth cone during the establishment of neuronal networks and, in neurons from *Aplysia*, ROS produced by NOX promote axonal growth. In addition, ROS produced by NOX critically influence the neuronal proliferation and neurogenesis and they have been implicated in the progression of the programmed cell death of neurons during cerebellar development.

Most of the physiological and pathological actions of ROS are mediated by modification of the redox state of several proteins. The oxidation of these proteins occurs in specific amino acid residues such as cysteine, tyrosine and tryptophan. In particular, the oxidation of cysteine residues is a major mechanism for the control of several

---

* E-mail: albuerne@email.ifc.unam.mx.
† E-mail: zaragoza@email.ifc.unam.mx.
‡ Tel.: (5255) 56 22 56 16, Fax: (5255) 56 22 56 07, E-mail: jmoran@ifc.unam.mx. Both (I and II) authors contributed equally to this work.

proteins. These molecules include channels, enzymes and proteins from the cytoskeleton. For example, in the striatum, the hydrogen peroxide modulates dopamine release by the oxidation of the ATP-sensitive K^+ channels and, in dorsal root ganglion neurons, ROS induce the growth cone collapse by the oxidation of CRMP2.

It has been proposed that ROS also alter the redox state of the proteins of the signaling pathways. For example, ROS produced in response to growth factors control the proliferation and neurogenesis of neural precursor cells through the redox regulation of PI3K/Akt pathway. On the other hand, the oxidation of thioredoxins (Trx) and glutaredoxins (Grx1) leads to their dissociation from ASK1 that dephosphorylates and promotes its activation and the consequent stimulation of JNK and p38, which are involved in several physiological processes such as apoptosis. Other proteins such as thioredoxin-interacting protein (TXNIP) negatively regulates Trx1 and controls the cellular redox state. Finally, Akt has also been reported to be inactivated by direct oxidation, but it can also be activated by the oxidation of PTEN.

In this chapter, we review the experimental evidences supporting a role for ROS in cell signaling in the nervous system and we discuss the interactions of ROS with several proteins as part of the mechanisms that regulates neuronal physiology.

ABBREVIATIONS

AMPA: α-amino-3-hydroxy-5-methyl-4-isoxazole propionic acid
AP5: 2-amino-5-phosphonopentanoic acid
apCAM: *Aplysia* cell adhesion molecule
ASK1: Apoptosis signal-regulating kinase 1
Bcl-X_L: B-cell lymphoma-extra large
CNS: Central Nervous System
CRMP2: Collapsin response mediator protein 2
DPI: Diphenyleneiodonium chloride
EGF: Epidermal growth factor
ERK1/2: Extracellular signal-regulated kinases-1/2
FGFR: Fibroblast growth factor receptor
GAP-43: Growth-associated protein-43
Grx: Glutaredoxin
GST: Glutathione S-Transferase
H_2O_2: Hydrogen peroxide
JNK: Jun N-terminal kinase
MAPK: Mitogen-activated protein kinase
MAPKK: Mitogen-activated protein kinase kinase
MAPKKK: Mitogen-activated protein kinase kinase kinase
MSN: Medium spiny neurons
NADPH: Nicotinamide adenine dinucleotide phosphate
NGF: Nerve Growth Factor
NMDA: N-methyl-D-aspartate
NOX: NADPH oxidase
OPA1: Optic atrophy 1
PDGF: Platelet-derived growth factor
PDK1: Phosphoinositide dependent kinase 1

PI3K: Phosphatidylinositol 3-kinase

PIP_2: Phosphatidylinositol (4, 5)-bisphosphate

PIP_3: Phosphatidylinositol (3, 4, 5)-triphosphate

PKCε: Protein kinase C ε

PTEN: Phosphatase and tensin homolog deleted on chromosome ten

ROMO1: Reactive oxygen species modulator 1

ROS: Reactive oxygen species

RTK: Receptor tyrosine kinase

SCG10: Superior cervical ganglion-10

TNF-α: Tumor necrosis factor-α

Trk: Tropomyosin-related receptor kinase

Trx: Thioredoxin

TrxR1: Thioredoxin reductase 1

TXNIP: Thioredoxin-interacting protein

USP9X: Ubiquitin-specific peptidase 9, X-linked

VEGFR: Vascular endothelial growth factor receptor

INTRODUCTION

It is well known that reactive oxygen species (ROS) are important regulators of numerous cellular functions. Many advances in the field have been achieved in recent years due in part to the advances in the methodologies employed for the study of the actions of ROS. This has allowed to increase our knowledge about the role of ROS as mediators of different physiological events. In the nervous system, the majority of these studies have focused on elucidating the role of ROS in the neuropathologies and neurodegenerative diseases, which have contributed to the understanding of the mechanisms by which the ROS are produced and regulate these processes. Although there have been important advances in the field, there are still many gaps in our knowledge about the role of ROS in the physiology of the nervous system. In this chapter we will detail some studies on the nervous system in which the ROS play a role as regulators of cellular function in the physiology, as well as the generation and progress of certain pathological conditions of the nervous system.

GENERAL MECHANISMS OF ROS ACTIONS

Several studies have described different physiological processes in which ROS act as cellular regulators through the oxidation of specific proteins, leading to a modification of their state of activation and influencing specific signaling pathways and cell function. This occurs mainly through the oxidation of proteins in specific amino acid residues such as cysteine, tyrosine and tryptophan [1]. Particularly, the oxidation of cysteines is a major target to control protein functions. For example, it is well known that ROS, particularly H_2O_2, induce the activation of several protein kinases, as well as the activation or inactivation of several protein phosphatases mediated by the oxidation of cysteines [2-5]. Hydrogen peroxide exerts different modifications depending on the type of reaction. In this chapter we review different examples in which H_2O_2 alters the function of the proteins through the modification of cysteine residues of different proteins, as well as the protein-glutathione and protein-thioredoxin complexes.

CYSTEINE MODIFICATIONS

The functionality of a wide variety of proteins depends on a series of reversible reactions that are controlled by the redox state of the cell. In this regard, the oxidation of cysteines by hydrogen peroxide is a main mechanism. Once the thiolate group of reactive cysteines interacts with H_2O_2, it is converted to sulfenic acid (R-SOH). At this point, different reactions may occur in the absence of glutathione, thioredoxin and glutaredoxin. The highly reactive sulfenic acid can reduce an adjacent thiol group, and a disulfide bond will be formed. Alternatively, sulfenic acid can further be oxidized by hydrogen peroxide, forming sulfinic acid (R-SO_2H). This group is important in the redox regulation of some proteins such as peroxiredoxins. Despite its stability, sulfinic acid can be reduced by sulfiredoxins and sestrins to sulfenic acid [6, 7], or it can be oxidized by hydrogen peroxide forming sulfonic acid (R-SO_3H); so far it is not known any enzymatic reaction to reduce the sulfonic acid [8, 9]. On the other hand, sulfenic acid can also form a disulfide link between reduced glutathione and the cysteine residue of another protein, forming a glutathionylated protein; however, if glutathione is in an oxidized form, it can be established a bond with the thiolate group of a cysteine residue. In addition, the disulfide bonds formed between cysteines can be reduced by thioredoxin or glutaredoxin, forming a disulfide bond between the protein and any of these proteins. Both processes may be important for the regulation of the activity of several proteins, as it is the case for ASK1 and CRMP2. The bond formed between protein-thioredoxin and protein-glutaredoxin can be broken by hydrogen peroxide (Figure 1) [10-12].

OXIDATIVE MODIFICATIONS OF SIGNALING PROTEINS

It is known that the oxidation of proteins involved in cellular signaling represents a critical posttranslational regulatory mechanism [13]. The redox regulation of intracellular signals involved in physiological processes requires efficient cellular sources of ROS (NADPH-oxidase, electron chain transport, etc.), as well as proteins sensitive to the redox state. There are several examples that fulfill these features and that involve not only signaling proteins, but also other type of proteins such as receptors.

Most of these studies have been focused on the regulation of signaling molecules through the oxidation of cysteine residues. In this chapter, we describe some examples.

a) Trx /Grx and ASK1

The reductive activity of Trx1 thiols depends on the cysteine 32 (Cys32) and 35 (Cys35), while that from the mitochondrial isoform (Trx2) depends on Cys90 and Cys93 [14], which constitute a redox catalytic CGPC motif [15, 16].

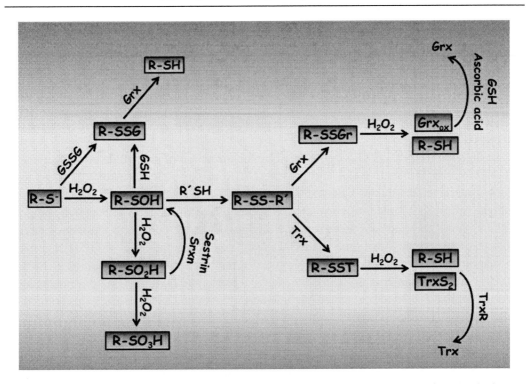

Figure 1. *Mechanisms of cysteine oxidation involved in redox signaling.* The reaction between hydrogen peroxide and the reactive cysteine thiolate group (R-S$^-$) produces sulfenic acid (R-SOH), which increases the probability to generate a disulfide bridge (R-SS-R$'$) with an adjacent thiol group (R$'$SH). If R-SOH is oxidized by H_2O_2 then sulfinic acid (R-SO$_2$H) is formed, which is a reaction that can be reduced by sestrin and sulfiredoxin (Srxn). When H_2O_2 oxidizes R-SO$_2$H then sulfonic acid (R-SO$_3$H) is formed. The presence of reduced glutathione (GSH) and proteins containing an R-SOH group generates glutathionylated proteins (R-SSG), but if glutathione is in the oxidized form (GSSG), it binds to the thiolate group of cysteine residues, forming R-SSG. Thioredoxins and glutaredoxins can reduce the disulfide bonds between oxidized proteins through the formation of intermolecular disulfide bonds, which can be dissociated by H_2O_2.

Proline is the key amino acid for the reductive action of the CGPC motif. In Trx1, when proline is replaced by serine or threonine, the protein experiences marked changes in its redox properties, as well as in the stability between the oxidized and reduced forms [17]. Similarly, the active catalytic site CPYC of Grx contains two cysteine residues (Cys22 y Cys25) susceptible to be oxidized [18]. In contrast to Trx that forms an intramolecular disulfide bond between the cysteines of its catalytic site Trx-[S-S], Grx specifically form disulfide bonds with glutathione. During its catalytic cycle a covalent intermediary is formed between the Cys22 of Grx and glutathione (Grx-S-S-glutathione) [19]. During oxidative stress, Grx-S-S-glutathione seems to be the predominant form, instead of Grx-[S-S] [20, 21].

It is suggested that the Cys250 of ASK1 binds to the Cys32 or Cys35 of Trx1 via an intermolecular disulfide bridge, which can be broken by ROS [14, 22]. This interaction can also be eliminated by TXNIP, which binds to the Cys 32 of Trx1 therefore reducing the ability of Trx1 to bind ASK1 [23]. It has been shown that the Cys30 of ASK1 forms an intermolecular disulfide bridge with the Cys90 of Trx2 [14]. On the other hand, the cysteines of the active site of Grx (Cys22 and Cys25) are responsible for the interaction between Grx and ASK1, probably through the formation of an intramolecular disulfide bond in Grx [24].

b) Trx and PTEN

PTEN is a tumor suppressor protein that can be reduced by intracellular agents, supporting the idea that the reversible oxidation and reduction of cysteines in the active site represents a key mechanism for PTEN regulation [25]. It is known that H_2O_2 oxidizes Cys124 in the active site of PTEN that forms an intramolecular disulfide bond with Cys71, leading to PTEN inactivation [25].

The binding of Trx1 to PTEN is mediated by the formation of a disulfide bridge between the Cys32 of the Trx1 active site and the Cys212 from the C2 domain of PTEN, which induces a steric effect in the catalytic site of PTEN and the C2 domain that binds to membrane lipids. This condition obstructs the access of the substrate to the catalytic site of the PTEN phosphatase domain as well as the binding of the C2 domain to the inner side of the plasmatic membrane [26]. Due to the fact that Trx directly interacts with PTEN, it has been suggested that the reduction of PTEN is carried out by the binding of oxidized PTEN to Trx1 in a reduced state. It is unknown whether the reductase TrxR1 reverts the interaction between Trx1 and PTEN and cannot be excluded that glutathione and Grx break this union.

c) Trx and TXNIP

It has been shown that during oxidative conditions, TXNIP contains an intramolecular disulfide bond formed by Cys63 and Cys247, which is able to interact with the reduced form of Trx by forming an intermolecular disulfide bond between Cys247 from TXNIP and Cys32 from Trx [27]. Hwang et al. [28] recently showed that ROS can oxidize the intermolecular disulfide bond between TXNIP and Trx leading to their dissociation. After restoration of the redox potential by antioxidant conditions, the Trx reactive cysteines interact with the bond formed between Cys63 and Cys247 from two TXNIP molecules. After that, these two TXNIP molecules undergo a structural rearrangement that involves the exchange of the former disulfide bond to a new one between the Cys63 and Cys190 from two TXNIP molecules and then the *novo* formation of the intermolecular disulfide bond between the Trx Cys32 and the Cys247 from TXNIP [28].

d) Akt

Murata *et al.* [29] reported that the exposure of cardiac cells to H_2O_2 induces the formation of an intramolecular disulfide bond between Cys297 and Cys311 of the Akt kinase domain, which leads to its dephosphorylation. These cysteines are conserved in the three Akt isoforms. By using site-directed mutagenesis, they also showed that the formation of this bond leads to Akt proteasomal degradation [29]. It has been shown that the PDGF induces ROS generation in smooth muscle cells [30] and that the Akt2 redox-regulation participates in the glucose consumption induced by PDGF. In this regard, it was recently reported by Wani *et al.* [31] that ROS induced by PDGF cause the oxidation of the Cys124 of Akt2, modulating its inactivation... Cys124 is not conserved in Akt1 and Akt3. These results point to the Cys124-Cys297 or Cys124-Cys311 intramolecular bonds as responsible for the Akt2 inhibition by oxidation [31]. Interestingly, the exogenous H_2O_2 administration activated Akt1 y Akt2, but intracellular accumulation of H_2O_2 resulted in the inactivation of Akt2 only, suggesting a differential action of the ROS source on Akt isoforms activation. It is proposed that the activation of Akt2 by phosphorylation is inhibited by oxidation. This highlights that Akt signaling can be modulated by physiological levels of ROS with functional consequences on the cellular and molecular processes induced by PDGF [31].

e) MAPKs (JNK, p38 and ERK)

JNK activity can be modulated by ROS by an indirect way. For example, it has been shown that GSTπ is inactivated in vitro by H_2O_2 by forming both an intramolecular disulfide bond between the Cys47 and the Cys101 and an intermolecular bond between the Cys47 of two monomers of GST [32]. On the other hand, it is known that the binding of the monomeric GSTπ to JNK inhibits the activation of JNK. Therefore, ROS allow the JNK activation by favoring the formation of GSTπ oligomers that are unable to bind JNK. This has been shown in cultured mouse fibroblasts exposed to pro-oxidant conditions. Under these conditions it is observed the formation of dimers and larger aggregates of GSTπ, JNK activation and the consequent phosphorylation of c-Jun and apoptosis [33].

It was recently reported that p38 is oxidized upon exposure to exogenous H_2O_2 or prostaglandin J2 (an inflammatory mediator), resulting in the inactivation of its kinase activity despite of being phosphorylated. Both, the Cys119 and the Cys162 of p38 were identified as sites of oxidation, with no formation of disulfide bridges. As p38 can be oxidized under micromolar concentrations of the prostaglandin J2, this could represent a signaling event physiologically relevant during inflammation [34].

ROS may exert different actions on the signaling molecules depending on their concentration. In a previous study [35], it was reported that low concentrations of H_2O_2 (0.1 μM) oxidize the Cys38 and Cys214 of ERK2, which does not occur with higher concentrations (10 μM). It was also found that the Cys162 of p38 was also oxidized, but only at a concentration of 20 μM of H_2O_2. In the case of JNK2, several cysteines are directly oxidized with 1 μM of H_2O_2: Cys41, Cys116, Cys137, Cys177 and Cys222, but none of these are oxidized at a concentration of 0.1 μM of H_2O_2. These variable actions of ROS in the oxidation of MAPKs could contribute to the differential control of events such as proliferation and disruption of the cell cycle in some cells [35]. This is an example that low and high concentrations of ROS may produce opposite effects depending on the cysteines oxidized..

f) Receptor Tyrosine Kinase

It is known that one of the consequences of an increase in ROS levels is the inhibition of protein phosphatases, which regulate the activity of several intracellular signaling pathways, including the PI3K/Akt, PLCγ, MAPK and JAK/STAT pathways. For example, some of the physiological and pathological effects of the inhibition of protein tyrosine phosphatases induced by ROS is the activation of cell signals mediated by the receptor tyrosine kinase (RTKs) [36, 37]. Recently, several studies have implicated ROS in the transactivation of RTKs, i.e., in the activation of the receptor independent of its ligand [38-40].

Among the three types of Trk receptors, the BDNF receptor, TrkB, is the most studied RTK in the CNS of mammals. This receptor is widely expressed in both mature and developing neurons and participates in various biological processes such as survival and neuronal differentiation, as well as the physiology, structure and plasticity of synapses [41]. Recently, it was reported in cortical neurons that endogenous and exogenous ROS directly activate TrkB receptor by a mechanism that requires the Src family kinases, i.e., TrkB is activated by a transactivation mechanism mediated by physiological levels of ROS without the participation of BDNF. One of the functional consequences of this ROS-mediated TrkB transactivation is an increase of the survival of cultured neurons [40]. In addition, both the H_2O_2 and BDNF induced the activation of ERK1/2, a signaling protein downstream of TrkB receptors [40].

Furthermore, a recent study in mouse cortical neurons showed that ROS and the NADPH-oxidase (NOX) activity are required for the transactivation of TrkB and PDGFβ by serotonin (5-HT) [42]. This study suggests that serotonin activates their Gαi coupled receptors, leading to PLC activation, which induces calcium release from the endoplasmic reticulum and the activation of PKC. It is suggested that PKC activates NOX, resulting in ROS production. This condition or the exogenous application of H_2O_2 can induce the phosphorylation/activation of the TrkB receptors and PDGFβ. [42]. In the case of the NGF receptor, TrkA, it has also been reported that the redox state regulates its activity through tyrosine phosphatases [43]. There is no much evidence to explain the mechanism by which ROS promote the phosphorylation of TrkA, TrkB and PDGFβ receptors. In the case of the PDGFβ receptor, it has been identified two conserved cysteine residues, which are critical for the RTK kinase activity: Cys822 and Cys940. In this regard, it has been observed that the kinase activity of the receptor is not due to the formation of a disulfide bond between these cysteines, and that the Cys940 mutation only induces a conformational change in the protein [44].

It is known that ROS can also transactivate the EGF receptor [45] and that the activation of this receptor induces an increase in the endogenous levels of H_2O_2 [46], suggesting that the EGF receptor is sensitive to the redox state, and that it induces the generation of ROS. In this context, it was recently demonstrated in cells stimulated with EGF that the Cys797 of the catalytic site of the EGF receptor is directly oxidized by endogenous H_2O_2 that further increases its kinase activity. ROS are apparently produced through the association of EGF receptor with NOX2, one of the 7 homologues of NOX. This highlights the importance of endogenous H_2O_2 in the signaling of the EGF receptor as a result of the activation of NOX [47].

The VEGF receptor (VEGFR) is another example of an RTK that is regulated by direct oxidation of cysteines. In particular, a recent study in endothelial cells showed that VEGFR-2 activity is negatively regulated by the reversible formation of a disulfide bond between the Cys1199 and Cys1206, where the Cys1206 is the direct target of the oxidation by ROS in the absence of the antioxidant enzyme PrxII. Therefore, under physiological conditions, PrxII preserves the reduced state of VEGFR-2 by blocking its oxidative inactivation by H_2O_2 [48].

The FGF type 1 receptor (FGFR-1) also contains a cysteine (Cys488) that is susceptible to be oxidized. This residue was first characterized in the corresponding Cys277 of Src kinase [49]. This study showed that Src in its reduced form is fully active, but it becomes partially inactivated under oxidizing conditions. It is known that the oxidation of the Src Cys277 generates an intermolecular disulfide bond with the Cys277 of other monomer of Src, forming a dimer linked by the disulfide bridge Cys277-Cys277. However, other study shows that H_2O_2 induces Src activation through the formation of an intramolecular disulfide between Cys245 and Cys487, which takes place during cell adhesion [50]. The Cys277 of Src is located in the sequence GQGCFG of its catalytic domain called "Gly loop". Similarly, FGFR-1 contains the Cys488 in the corresponding conserved sequence. In this regard, FGFR-1 is also inactivated by oxidation of the Cys488, which also generates a dimer linked by an intermolecular disulfide bridge; although, in this case, other cysteines seem to participate to stabilize the dimer by oxidation [49].

All these studies suggest that ROS represent a key component for the transactivation pathways in neurons and highlight the physiological relevance of ROS in the mechanisms of transactivation, where ROS could activate multiple RTKs through the inactivation of phosphatases of tyrosine, rather than the transactivation of RTK by GPCR. Table 1 shows the redox sensitive cysteines of some signaling proteins.

PHYSIOLOGICAL ROLE OF ROS IN THE NERVOUS SYSTEM

ROS act as signal molecules that regulate different processes in the adult and developing brain [64-68]. Coincidently, it is in the neurogenic regions of the developing and adult brain where ROS are relatively elevated in physiological conditions [65, 66, 69]. Particularly, during nervous system development, ROS have been shown to regulate the proliferation of neural stem cells and the neuronal differentiation [64-68]. ROS have also been shown to act as morphogens during brain development. For example, it has been observed an increased mitochondrial ROS levels, aberrant axonal targeting and abnormal brain formation when the mitochondrial SOD of the fruit fly *Drosophila* is mutated.

Table 1. Cysteine oxidation with physiological relevance in cell signaling

Protein	Cysteine	Oxidative modification	Physiological result	Refs
Trx1	Cys32 and Cys35	Intramolecular disulfide bond	Dissociates from ASK1 in the cytosol inducing apoptosis	[15, 51, 52]
	Cys32 or Cys35	Intermolecular disulfide bond with Cys250 of ASK1	Inhibits the activity of ASK1 in the cytosol	[14, 22]
Trx2	Cys90 and Cys93	Intramolecular disulfide bond	Dissociates from ASK1 in the mitochondrion inducing apoptosis	[14]
	Cys90	Intermolecular disulfide bond with Cys30 of ASK1	Inhibits the activity of ASK1 in the mitochondrion	[14, 53, 54]
Grx	Cys22 and Cys25	Glutathionylation and/or intramolecular disulfide bond	Dissociates from ASK1 inducing apoptosis	[18, 24, 55]

Table 1. (Continued)

Protein	Cysteine	Oxidative modification	Physiological result	Refs
TXNIP	Cys63 and Cys247 Cys247	Intramolecular disulfide bond Intermolecular disulfide bond with Cys32 of Trx1	Interaction with Trx1 Inhibition of reducing activity of Trx1 inducing cell death	[27] [27, 28, 56]
Akt	Cys297 and Cys311	Intramolecular disulfide bond	Binding of PP2A and inhibition of cell survival	[29, 57, 58]
Akt2	Cys124	Intramolecular disulfide bond with Cys297 o Cys311	Inactivation of Akt2, glucose uptake	[31]
JNK	Cys41, Cys162, Cys137, Cys177, Cys222	Direct oxidation	Cell cycle arrest	[35]
p38	Cys119 and Cys162	Direct oxidation	Inactivation of p38, inflammation	[34, 35]
ASK1	Cys250	Conformational change by direct oxidation	Formation of multimers of ASK1 which activates cell apoptosis	[59, 60]
PTEN	Cys124 and Cys71 Cys212	Intramolecular disulfide bond Intermolecular disulfide bond with Cys32 of Trx1	Inactivation of PTEN Inhibition of the phosphatase activity of PTEN inducing proliferation and cell survival	[25, 61, 62] [26]
ERK2	Cys38 and Cys214	Direct oxidation	Promotes proliferation	[35]
PKC	Cysteine-rich regions	Direct oxidation	Neuronal differentiation	[63]
Src	Cys277 Cys245 and Cys487	Intermolecular disulfide bond with Cys277 between two Src Intramolecular disulfide bond	Inactivation by the formation of a dimer Activation of Src in cell adhesion events	[49] [50]
EGFR	Cys797	Direct oxidation	Activation of EGFR	[47]
VEGFR-2	Cys1199 and Cys1206	Intramolecular disulfide bond	Inactivation kinase of VEGFR-2	[48]
FGFR-1	Cys488	Direct oxidation	Inactivation by the formation of a dimer	[49]
GSTπ	Cys47 and Cys101	Intramolecular disulfide bond	Formation of oligomers of GSTπ that cannot bind to JNK inducing apoptosis	[32, 33]
CRMP2	Cys540	Intermolecular disulfide bond with Cys540 between two CRMP2	Induce growth cone collapse	[64]

These flies also present clusters of nuclei located in the neuropile of the central brain, where normally does not contain these organelles [70].

In mammals, during the postnatal development of rat cerebellum, ROS is transiently produced at different stages of development and is restricted to specific regions of the developing cerebellar cortex. In addition, different members of the NOX family are differentially expressed during cerebellar development. The inhibition of ROS during rat development, leads to changes in cerebellar folia formation, as well as an alteration in motor behavior [65]. These studies suggest that the proper regulation of ROS during critical periods of time is required for normal brain development.

Little is known about the mechanisms related to the physiological actions of ROS in the nervous system, but three different conditions have been identified in these processes: 1) ROS are produced in response to a physiological stimulus induced by a growth factor or a neurotransmitter and the most likely source is a NOX and/or the mitochondria. 2) It is necessary a target protein with specific chemical features that allow to interact with ROS, as it was previously described. 3) These events should occur restrained in time and space in order to be specific; otherwise ROS could trigger unspecific responses, including cell death. In this chapter we describe some studies that exemplify the physiological actions of ROS in the nervous system.

a) Proliferation

A growing body of experimental evidence suggests that ROS induce proliferation of neural cells. It has been shown that the neural progenitor cells derived from embryonic hippocampus generate ROS under basal conditions and that the antioxidants and inhibitors of the ROS-producing enzyme NOX reduce their proliferation [71]. In these cells, it has been observed a correlation between the levels of ROS and proliferation [72]. Furthermore, *in vivo* administration of the antioxidant α-lipoic acid reduced cell proliferation in the dentate subgranular zone of the hippocampus [72].

Le Belle and collaborators [66] demonstrated in neurosphere cultures obtained from the subventricular zone that H_2O_2 promoted self-renewal of neural progenitor cells. Also, when ROS levels were lowered, the number of neurospheres was decreased and restored by exogenous addition of H_2O_2. Consistent with these studies, high levels of ROS have been detected in the neurogenic regions of the subventricular zone, the glomerular layer of the olfactory bulb and the subgranular zone [66, 69]. In addition, BDNF also increased the levels of ROS and self-renewal of progenitor cells; however, none of these effects were observed in BDNF-treated cells derived from KO NOX2 mice. Besides, the KO NOX2 mice have less proliferating cells in the subventricular zone than wild type mice and the pharmacological inhibition of NOX diminished both the generation of ROS and proliferation in the subventricular zone. These results suggest that the ROS produced by BDNF are implicated in the proliferation and that the ROS source is NOX2.[66]. Furthermore, H_2O_2 also induced the oxidation of PTEN in these cells.

Finally, H_2O_2 activates the pathway PI3K/Akt/mTOR through the inactivation of PTEN [73]. In KO PTEN mice neither H_2O_2 nor BDNF were able to stimulate neurosphere formation. Thus, the effect of ROS in neural precursor cells seems to be mediated by the redox inactivation of PTEN [66].

b) Neuronal Differentiation

It has been found that ROS are critical determinants of neuronal differentiation in several experimental models. Part of this idea is supported by the *in vivo* observations of a transient ROS production in response to trophic conditions that induce neuronal differentiation in specific neurogenic regions of the brain [65, 66, 69]. Under these conditions, the differentiation process is delayed or diminished when ROS are decreased by antioxidants or inhibitors of the ROS sources.

Many of the studies on neuronal differentiation have been performed in the PC12 cell line. When these cells are treated with the neurotrophin NGF, these cells develop neurites (neuritogenesis) and express different neuronal markers, including βIII-tubulin, GAP-43 and neurofilament L, among others. This process begins with the activation of TrkA, which leads to the activation of PLCγ-PKC-Raf and the subsequent activation of the signaling pathway Ras-Raf-MEK-ERK. The sustained activity of ERK is necessary for the achievement of the neuronal-like characteristics of PC12 cells. Finally, TrkA also activates the PI3K-Akt signaling pathway that promotes cell survival [74, 75].

In this regard, neuronal differentiation of PC12 is ROS dependent. For example, hyperoxia and xanthine/xanthine oxidase activation induce the formation of neurites trough a sustained activation of ERKs in a process that is mediated by ROS production [76]. In particular, the activation of ERKs is affected by ROS in different points of the signaling cascade. In PC12 cells it has been demonstrated that ROS induce the phosphorylation of TrkA through the inhibition of PTPs (protein tyrosine phosphatases), and also promote the activation of PLCγ and PI3K, as well as the formation of the receptor complexes with the scaffold proteins Shc, Grb2 and Sos, which are indispensable for the activation of the MAPK pathway [77]. Although it is not clear how ROS induce the formation of the complex formed by the TrkA receptor and the scaffold proteins, it has been proposed that H_2O_2 induces the activation of ERKs by Src through the Ras-Raf pathway [78] and by Fyn through the Jak2-Shc-Grb2-Sos-Ras pathway [79]. Furthermore, neurite outgrowth of PC12 induced by NGF is mediated by Fyn [80], while Src is required for neurite outgrowth induced by cAMP, but not by NGF [81]. Thereby these kinases seem to be involved in the neuronal differentiation of PC12 induced by ROS and one of the possible targets of ROS produced by NGF might be Fyn that acts upstream ERKs activation.

It is not conclusive the role played by the different sources of ROS during the differentiation processes; however, it seems that different sources might have different effectors, which could have diverse effects in cells. For example, in PC12 cells, NGF induces a peak of ROS levels after 10 min of treatment. This production of ROS is inhibited by DPI, an inhibitor of NOX, suggesting that NOX is the ROS source induced by NGF at this time [82]. On the other hand, the NGF treatment produces a time dependent reduction of the expression of NOX2 at 48 h, with a concomitant increase in the expression of NOX1. After 72 h, there is a second peak of ROS, which is produced by NOX1, since the elimination of NOX1 abolishes this peak. Under this scenario, the inhibition of ROS production by NOX inhibitors and a mimetic of catalase (Euk-8) after 48 h of NGF treatment, increases the neurite length and the expression of βIII-tubulin. However, when catalase is applied together with NGF from the beginning, the differentiation of PC12 cells is reduced [83]. These results suggest that ROS produced by different sources at different stages of PC12 cells differentiation have different effects in the differentiation process. The first peak of ROS, probably produced by NOX2, is critical to initiate the observed changes, while the second peak of ROS, which is produced by NOX1, negatively regulate neurite outgrowth of differentiated PC12 cells.

The counterpart of ROS produced are the antioxidant systems. In this regard, it has been reported in PC12 cells that NGF induces the expression of the antioxidants glutathione peroxidase and catalase after 3 days of treatment [84]. This regulation of the antioxidant systems allows the cells to contend with the H_2O_2 chronically produced by NGF [85]. However, the role of the antioxidant systems in neuronal differentiation has not been completely determined. When PC12 cells are treated with NGF, there is an induction of the phosphorylation of ERKs from 5 min to 30 min, which is crucial to induce the expression and activity of the mitochondrial MnSOD that is necessary to induce differentiation. MnSOD is required to induce a second peak of the phosphorylation of ERKs at 180 min after NGF treatment. If MnSOD is overexpressed, it is induced the neural specific transcription of NGF1a in the absence of NGF; while MnSOD silencing leads to a reduction in the phosphorylation of ERKs. It is proposed that the mechanism by which MnSOD induces the phosphorylation of ERKs at 180 min is through the conversion of superoxide anion into H_2O_2, which is indispensable to induce the long term phosphorylation of ERKs. When H_2O_2 is reduced by the mimetic of glutathione peroxidase Ebselen, the second peak of ERKs phosphorylation is also inhibited and the neurite outgrowth is completely prevented [86].

It is not completely understood how ROS participate in the activation of ERKs. Gopalakrishna *et al.* [63] employed the xanthine/xanthine oxidase system and $CoCl_2$ as pro-oxidants to induce cell differentiation. Both oxidants were able to induce neuronal differentiation of PC12 measured as neurite outgrowth, the expression of neurofilament-L, GAP-43 and SCG10. The differentiation induced by oxidants was mediated by PKC, since the non-selective inhibitors of PKC, calphostin C and chelerythrine, reduced neurite outgrowth. Also, $CoCl_2$ induced the translocation of PKC from the cytosol to the membrane. During the period of activation the capacity of PKC to bind phorbol esters was reduced, suggesting that there is a redox modification of the regulatory domain of PKC. Further exposure to higher concentrations of $CoCl_2$ induced the inactivation of PKC. The exposure of cells to $CoCl_2$ oxidized 7 of the 18 sulfhydryls detected in PKC and exposure to higher concentrations of $CoCl_2$ induced the oxidation of 3 more PKC sulfhydryls. Thus, the increasing oxidation of sulfhydryls residues decreases PKC activity. In this study, the MEK inhibitor PD98059 did not affect the activation of PKCε, but substantially decreased the activation of ERKs, CREB and neurite outgrowth induced by CoCl2. This suggests that PKCε couples the oxidative signal to the final activation of ERKs, and that there are more possible targets of oxidative modification upstream of MEK. Finally, in a context of NGF treatment, ROS produced during the first minutes activate PKCε [63], indicating that the oxidation of PKCε is an important event in the neuronal differentiation induced by NGF (Figure 2).

In primary cultures of neural precursor cells obtained from cerebral cortex, ROS control neuronal fate. In this model, those cells producing high levels of ROS were differentiated to neurons [87]. The same occurs in primary cultures of neural precursor cells obtained from the subventricular zone, where exogenous administration of H_2O_2 produced more differentiated neurons. Conversely, the inhibition of NOX or PI3K diminished the number of neurons, while the effect of the exogenous administration of H_2O_2 was abolished by the pharmacological inhibition of PI3K. Furthermore, cultures derived from KO NOX2 mice produced significantly lesser neurons than those from wild type animals [66].

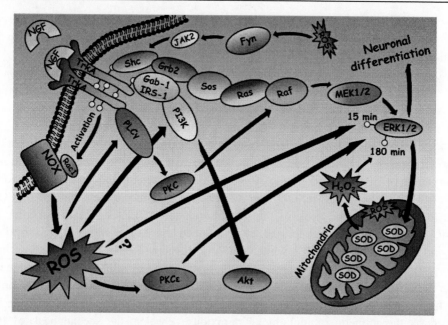

Figure 2. *Redox regulation of PC12 cells differentiation*. When PC12 cells are treated with NGF, there occurs a TrkA transphosphorylation, which induces the recruitment of adapter proteins leading to the activation of the signaling pathway Ras-Raf-MEK1/2-ERK1/2 that promotes differentiation. On the other hand, it is proposed that ROS produced by NOX induce a maximal phosphorylation of ERK at 15 min, which is crucial to induce the expression and activity of the mitochondrial MnSOD required for the conversion of superoxide anion into H2O2. The generation of H_2O_2 is necessary to generate a second peak of the phosphorylation of ERKs at 180 min. ROS generated by NOX may also induce the activation of PKC, coupling the oxidative signal to ERK activation. NGF binding to TrkA also leads to the activation of the signaling pathway PLCγ-PKC-Raf and the subsequent activation of ERK. ROS may also activate Fyn, coupling the signaling pathway Shc-Ras-Raf-MEK1/2-ERK1/2. It has also been suggested that PKC and Akt induce the activation of NOX.

Tsatmalli et al. also demonstrated that neuronal differentiation of neural precursor cells from cortex are influenced by ROS in multiple aspects. When neural precursor cells are selected according to their ROS production, it was found that high ROS producer cells generated neurons, while low ROS producer cells generated astrocytes, oligodendrocytes and a different type of neurons. These former neurons were classified in two types: the type 1 neurons were predominant in number (around 65%) and had pyramidal morphology, multiples neurites and fired a single action potential, while the type 2 neurons were less in proportion (around 35%), had rounded soma, less neurites and fired repetitive action potentials. When low ROS producer cells are treated with antioxidants, the proportion of the generated neurons are reverted, increasing the number of neurons type 2 (around 80%) [69]. Overall, these results strongly suggest that ROS promotes neuronal differentiation of neural precursor cells in different regions of the brain.

c) Axonal Growth and Guidance

The participation of the ROS in axonal growth is a process that has extensively been studied in the axon growth cones of *Aplysia* neurons. Munnammalai *et al.* [67] found in this model that axonal growth cones have high concentrations of ROS, which favor the axonal growth, since the decrease of ROS by treatments with antioxidants, inhibitors of NOX or lipoxygenase decreased the axonal growth. ROS modulate different aspects of the dynamics of the actin cytoskeleton. This regulation is determined by both the ROS levels and its source, which could define the compartmentalization of ROS. For example, physiological levels of ROS promote the assembly and protrusion of the actin filaments, while the inhibition of NOX prevents this process. On the other hand, lipoxygenase inhibition influences the assembly of actin in the actin arches, but not in the filopodia [67].

In further studies, Munnammalai et al. [68] determined that NOX2 is localized in the plasma membrane of the axonal growth cones. The activation of NOX2 increased the levels of ROS in the P domain, while the pharmacological inhibition of NOX2 impaired actin dynamics and axonal growth. Interestingly, the localization of active NOX2 was elevated in F-actin bundles in non-stimulated growth cones, which was reduced when F-actin bundles were disrupted with cytochalasin B treatments. Finally, the activity of NOX2 was increased when neurons were grown in beds of apCAM (*Aplysia* cell adhesion molecule), which evoke growth in the apCAM zones [68], indicating that the dynamics of the axonal growth cones are importantly affected by a bidirectional relationship between actin cytoskeleton and NOX2 [68].

As mentioned, the specific localization of ROS in the axonal growth cone might affect different aspects of axonal growth cone dynamics. In this regard, Zhang et al. [88] characterized in *Aplysia* neurons the relationship between ROS production and calcium. In this model, calcium is elevated in the axonal growth cone in response to serotonin, which is dependent on ROS produced by NOX. This relationship involves the regulation of microtubule dynamics and ROS production dependent on Rac1. Under control conditions, nearly 13% of the neurons showed increased levels of calcium, which was increased by 80% when the constitutive active form of Rac1 was injected into the cells. This constitutive active form of Rac1 promoted the movement of microtubules and endoplasmic reticulum Ca^{2+} stores towards the P-domain of the axonal growth cone. On the other hand, the constitutive active form of Rac1 promoted ROS formation in response to serotonin, while the dominant-negative form had the opposite effect. When ROS were inhibited by antioxidants in the presence of the constitutive active form of Rac1, the observed increase of calcium release evoked by serotonin was completely blocked. Conversely, the dominant-negative of Rac1, restored calcium release when low concentration of exogenous H_2O_2 was added. This effect of ROS is dependent on IP_3 receptors, since the blockade of these receptors with xestopongin C did not restore calcium release [88]. This is in line with the idea that ROS oxidizes the IP_3 receptors, which favor calcium release [89]. Furthermore, the regulation of calcium release by ROS in the axonal growth cone might regulate axonal growth cone dynamics, since calcium has pleiotropic effects in the growth cone motility [90].

During nervous system development, neurons tend to establish the proper contact with specific targets through a complex process that is regulated by extracellular cues that guide the axons. A group of proteins that guide the axonal growth cone are the semaphorins, whose mechanisms of action requires the activation of their receptors [91], which couple specific signaling pathways that regulate repulsive axon guidance and cell migration. In dorsal root ganglion neurons, semaphorin3A induces growth cone collapse by the cytoskeleton regulation through the collapsin response mediator protein 2 (CRMP2). The phosphorylation of CRMP2 by GSK3-β and Cdk5 promotes microtubule disassembly, which produces the growth cone collapse [92]. In these cells, Morinaka et al. [64] found that the phosphorylation of CRMP2 is specifically regulated by ROS. Semaphorine3A induces the generation of H_2O_2 in the axonal growth cone through the participation of the Molecule Interacting with CasL (MICAL), which oxidizes CRMP2 and induces the formation of a transient disulfide-linked homodimer between the cysteines 504 of two CRMP2 proteins. Then, this homodimer is reduced by Trx that forms a disulfide bond with one molecule of CRMP2. This complex is crucial for CRMP2 phosphorylation by GSK3-β, which ultimately produces the growth cone collapse of these neurons [64]. Together, these studies demonstrate the importance of local ROS production in developing neurons, which can affect nervous system development and the proper establishment of neuronal circuits.

d) Apoptosis and Survival

i) Trx, Grx and the MAPK Pathway

During the last decade there has been a remarkably advance in the knowledge of the role of ROS as signal molecules involved in programmed cell death. Oxidative stress can alter the cell homeostasis at different level. For example, ROS can induce modifications of the sulfhydryl groups leading to modifications of the functional characteristics of proteins with reactive cysteine residues. This condition might be strengthened if ROS also inhibit the thioredoxin (Trx) and/or glutaredoxin (Grx) system, which are responsible for reversing the inter- or intramolecular disulfide bonds, as well as the S-glutathionylation of proteins, respectively [93].

As all redox proteins, both Trx and Grx can exist in an oxidized or reduced form, which accounts a critical feature for their interaction with other proteins. One of these proteins is ASK1, a member of the MAPKKK, which is expressed in the cytosol and mitochondria [14] and that is involved in the signaling initiated by oxidative stress that leads to apoptosis [94, 95]. Although ASK1 is involved in proliferation and differentiation in several cell types, its role in apoptosis has been the most widely characterized [96-99]. It has been proposed that ASK1 regulates the intrinsic, extrinsic and caspase-independent apoptotic pathways, which can be induced by conditions such as stimulation of death receptors, DNA damage, oxidative stress and stress of the endoplasmic reticulum [99]. ASK1 is also the target of many proteins related to survival, which bind to different domains of ASK1. Trx and Grx are part of this group of proteins. Trx binds to the N-terminal domain, while the Grx binds to the C-terminal domain of ASK1, inhibiting the activity of ASK1 [15, 24, 51].

Trx1 was the first identified negative regulator of the activity of ASK1 [15]. It has been described that under basal conditions, ASK1 forms homo-oligomers through their coiled-coil domains in the carboxyl terminal (CCC). Also, both Trx1 and 14-3-3 proteins, bind to ASK1 forming what is called the signalosome that negatively regulates ASK1 activity [52]. The 14-3-3 proteins bind to ASK1 in the phosphorylated Ser967 [94]. In response to ROS generation, Trx1 is oxidized and Cys35 and Cys32 form an intramolecular disulfide bridge with the consequent conformational change of Trx1 leading to its dissociation from ASK1 and the release of 14-3-3 proteins. Subsequently, TRAF2 and/or TRAF6, which act as positive regulators, are recruited to ASK1, which promotes the interaction between ASK1 molecules through their domains coiled-coil in the amino terminal (NCC) and allows the autophosphorylation of T845 in ASK1 and completing the ASK1 activation triggered by the oxidative stimulus [52]. Under oxidative stress ASK1 is ubiquitinated and may be degraded; however, the peptidase USP9X promotes the deubiquitination of active ASK1 to counteract its proteasome-dependent degradation. In this way, USP9X stabilizes the activity of ASK1 [100]. Once active, ASK1 activates JNK and p38, which triggers the apoptotic cell death.

Alternatively, Nadeau et al. [59, 60] proposed another mechanism for Trx1 in the regulation of ASK1 in response to H_2O_2. They showed that H_2O_2 induces ASK1 oxidation leading to the formation of multimers of ASK1 linked by disulfide bonds. They also identified the Cys250 in ASK1 as the critical residue for JNK activation in response to H_2O_2-induced oxidative stress. When they mutated the Cys250 of ASK1, the binding of ASK1 to Trx1 was blocked; however, although the ASK1 multimers linked by disulfide bridges are still formed, no longer phosphorylation in T845 (related to activation) and downstream activation of the MAPKs pathway is observed.

These results suggest that the dissociation of ASK1 from Trx1 is not enough to promote ASK1 signaling, but it is required the oxidation of the Cys250 of ASK1 to induce a conformational change that allows the activation of the protein [59, 60]. It is necessary more experimental evidences to understand the role that plays the Cys250 in the activation of ASK1 in response to H_2O_2.

In cerebellar granule neurons it has been shown that staurosporine (Sts) and potassium deprivation (K5) cause apoptotic death [101, 102]. In addition, both K5 and Sts induce the generation of ROS, which is transient and occurs during the 4 h after treatment [101, 103]. In this regard, it was found that K5 activated both ASK1-JNK-cJun and ASK1-p38-ATF2 pathways, where ROS acted upstream ASK1 [101, 102]. On the other hand, Sts induced apoptotic death only through the ASK1-p38-ATF2 pathway, indicating that ROS generated by Sts seems to act at a different level [102].

On the other hand, it has been observed that the overexpression of Grx protects cells from metabolic oxidative stress induced by glucose deprivation by a mechanism that suppresses the redox activation of ASK1 and its targets downstream, including the JNK pathway [24, 55]. These results support the hypothesis that the Grx-ASK1 interaction sensitive to the redox state is regulated by the Grx through the regulation of the intracellular glutathione-dependent redox reactions that involve the participation of H_2O_2 [24]. The oxidative stress induced by glucose deprivation can activate ASK1 through two different pathways: the glutathione-dependent Grx-ASK1 and the Trx-ASK1 independent of glutathione. It is proposed that the release of either Grx or Trx is sufficient for activating ASK1 [55].

It has been observed that the knockdown of ASK1 protects the neuronal cells SHSY5Y from L-DOPA-induced apoptosis [104, 105]. These results support the idea that the possible regulation of Grx of apoptosis induced by oxidants in neurons is mediated via ASK1. However, there are many potential effectors for ASK1 activation and many of them are also sensitive to oxidation and potential targets of Grx; therefore, additional studies are needed to outline the specific role of Grx under this condition [106].

The reversible inactivation of PTEN has also been described in studies using H_2O_2 or ROS produced by NOX in macrophages [61, 62]. As already mentioned, Trx1, in its reduced state, directly binds to PTEN in a redox-dependent way to inhibit its phosphatase activity on PIP_3, resulting in an increase in the activity of Akt [26]. Akt binds to PIP_3 through their PH domains (domains of homology to pleckstrine), which allows that PDK1 phosphorylates Akt T803 (PDK2 phosphorylates the Ser473), leading to full Akt activation. In this regard, it is proposed that under basal conditions PTEN is active, carrying out the dephosphorylation of

PIP$_3$, and therefore decreasing the Akt activity. Under oxidative stress, Trx1 binds PTEN avoiding PIP$_3$ dephosphorylation and inducing a constitutive activation of Akt, which triggers the antiapoptotic signals.

As mentioned previously, under oxidative stress, Trx1 oxidizes and releases from ASK1. Therefore it is possible that Trx1, once reduced by the Thioredoxin reductase 1 (TrxR1), binds PTEN generating survival signals to counteract the apoptotic signals triggered by ASK1. The inhibition of ROS-dependent phosphatase activity of PTEN also suggests that ROS produced under pathological conditions could contribute to the apoptosis inhibition and subsequent formation of tumors in the nervous system.

ii) Redox Regulation of Akt

As mentioned above, it is known that Akt is sensitive to the redox state and that the oxidative modification of the Akt reactive cysteines are critical for its activity [29, 31, 57, 58]. Also, H$_2$O$_2$ induces the formation of disulfide bridges between Cys297 and Cys311 in Akt, as well as the subsequent dephosphorylation mediated by PP2A. Overexpression of Grx reduces Akt, which abolishes its binding to PP2A, then allowing a sustained Akt phosphorylation, inducing an inhibition of apoptosis in cardiac cells [29], indicating an antiapoptotic action of Grx through a redox regulation of Akt. Interestingly, it has been found that inactive Akt is fully oxidized, while the active form is only partially oxidized. In this regard, it was recently reported that ROS produced by NOX1 oxidize the Akt reactive cysteines promoting its interaction with PP2A, which inhibits Akt and therefore induces apoptosis in cardiomyocytes [57].

In the nervous system, it has been found that mice treated with MPTP, a neurotoxin which selectively damage dopaminergic neurons from the ventral midbrain, the critical cysteines of Akt are oxidized, increasing its association with PP2A, and therefore lowering the levels of Akt selectively phosphorylated. The presence of antioxidants fully reversed these effects [58]. Grx1 overexpression in primary neurons derived from human stem cells maintains the reduced state of Akt and inhibits the MPTP-mediated loss of phosphorylation [58], indicating that the preservation of the redox homeostasis by the overexpression of Grx1 can preserve the levels of phosphorylated Akt.

On the other hand, the inhibition of Akt induces an activation of p38 and JNK that promotes apoptosis, whereas active Akt directly phosphorylates ASK1 Ser83, which leads to apoptosis inhibition [107]. Min and collaborators [108] proposed that the regulation of Akt on ASK1 for the control of apoptosis occurs through the interaction between Hsp90, Akt and ASK1 to keep ASK1 in an inactive state. They suggest that this interaction allows Akt to be in the proximity of the N-terminal domain of ASK1 to phosphorylate it in the Ser83. In response to an apoptotic condition, such as H$_2$O$_2$, the Hsp90-Akt-ASK1 complex becomes more stable, since Akt moves to the ASK1 C-terminal domain, which causes a decrease in the phosphorylation of the Ser83 and the subsequent activation of ASK1 that activates p38 pathways and/or JNK leading to apoptosis.

In this model, Hsp90 would serve as a protein scaffold to keep Akt and ASK1 in proximity. Unlike Trx and Grx, Hsp90-Akt complex does not dissociate from ASK1 in response to oxidative stress, but it undergoes a conformational change that generates a more stable complex [108]. Thus, the regulation of apoptotic death through the ROS-mediated ASK1 activation is complex and represents an active research field (Figure 3).

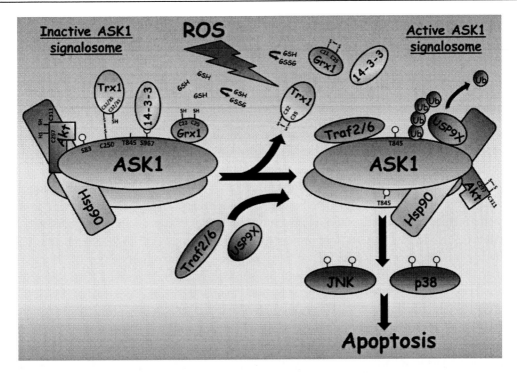

Figure 3. *Participation of the reactive oxygen species in the activation of ASK1 through its different redox sensitive controllers.* During the inactive condition, ASK1 forms homo-oligomers through their CCC domains. Each monomer binds Trx1, Grx1, 14-3-3 proteins, Akt, and Hsp90, which negatively regulate the activation of ASK1, forming the so called signalosome. HSP90 acts as a scaffold protein that maintains ASK1 bound to Akt, allowing the Ser83 ASK1 phosphorylation by Akt. Trx1 forms an intermolecular disulfide bridge with the Cys250 of ASK1, while Grx1 is attached to the c-terminus of ASK1 and 14-3-3 protein binds to the phosphorylated Ser967 of ASK1. In response to ROS generation, Trx1, Grx1 and 14-3-3 protein dissociate from ASK1 and Hsp90 and Akt undergoes a conformational rearrangement with respect to ASK1, which physically prevents that Akt negatively phosphorylates ASK1. Akt is inactivated when it forms an intramolecular disulfide bridge between the Cys297 and Cys311. Meanwhile, TRAF2 and/or TRAF6 join ASK1, which results in the homophilic interaction between the two ASK1 proteins through their NCC, allowing the autophosphorylation of T845 in ASK1. USP9X joins the signalosome and stabilizes active ASK1 by avoiding its proteasomal degradation by deubiquitination. Once ASK1 is totally active, it phosphorylates MAPKK, which in turn phosphorylates JNK and p38 MAPK, inducing apoptosis. See text for more details.

iii) TXNIP and TRX

Although most of the studies have focused on the interaction between Trx1 and cytosolic ASK1, it is also known that the mitochondrial isoform of thioredoxin (Trx2) also interacts with the mitochondrial ASK1 and inhibits its activity preventing the apoptosis induced by ASK1 in endothelial cells and hepatocytes [14, 53]. Trx2 has a critical role in the control of mitochondrial oxidative stress and mitochondria-dependent apoptosis [54]. Thus, Trx2 helps to repair the oxidative damage of proteins by reducing the disulfide bonds formed by the cysteines oxidation.

Unlike Trx1, Trx2 specifically regulates the JNK-independent apoptotic intrinsic pathway in vascular endothelial cells, suggesting that Trx1 and Trx2 control different apoptotic pathways [14].

On the other hand, TXNIP also known as VDUP1 (vitamin D3 up-regulated protein-1) or TBP2 (thioredoxin-binding protein-2), is a redox protein ubiquitously expressed that promotes apoptosis [56]. In mouse pancreatic beta cells, it has been described that under basal conditions, TXNIP is predominantly located in the nucleus. In response to oxidative stress, TXNIP translocates from the nucleus to the mitochondria, where it forms a complex with Trx2, removing Trx2 from ASK1. The Trx2-mediated inhibition of ASK1 elimination leads to cytochrome c release, caspase-3 activation and apoptosis [56]. The TXNIP translocation to the mitochondria induced by oxidative stress fits well with the role that TXNIP has as regulator of the redox state and the mitochondrial death pathway.

It is believed that under physiological levels of ROS, the TXNIP-Trx1 complex formation is favored. In endothelial cells, this complex translocates from the nucleus to the plasmatic membrane, activating the inflammatory processes and promoting cell survival. In this context, TXNIP acts as a scaffold protein for the transport of Trx1 to the membrane. This translocation is required, for example, to carry out the trans-activation of the VEGF type 2 receptor (VEGFR-2) mediated by H_2O_2 and the subsequent activation of ERK1/2. Here, the TXNIP-Trx1 complex acts as a redox sensitive mediator for the control of VEGFR-2 signaling, which promotes cell survival under physiological ROS levels [109]. Thus, TXNIP can function as an intermediary in the signaling depending on the cell compartment and can be proapoptotic under high concentrations of ROS or a survival protein in cells with physiological levels of ROS (Figure 4). Recently, it has been proposed the concept of "Redoxisome" to refer to the complex Trx-TXNIP as a signaling transducer relative to the redox state under normal and pathological conditions [110].

In the nervous system, the role played by these molecules and their interaction with ROS in the apoptotic death has not been explored in detail. It has been reported that the activation of ASK1 is involved in neuronal apoptosis, as occurs in NGF-deprived sympathetic neurons [111]. In addition, Trx attenuates neuronal damage [112], regulates the MAPK cascade through the suppression of ASK1 activation and increases the transcription factors activation [15]. In cerebellar granule neurons, it has been described that the TXNIP gene corresponds to the early response genes whose expression is directly regulated by the flow of calcium during neuronal apoptosis [32]. Therefore, it is possible that TXNIP regulates the MAPKs pathway forming a complex net of signal transduction in neuronal apoptosis. It is likely that these mechanisms have variations due to the fact that in other cell types TXNIP has been described as a cytosolic protein [23, 113, 114].

It is known that the overstimulation of NMDA receptors (NMDAR) leads to the generation of free radicals in neurons that causes an oxidative damage associated with neuronal death and several neurodegenerative diseases [115]. On the other hand, it has been reported that physiological synaptic activity increases the expression of antioxidant defenses (thioredoxin, peroxiredoxin and sulfiredoxin) in neurons. It was found that the blockade of the NMDAR under basal conditions promoted an increased vulnerability to oxidative insults [116].

The stimulation of the NMDAR activates the PI3K/Akt pathway leading to the phosphorylation of the transcription factor FOXO in the nucleus, causing its dissociation from the TXNIP promoter and inducing the release of FOXO from the nucleus, reducing TXNIP levels. Thus, a low TXNIP transcription results in less inhibition of Trx, and therefore promotes a neuroprotective action against oxidative damage under physiological conditions [116].

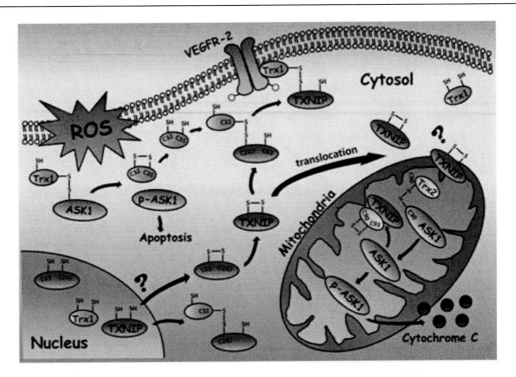

Figure 4. *Participation of TXNIP in the cascade of signal transduction that promotes survival and cell death.* Under basal conditions, TXNIP is located in the nucleus, while Trx1 is found both in the cytosol and the nucleus and Trx2 is located only in the mitochondria. The inactive form of ASK1 is located both in the cytosol (interacting with reduced Trx1), and in the mitochondria (bound to reduced Trx2). In response to oxidative stress, TXNIP translocates from the nucleus to the mitochondria, where it binds Trx2, which relieves the inhibition of ASK1 by Trx2 that is now in its oxidized form. This allows ASK1 activation in the mitochondria inducing signals that lead to apoptotic death. Meanwhile, Trx1 is oxidized and released from ASK1, which activates and induces apoptotic death. The antioxidant mechanisms activated by ROS can reduce the levels of oxidized Trx1. On the other hand, under physiological levels of ROS, the formation of the TXNIP-Trx1 complex is induced in the nucleus and in the cytosol. In the case of the VEGF receptor (VEGFR-2), this complex translocates to the membrane, where it carries out the trans-activation of the receptor, which activates ERK1/2 that promotes cell survival. See text for more details.

iv) ROS, Mitochondria and Apoptosis

The mitochondrion is one of the main sources of ROS in the cell. It has been suggested that the mitochondrial ROS are involved in several pathologies, including neurodegenerative diseases [117]. Interestingly, new mechanisms have been proposed to explain how changes in the redox state of a mitochondrial protein may lead to cell death/survival through a mechanism associated with changes in the mitochondrial morphology. It is known that dynamics of mitochondrial fusion and fragmentation regulates many mitochondrial functions necessary for cell physiology. Although the machinery that catalyzes these processes has been described, little is known about the signaling components that regulate these phenomena [118]. In this regard, in the nervous system, it is known that the inhibition of mitochondrial fission in cortical neurons blocks the ROS production and cell damage produced by inhibitors of the electron transport chain [119]. Also, the ROS overproduction observed in a condition of hyperglycemia requires an increase in mitochondrial fission [120].

Recently, it has been described that Romo1 (reactive oxygen species modulator 1) represents a fundamental element in the generation of mitochondrial ROS. Romo1 is a 79 amino acids transmembrane protein, which is located in the mitochondria and that induces the production of mitochondrial ROS through the complex III of the electron transport chain [121-123]. In this regard, Screaton and cols. [118] reported that Romo1 is sensitive to the redox state and that this molecule represents a molecular switch (or redox switch) that links ROS and the mitochondrial morphology by modulating the mitochondrial fusion and the remodeling of the mitochondrial crests. This group found that the loss of Romo1 induces the deoligomerization of OPA1 (optic atrophy 1), which is required for mitochondrial fusion. Under this condition occurs a mitochondrial crests remodeling, which increases the probability of cytochrome c release and apoptosis [124]. In spite of the evidences of Romo1 as a protein involved in the morphological modeling of mitochondria and sensitive to the redox state, there is no enough information about the direct regulation of ROS on the components of the machinery responsible for the mitochondrial fission and fusion, therefore further research on this field is required.

In addition to its role in mitochondrial fusion, it has also been suggested that Romo1 may serve as a molecular link between TNF-α and the mitochondrial ROS during TNF-α-mediated apoptosis. In this regard, the complex II of TNF-α binds to the C-terminus of Romo1, which recruits Bcl-X_L and reduces the mitochondrial membrane potential, resulting in ROS production and apoptotic cell death [125]. Since Romo1 seems to participate in the modulation of the intrinsic pathway of apoptosis, its inhibition might have therapeutic applications by promoting the apoptotic death of cancer cells and by disrupting the ROS production involved in the signaling pathways responsible for cell proliferation.

ROS AND BRAIN FUNCTION

ROS play an important role in the regulation of normal brain function. For example, ROS is a regulator of dopamine release in the striatum and in the long term potentiation (LTP) and plasticity in the hippocampus. However, the underlying mechanisms by which ROS regulate these functions are not fully understood.

a) ROS as Neuromodulator

The group of Rice has significantly contributed to the understanding of the ROS function as neuromodulators of dopamine release in nigrostriatal pathway [126-130]. This system regulates motor movement [131-134], receives synaptic inputs from the cerebral cortex, thalamus and substantia nigra [135] and the degeneration of neurons from the substantia nigra has been related to Parkinson's disease [136, 137]. Avshalumov et al. [126] demonstrated in coronal striatal slices that endogenous glutamate release produces H_2O_2 under physiological conditions and that the blockade of glutamate receptors produced an increase in the release of dopamine by these neurons. The effect of glutamate on dopamine release seems to be indirect [126, 127], probably mediated by H_2O_2. This is supported by the fact that dopamine release was prevented in the presence of catalase or glutathione peroxidase. On the other hand, the effect of GABA-dependent modulation of dopamine release is also mediated by H_2O_2 since catalase completely prevented the effect of picrotoxin (a blocker of $GABA_A$ receptors). On the other hand, when endogenous glutathione peroxidase was inhibited by mercaptosuccinate, the increased H_2O_2 markedly inhibits dopamine release, an effect that was blocked by catalase [126].

The modulation of H_2O_2 on dopamine release occurs in a physiological time scale. In experiments where a single pulse of electrical stimulation elicited dopamine release, glutathione peroxidase inhibition did not have any effect on dopamine release; however, if subsequent pulses are applied, it can be appreciated a decrease in dopamine release by decreasing glutathione peroxidase with mercaptosuccinate within the first three to five electrical pulses train. Thus, H_2O_2 produced during the first pulse seems to be responsible for dopamine release inhibition elicited by the subsequent pulses. The effect of glutamate and GABA occurs in the same neurons that produce H_2O_2 since the activation of $GABA_A$ receptors has no effect when glutamate receptors are blocked, which indicates that GABA has no effect on dopamine release. Since the antioxidant enzymes catalase and glutathione peroxidase are not expected to enter the cells, their effect most be in the extracellular space. Thus the release of H_2O_2 produced by neurons in the striatum diffuse from the postsynaptic sites to inhibit the presynaptic dopamine release [126].

The activity-dependent production of H_2O_2 also occurs in neurons from substantia nigra pars compacta (SNpc). An increase in the firing rate of these neurons by depolarizing current injection induces elevated H_2O_2 levels. The presence of catalase produced an increase in the firing rate. In contrast, high concentrations of mercaptosuccinate (1 mM) produced a marked hyperpolarization and cease of firing in one population of dopamine neurons. These results can be mimicked by adding exogenous H_2O_2 (1.5 mM) which also inhibits dopamine release [128]. Thus, two groups of SNpc neurons can be distinguished by their capacity to respond to H_2O_2 [129]. Avshalumov and collaborators [129, 130] also determined that the target upon which H_2O_2 acts to modulate dopamine release are the ATP-sensitive K^+ channels (K_{ATP}). These channels are activated by a decrease in the ATP/ADP ratio and are composed by inwardly rectifying pore-forming subunits ($K_{ir}6.2$ in neurons) and sulfonylurea receptor subunits (SUR1/SUR2) [138-140].

Mitochondria seem to be the source of H_2O_2 that regulates the dopamine release in the dorsal striatum. Bao et al. [141] demonstrated that inhibiting mitochondrial ROS by using succinate and rotenone inhibits glutamate-dependent regulation of dopamine release. The already mentioned increased of dopamine release induced by the blockade of glutamate receptors was completely prevented in the presence of succinate and rotenone. On the other hand, an increase the levels of H_2O_2 by mercaptosuccinate produced the typical 35% decrease in the evoked dopamine release, which was completely prevented by succinate and rotenone. Together, these results indicate that mitochondria are a primary source of ROS in the glutamate-dependent modulation of dopamine release [141].

b) ROS as Regulators of Synaptic Plasticity

ROS have also been identified as regulators of synaptic plasticity. Neurons have the ability to change their activity in response to experience through a modification in the efficiency of the synapses. Long-term potentiation (LTP) and long-term depression (LTD) are two elements of synaptic plasticity in hippocampus that have been proposed as the cellular processes that are essential for the memory and learning. LTP is a long-lasting strengthening in the efficacy of synaptic transmission, while LTD is an activity-dependent reduction in synaptic efficiency [142, 143]

The molecular mechanisms of the LTP have been widely described in the CA1 region of hippocampus. In this region, the dendrites of pyramidal neurons receive synaptic inputs from the Shaffer collaterals of the CA3 region. Different studies have addressed the effects of ROS in LTP, which are diverse and seem to be related to the concentration of H_2O_2 and/or superoxide anion. In this regard, Kamsler et al. [43] demonstrated that H_2O_2 (20 µM) prevented the establishment of new LTP and enhanced LTD, while H_2O_2 (1 µM) markedly increased LTP and suppressed LTD [43]. On the other hand, brief incubations of hippocampal slices with H_2O_2 promoted LTP [144], while long time incubations prevented LTP [145]. In addition, the administration of antioxidants such as catalase or cell-permeable scavengers of superoxide or H_2O_2 impaired LTP [146, 147]. These experiments demonstrate that ROS are strong regulators of LTP.

Based on different models of transgenic mice, it has been possible to comprehend more about the role of ROS in synaptic plasticity. KO NOX2 mice have deficient LTP and suffer hippocampus-dependent memory impairments, as well as a slight motor coordination impairment and motor memory alterations [148]. On the other hand, in a mouse model that overexpresses extracellular superoxide dismutase (EC-SOD), hippocampal slices fail to show LTP and the contextual fear conditioning is markedly impaired as compared to wild type mice [149]. These evidences demonstrate that the regulation of ROS during LTP is related to the consolidation of hippocampus-dependent memories. Interestingly, these findings are reverted during aging, since hippocampal slices obtained from aged EC-SOD mice exhibit an enhanced LTP in comparison with wild type mice. Furthermore, aged EC-SOD mice exhibit better hippocampus-dependent spatial learning and better cerebellum-dependent learning than in aged wild type mice, which correlates with lower levels of ROS in hippocampus and cerebellum in aged EC-SOD mice [150]. These results emphasize the changes in ROS production during the lifespan and their implications in learning and memory.

CONCLUSION

Reactive oxygen species play a critical role in cellular physiology. An increasing body of evidence supports a role of ROS as signaling agents. The regulation of physiological and pathologic processes by ROS is mediated by specific proteins mainly involved in intracellular signaling. The mechanisms by which ROS modulate these processes involve the direct oxidation of cysteine residues of several proteins involved in redox signaling. This generates disulfide bonds between cysteine residues in the same protein or between two proteins. It is noteworthy to mention that ROS actions depend on the cellular context, as well as the specific time and particular location of ROS produced. This represents a very fine mechanism of regulation that also involves the antioxidant systems, the ROS sources and the target proteins. Direct oxidative modification of cysteines leads to the activation of specific signaling pathways that modify different physiological processes such as proliferation, neuronal differentiation, axonal growth and guidance and apoptosis. This can occur in a time scale that goes from minutes to hours, but also in the order of seconds, as it occurs in the oxidation of receptors and channels. The importance of these studies underlie in our comprehension of nervous system function, as well as the redox biology. There are still many gaps in our knowledge about the mechanisms of action involving ROS as signaling molecules. Thus, many studies should be addressed to solve these subjects.

ACKNOWLEDGMENTS

This work was partially supported by a grant from DGAPA-PAPIIT, UNAM, México (IN206213) and from CONACYT, México (179234).

REFERENCES

[1]   Droge W. Free radicals in the physiological control of cell function. *Physiological reviews,* 2002;82(1):47-95.

[2]   Valko M., Leibfritz D., Moncol J., Cronin M. T., Mazur M., Telser J. Free radicals and antioxidants in normal physiological functions and human disease. *The international journal of biochemistry and cell biology,* 2007;39(1):44-84.

[3]   Tonks N. K. Redox redux: revisiting PTPs and the control of cell signaling. *Cell,* 2005;121(5):667-70.

[4]   Pourova J., Kottova M., Voprsalova M., Pour M. Reactive oxygen and nitrogen species in normal physiological processes. *Acta physiologica,* 2010;198(1):15-35.

[5]   Kamata H., Hirata H. Redox regulation of cellular signalling. *Cellular signalling,* 1999;11(1):1-14.

[6]   Day A. M., Brown J. D., Taylor S. R., Rand J. D., Morgan B. A., Veal E. A. Inactivation of a peroxiredoxin by hydrogen peroxide is critical for thioredoxin-mediated repair of oxidized proteins and cell survival. *Molecular cell,* 2012;45(3):398-408.

[7]   Jonsson T. J., Lowther W. T. The peroxiredoxin repair proteins. *Sub-cellular biochemistry,* 2007;44:115-41.

[8]   Finkel T. Signal transduction by reactive oxygen species. *The Journal of cell biology,* 2011;194(1):7-15.

[9]   Lo Conte M., Carroll K. S. The redox biochemistry of protein sulfenylation and sulfinylation. *The Journal of biological chemistry,* 2013;288(37):26480-8.

[10]   Rinna A., Torres M., Forman H. J. Stimulation of the alveolar macrophage respiratory burst by ADP causes selective glutathionylation of protein tyrosine phosphatase 1B. *Free radical biology and medicine,* 2006;41(1):86-91.

[11]   Forman H. J., Fukuto J. M., Torres M. Redox signaling: thiol chemistry defines which reactive oxygen and nitrogen species can act as second messengers. *American journal of physiology Cell physiology,* 2004;287(2):C246-56.

[12]   Forman H. J., Ursini F., Maiorino M. An overview of mechanisms of redox signaling. *Journal of molecular and cellular cardiology,* 2014.

[13]   Cross J. V., Templeton D. J. Regulation of signal transduction through protein cysteine oxidation. *Antioxidants and redox signaling*, 2006;8(9-10):1819-27.

[14]   Zhang R., Al-Lamki R., Bai L., Streb J. W., Miano J. M., Bradley J., et al. Thioredoxin-2 inhibits mitochondria-located ASK1-mediated apoptosis in a JNK-independent manner. *Circulation research,* 2004;94(11):1483-91.

[15]   Saitoh M., Nishitoh H., Fujii M., Takeda K., Tobiume K., Sawada Y., et al. Mammalian thioredoxin is a direct inhibitor of apoptosis signal-regulating kinase (ASK) 1. *The EMBO journal,* 1998;17(9):2596-606.

[16]   Holmgren A. Thioredoxin structure and mechanism: conformational changes on oxidation of the active-site sulfhydryls to a disulfide. *Structure,* 1995;3(3):239-43.

[17]   Roos G., Garcia-Pino A., Van Belle K., Brosens E., Wahni K., Vandenbussche G., et al. The conserved active site proline determines the reducing power of Staphylococcus aureus thioredoxin. *Journal of molecular biology,* 2007;368(3):800-11.

[18]   Chrestensen C. A., Eckman C. B., Starke D. W., Mieyal J. J. Cloning, expression and characterization of human thioltransferase (glutaredoxin) in E. coli. *FEBS letters,* 1995;374(1):25-8.

[19]   Yang Y., Jao S., Nanduri S., Starke D. W., Mieyal J. J., Qin J. Reactivity of the human thioltransferase (glutaredoxin) C7S, C25S, C78S, C82S mutant and NMR solution structure of its glutathionyl mixed disulfide intermediate reflect catalytic specificity. *Biochemistry,* 1998;37(49):17145-56.

[20]   Chai Y. C., Ashraf S. S., Rokutan K., Johnston R. B., Jr., Thomas J. A. S-thiolation of individual human neutrophil proteins including actin by stimulation of the respiratory burst: evidence against a role for glutathione disulfide. *Archives of biochemistry and biophysics,* 1994;310(1):273-81.

[21]   Ciriolo M. R., Palamara A. T., Incerpi S., Lafavia E., Bue M. C., De Vito P., et al. Loss of GSH, oxidative stress, and decrease of intracellular pH as sequential steps in viral infection. *The Journal of biological chemistry,* 1997;272(5):2700-8.

[22]   Liu Y., Min W. Thioredoxin promotes ASK1 ubiquitination and degradation to inhibit ASK1-mediated apoptosis in a redox activity-independent manner. *Circulation research,* 2002;90(12):1259-66.

[23]   Junn E., Han S. H., Im J. Y., Yang Y., Cho E. W., Um H. D., et al. Vitamin D3 up-regulated protein 1 mediates oxidative stress via suppressing the thioredoxin function. *Journal of immunology,* 2000;164(12):6287-95.

[24]   Song J. J., Rhee J. G., Suntharalingam M., Walsh S. A., Spitz D. R., Lee Y. J. Role of glutaredoxin in metabolic oxidative stress. Glutaredoxin as a sensor of oxidative stress mediated by H2O2. *The Journal of biological chemistry,* 2002;277(48):46566-75.

[25]   Lee S. R., Yang K. S., Kwon J., Lee C., Jeong W., Rhee S. G. Reversible inactivation of the tumor suppressor PTEN by H2O2. *The Journal of biological chemistry,* 2002;277(23):20336-42.

[26]   Meuillet E. J., Mahadevan D., Berggren M., Coon A., Powis G. Thioredoxin-1 binds to the C2 domain of PTEN inhibiting PTEN's lipid phosphatase activity and membrane binding: a mechanism for the functional loss of PTEN's tumor suppressor activity. *Archives of biochemistry and biophysics,* 2004;429(2):123-33.

[27]   Patwari P., Higgins L. J., Chutkow W. A., Yoshioka J., Lee R. T. The interaction of thioredoxin with Txnip. Evidence for formation of a mixed disulfide by disulfide exchange. *The Journal of biological chemistry,* 2006;281(31):21884-91.

[28] Hwang J., Suh H. W., Jeon Y. H., Hwang E., Nguyen L. T., Yeom J., et al. The structural basis for the negative regulation of thioredoxin by thioredoxin-interacting protein. *Nature communications,* 2014;5:2958.

[29] Murata H., Ihara Y., Nakamura H., Yodoi J., Sumikawa K., Kondo T. Glutaredoxin exerts an antiapoptotic effect by regulating the redox state of Akt. *The Journal of biological chemistry,* 2003;278(50):50226-33.

[30] Sundaresan M., Yu Z. X., Ferrans V. J., Irani K., Finkel T. Requirement for generation of H2O2 for platelet-derived growth factor signal transduction. *Science,* 1995;270(5234):296-9.

[31] Wani R., Qian J., Yin L., Bechtold E., King S. B., Poole L. B., et al. Isoform-specific regulation of Akt by PDGF-induced reactive oxygen species. *Proceedings of the National Academy of Sciences of the United States of America,* 2011;108(26):10550-5.

[32] Bernardini S., Bernassola F., Cortese C., Ballerini S., Melino G., Motti C., et al. Modulation of GST P1-1 activity by polymerization during apoptosis. *Journal of cellular biochemistry,* 2000;77(4):645-53.

[33] Adler V., Yin Z., Fuchs S. Y., Benezra M., Rosario L., Tew K. D., et al. Regulation of JNK signaling by GSTp. *The EMBO journal,* 1999;18(5):1321-34.

[34] Templeton D. J., Aye M. S., Rady J., Xu F., Cross J. V. Purification of reversibly oxidized proteins (PROP) reveals a redox switch controlling p38 MAP kinase activity. *PloS one,* 2010;5(11):e15012.

[35] Galli S., Antico Arciuch V. G., Poderoso C., Converso D. P., Zhou Q., Bal de Kier Joffe E., et al. Tumor cell phenotype is sustained by selective MAPK oxidation in mitochondria. *PloS one,* 2008;3(6):e2379.

[36] Trachootham D., Lu W., Ogasawara M. A., Nilsa R. D., Huang P. Redox regulation of cell survival. *Antioxidants and redox signaling,* 2008;10(8):1343-74.

[37] Groeger G., Quiney C., Cotter T. G. Hydrogen peroxide as a cell-survival signaling molecule. *Antioxidants and redox signaling,* 2009;11(11):2655-71.

[38] Liu Y., Li M., Warburton R. R., Hill N. S., Fanburg B. L. The 5-HT transporter transactivates the PDGFbeta receptor in pulmonary artery smooth muscle cells. *FASEB journal : official publication of the Federation of American Societies for Experimental Biology,* 2007;21(11):2725-34.

[39] Moody T. W., Osefo N., Nuche-Berenguer B., Ridnour L., Wink D., Jensen R. T. Pituitary adenylate cyclase-activating polypeptide causes tyrosine phosphorylation of the epidermal growth factor receptor in lung cancer cells. *The Journal of pharmacology and experimental therapeutics,* 2012;341(3):873-81.

[40] Huang Y. Z., McNamara J. O. Neuroprotective effects of reactive oxygen species mediated by BDNF-independent activation of TrkB. *The Journal of neuroscience : the official journal of the Society for Neuroscience,* 2012;32(44):15521-32.

[41] Huang E. J., Reichardt L. F. Neurotrophins: roles in neuronal development and function. *Annual review of neuroscience,* 2001;24:677-736.

[42] Kruk J. S., Vasefi M. S., Heikkila J. J., Beazely M. A. Reactive oxygen species are required for 5-HT-induced transactivation of neuronal platelet-derived growth factor and TrkB receptors, but not for ERK1/2 activation. *PloS one,* 2013;8(9):e77027.

[43] Kamsler A., Segal M. Hydrogen peroxide modulation of synaptic plasticity. *The Journal of neuroscience : the official journal of the Society for Neuroscience,* 2003;23(1):269-76.

[44] Lee J. W., Kim J. E., Park E. J., Kim J. H., Lee C. H., Lee S. R., et al. Two conserved cysteine residues are critical for the enzymic function of the human platelet-derived growth factor receptor-beta: evidence for different roles of Cys-822 and Cys-940 in the kinase activity. *The Biochemical journal*, 2004;382(Pt 2):631-9.

[45] Goldkorn T., Balaban N., Matsukuma K., Chea V., Gould R., Last J., et al. EGF-Receptor phosphorylation and signaling are targeted by H2O2 redox stress. *American journal of respiratory cell and molecular biology*, 1998;19(5):786-98.

[46] Bae Y. S., Kang S. W., Seo M. S., Baines I. C., Tekle E., Chock P. B., et al. Epidermal growth factor (EGF)-induced generation of hydrogen peroxide. Role in EGF receptor-mediated tyrosine phosphorylation. *The Journal of biological chemistry*, 1997; 272(1): 217-21.

[47] Paulsen C. E., Truong T. H., Garcia F. J., Homann A., Gupta V., Leonard S. E., et al. Peroxide-dependent sulfenylation of the EGFR catalytic site enhances kinase activity. *Nature chemical biology*, 2012;8(1):57-64.

[48] Kang D. H., Lee D. J., Lee K. W., Park Y. S., Lee J. Y., Lee S. H., et al. Peroxiredoxin II is an essential antioxidant enzyme that prevents the oxidative inactivation of VEGF receptor-2 in vascular endothelial cells. *Molecular cell*, 2011;44(4):545-58.

[49] Kemble D. J., Sun G. Direct and specific inactivation of protein tyrosine kinases in the Src and FGFR families by reversible cysteine oxidation. *Proceedings of the National Academy of Sciences of the United States of America*, 2009;106(13):5070-5.

[50] Giannoni E., Buricchi F., Raugei G., Ramponi G., Chiarugi P. Intracellular reactive oxygen species activate Src tyrosine kinase during cell adhesion and anchorage-dependent cell growth. *Molecular and cellular biology*, 2005;25(15):6391-403.

[51] Liu H., Nishitoh H., Ichijo H., Kyriakis J. M. Activation of apoptosis signal-regulating kinase 1 (ASK1) by tumor necrosis factor receptor-associated factor 2 requires prior dissociation of the ASK1 inhibitor thioredoxin. *Molecular and cellular biology*, 2000;20(6):2198-208.

[52] Shiizaki S., Naguro I., Ichijo H. Activation mechanisms of ASK1 in response to various stresses and its significance in intracellular signaling. *Advances in biological regulation*, 2013;53(1):135-44.

[53] Lim P. L., Liu J., Go M. L., Boelsterli U. A. The mitochondrial superoxide/thioredoxin-2/Ask1 signaling pathway is critically involved in troglitazone-induced cell injury to human hepatocytes. *Toxicological sciences : an official journal of the Society of Toxicology*, 2008;101(2):341-9.

[54] Tanaka T., Hosoi F., Yamaguchi-Iwai Y., Nakamura H., Masutani H., Ueda S., et al. Thioredoxin-2 (TRX-2) is an essential gene regulating mitochondria-dependent apoptosis. *The EMBO journal*, 2002;21(7):1695-703.

[55] Song J. J., Lee Y. J. Differential role of glutaredoxin and thioredoxin in metabolic oxidative stress-induced activation of apoptosis signal-regulating kinase 1. *The Biochemical journal*, 2003;373(Pt 3):845-53.

[56] Saxena G., Chen J., Shalev A. Intracellular shuttling and mitochondrial function of thioredoxin-interacting protein. *The Journal of biological chemistry*, 2010;285(6):3997-4005.

[57] Matsuno K., Iwata K., Matsumoto M., Katsuyama M., Cui W., Murata A., et al. NOX1/NADPH oxidase is involved in endotoxin-induced cardiomyocyte apoptosis. *Free radical biology and medicine*, 2012;53(9):1718-28.

[58] Durgadoss L., Nidadavolu P., Valli R. K., Saeed U., Mishra M., Seth P., et al. Redox modification of Akt mediated by the dopaminergic neurotoxin MPTP, in mouse midbrain, leads to down-regulation of pAkt. *FASEB journal : official publication of the Federation of American Societies for Experimental Biology*, 2012;26(4):1473-83.

[59] Nadeau P. J., Charette S. J., Landry J. REDOX reaction at ASK1-Cys250 is essential for activation of JNK and induction of apoptosis. *Molecular biology of the cell*, 2009;20(16):3628-37.

[60] Nadeau P. J., Charette S. J., Toledano M. B., Landry J. Disulfide Bond-mediated multimerization of Ask1 and its reduction by thioredoxin-1 regulate H(2)O(2)-induced c-Jun NH(2)-terminal kinase activation and apoptosis. *Molecular biology of the cell*, 2007;18(10):3903-13.

[61] Kwon J., Lee S. R., Yang K. S., Ahn Y., Kim Y. J., Stadtman E. R., et al. Reversible oxidation and inactivation of the tumor suppressor PTEN in cells stimulated with peptide growth factors. *Proceedings of the National Academy of Sciences of the United States of America*, 2004;101(47):16419-24.

[62] Leslie N. R., Bennett D., Lindsay Y. E., Stewart H., Gray A., Downes C. P. Redox regulation of PI 3-kinase signalling via inactivation of PTEN. *The EMBO journal*, 2003;22(20):5501-10.

[63] Gopalakrishna R., Gundimeda U., Schiffman J. E., McNeill T. H. A direct redox regulation of protein kinase C isoenzymes mediates oxidant-induced neuritogenesis in PC12 cells. *The Journal of biological chemistry*, 2008;283(21):14430-44.

[64] Morinaka A., Yamada M., Itofusa R., Funato Y., Yoshimura Y., Nakamura F., et al. Thioredoxin mediates oxidation-dependent phosphorylation of CRMP2 and growth cone collapse. *Science signaling*, 2011;4(170):ra26.

[65] Coyoy A., Olguin-Albuerne M., Martinez-Briseno P., Moran J. Role of reactive oxygen species and NADPH-oxidase in the development of rat cerebellum. *Neurochemistry international*, 2013;62(7):998-1011.

[66] Le Belle J. E., Orozco N. M., Paucar A. A., Saxe J. P., Mottahedeh J., Pyle A. D., et al. Proliferative Neural Stem Cells Have High Endogenous ROS Levels that Regulate Self-Renewal and Neurogenesis in a PI3K/Akt-Dependant Manner. *Cell Stem Cell*, 2011;8(1):59-71.

[67] Munnamalai V., Suter D. M. Reactive oxygen species regulate F-actin dynamics in neuronal growth cones and neurite outgrowth. *Journal of neurochemistry*, 2009; 108(3): 644-61.

[68] Munnamalai V., Weaver C. J., Weisheit C. E., Venkatraman P., Agim Z. S., Quinn M. T., et al. Bidirectional interactions between NOX2-type NADPH oxidase and the F-actin cytoskeleton in neuronal growth cones. *Journal of neurochemistry*, 2014.

[69] Tsatmali M., Walcott E. C., Makarenkova H., Crossin K. L. Reactive oxygen species modulate the differentiation of neurons in clonal cortical cultures. *Molecular and cellular neurosciences*, 2006;33(4):345-57.

[70] Celotto A. M., Liu Z., Vandemark A. P., Palladino M. J. A novel Drosophila SOD2 mutant demonstrates a role for mitochondrial ROS in neurodevelopment and disease. *Brain and behavior*, 2012;2(4):424-34.

[71] Yoneyama M., Kawada K., Gotoh Y., Shiba T., Ogita K. Endogenous reactive oxygen species are essential for proliferation of neural stem/progenitor cells. *Neurochemistry international*, 2010;56(6-7):740-6.

[72] Limoli C. L., Rola R., Giedzinski E., Mantha S., Huang T. T., Fike J. R. Cell-density-dependent regulation of neural precursor cell function. *Proceedings of the National Academy of Sciences of the United States of America*, 2004;101(45):16052-7.

[73] Leslie N. R. The redox regulation of PI 3-kinase-dependent signaling. *Antioxidants and redox signaling*, 2006;8(9-10):1765-74.

[74] Patapoutian A., Reichardt L. F. Trk receptors: mediators of neurotrophin action. *Current opinion in neurobiology*, 2001;11(3):272-80.

[75] Kaplan D. R., Miller F. D. Neurotrophin signal transduction in the nervous system. *Current opinion in neurobiology*, 2000;10(3):381-91.

[76] Katoh S., Mitsui Y., Kitani K., Suzuki T. Hyperoxia induces the neuronal differentiated phenotype of PC12 cells via a sustained activity of mitogen-activated protein kinase induced by Bcl-2. *The Biochemical journal*, 1999;338 (Pt 2):465-70.

[77] Kamata H., Oka S., Shibukawa Y., Kakuta J., Hirata H. Redox regulation of nerve growth factor-induced neuronal differentiation of PC12 cells through modulation of the nerve growth factor receptor, TrkA. *Archives of biochemistry and biophysics*, 2005;434(1):16-25.

[78] Aikawa R., Komuro I., Yamazaki T., Zou Y., Kudoh S., Tanaka M., et al. Oxidative stress activates extracellular signal-regulated kinases through Src and Ras in cultured cardiac myocytes of neonatal rats. *The Journal of clinical investigation*, 1997;100(7): 1813-21.

[79] Abe J., Berk B. C. Fyn and JAK2 mediate Ras activation by reactive oxygen species. *The Journal of biological chemistry*, 1999;274(30):21003-10.

[80] Dey N., Howell B. W., De P. K., Durden D. L. CSK negatively regulates nerve growth factor induced neural differentiation and augments AKT kinase activity. *Experimental cell research*, 2005;307(1):1-14.

[81] Obara Y., Labudda K., Dillon T. J., Stork P. J. PKA phosphorylation of Src mediates Rap1 activation in NGF and cAMP signaling in PC12 cells. *Journal of cell science*, 2004;117(Pt 25):6085-94.

[82] Suzukawa K., Miura K., Mitsushita J., Resau J., Hirose K., Crystal R., et al. Nerve growth factor-induced neuronal differentiation requires generation of Rac1-regulated reactive oxygen species. *The Journal of biological chemistry*, 2000;275(18):13175-8.

[83] Ibi M., Katsuyama M., Fan C., Iwata K., Nishinaka T., Yokoyama T., et al. NOX1/NADPH oxidase negatively regulates nerve growth factor-induced neurite outgrowth. *Free radical biology and medicine*, 2006;40(10):1785-95.

[84] Sampath D., Jackson G. R., Werrbach-Perez K., Perez-Polo J. R. Effects of nerve growth factor on glutathione peroxidase and catalase in PC12 cells. *Journal of neurochemistry*, 1994;62(6):2476-9.

[85] Jackson G. R., Sampath D., Werrbach-Perez K., Perez-Polo J. R. Effects of nerve growth factor on catalase and glutathione peroxidase in a hydrogen peroxide-resistant pheochromocytoma subclone. *Brain research*, 1994;634(1):69-76.

[86] Cassano S., Agnese S., D'Amato V., Papale M., Garbi C., Castagnola P., et al. Reactive oxygen species, Ki-Ras, and mitochondrial superoxide dismutase cooperate in nerve growth factor-induced differentiation of PC12 cells. *The Journal of biological chemistry*, 2010;285(31):24141-53.

[87] Tsatmali M., Walcott E. C., Crossin K. L. Newborn neurons acquire high levels of reactive oxygen species and increased mitochondrial proteins upon differentiation from progenitors. *Brain research,* 2005;1040(1-2):137-50.

[88] Zhang X. F., Forscher P. Rac1 modulates stimulus-evoked Ca(2+) release in neuronal growth cones via parallel effects on microtubule/endoplasmic reticulum dynamics and reactive oxygen species production. *Molecular biology of the cell,* 2009;20(16): 3700-12.

[89] Joseph S. K., Nakao S. K., Sukumvanich S. Reactivity of free thiol groups in type-I inositol trisphosphate receptors. *The Biochemical journal,* 2006;393(Pt 2):575-82.

[90] Henley J., Poo M. M. Guiding neuronal growth cones using Ca2+ signals. *Trends in cell biology,* 2004;14(6):320-30.

[91] Sharma A., Verhaagen J., Harvey A. R. Receptor complexes for each of the Class 3 Semaphorins. *Frontiers in cellular neuroscience,* 2012;6:28.

[92] Zhou Y., Gunput R. A., Pasterkamp R. J. Semaphorin signaling: progress made and promises ahead. *Trends in biochemical sciences,* 2008;33(4):161-70.

[93] Mieyal J. J., Gallogly M. M., Qanungo S., Sabens E. A., Shelton M. D. Molecular mechanisms and clinical implications of reversible protein S-glutathionylation. *Antioxidants and redox signaling,* 2008;10(11):1941-88.

[94] Goldman E. H., Chen L., Fu H. Activation of apoptosis signal-regulating kinase 1 by reactive oxygen species through dephosphorylation at serine 967 and 14-3-3 dissociation. *The Journal of biological chemistry,* 2004;279(11):10442-9.

[95] Ichijo H., Nishida E., Irie K., ten Dijke P., Saitoh M., Moriguchi T., et al. Induction of apoptosis by ASK1, a mammalian MAPKKK that activates SAPK/JNK and p38 signaling pathways. *Science,* 1997;275(5296):90-4.

[96] Chang H. Y., Nishitoh H., Yang X., Ichijo H., Baltimore D. Activation of apoptosis signal-regulating kinase 1 (ASK1) by the adapter protein Daxx. *Science,* 1998;281(5384):1860-3.

[97] Hatai T., Matsuzawa A., Inoshita S., Mochida Y., Kuroda T., Sakamaki K., et al. Execution of apoptosis signal-regulating kinase 1 (ASK1)-induced apoptosis by the mitochondria-dependent caspase activation. *The Journal of biological chemistry,* 2000;275(34):26576-81.

[98] Charette S. J., Lambert H., Landry J. A kinase-independent function of Ask1 in caspase-independent cell death. *The Journal of biological chemistry,* 2001;276(39): 36071-4.

[99] Nishitoh H., Matsuzawa A., Tobiume K., Saegusa K., Takeda K., Inoue K., et al. ASK1 is essential for endoplasmic reticulum stress-induced neuronal cell death triggered by expanded polyglutamine repeats. *Genes and development,* 2002;16(11):1345-55.

[100] Nagai H., Noguchi T., Homma K., Katagiri K., Takeda K., Matsuzawa A., et al. Ubiquitin-like sequence in ASK1 plays critical roles in the recognition and stabilization by USP9X and oxidative stress-induced cell death. *Molecular cell,* 2009;36(5):805-18.

[101] Ramiro-Cortes Y., Moran J. Role of oxidative stress and JNK pathway in apoptotic death induced by potassium deprivation and staurosporine in cerebellar granule neurons. *Neurochemistry international,* 2009;55(7):581-92.

[102] Ramiro-Cortes Y., Guemez-Gamboa A., Moran J. Reactive oxygen species participate in the p38-mediated apoptosis induced by potassium deprivation and staurosporine in

cerebellar granule neurons. *The international journal of biochemistry and cell biology,* 2011;43(9):1373-82.

[103] Valencia A., Moran J. Role of oxidative stress in the apoptotic cell death of cultured cerebellar granule neurons. *Journal of neuroscience research,* 2001;64(3):284-97.

[104] Sabens E. A., Distler A. M., Mieyal J. J. Levodopa deactivates enzymes that regulate thiol-disulfide homeostasis and promotes neuronal cell death: implications for therapy of Parkinson's disease. *Biochemistry,* 2010;49(12):2715-24.

[105] Liedhegner E. A., Steller K. M., Mieyal J. J. Levodopa activates apoptosis signaling kinase 1 (ASK1) and promotes apoptosis in a neuronal model: implications for the treatment of Parkinson's disease. *Chemical research in toxicology,* 2011;24(10): 1644-52.

[106] Allen E. M., Mieyal J. J. Protein-thiol oxidation and cell death: regulatory role of glutaredoxins. *Antioxidants and redox signaling,* 2012;17(12):1748-63.

[107] Kim A. H., Khursigara G., Sun X., Franke T. F., Chao M. V. Akt phosphorylates and negatively regulates apoptosis signal-regulating kinase 1. *Molecular and cellular biology,* 2001;21(3):893-901.

[108] Zhang R., Luo D., Miao R., Bai L., Ge Q., Sessa W. C., et al. Hsp90-Akt phosphorylates ASK1 and inhibits ASK1-mediated apoptosis. *Oncogene,* 2005;24(24): 3954-63.

[109] World C., Spindel O. N., Berk B. C. Thioredoxin-interacting protein mediates TRX1 translocation to the plasma membrane in response to tumor necrosis factor-alpha: a key mechanism for vascular endothelial growth factor receptor-2 transactivation by reactive oxygen species. *Arteriosclerosis, thrombosis, and vascular biology,* 2011;31(8):1890-7.

[110] Yoshihara E., Masaki S., Matsuo Y., Chen Z., Tian H., Yodoi J. Thioredoxin/Txnip: Redoxisome, as a Redox Switch for the Pathogenesis of Diseases. *Frontiers in immunology,* 2014;4:514.

[111] Kanamoto T., Mota M., Takeda K., Rubin L. L., Miyazono K., Ichijo H., et al. Role of apoptosis signal-regulating kinase in regulation of the c-Jun N-terminal kinase pathway and apoptosis in sympathetic neurons. *Molecular and cellular biology,* 2000;20(1): 196-204.

[112] Takagi Y., Mitsui A., Nishiyama A., Nozaki K., Sono H., Gon Y., et al. Overexpression of thioredoxin in transgenic mice attenuates focal ischemic brain damage. *Proceedings of the National Academy of Sciences of the United States of America,* 1999; 96(7): 4131-6.

[113] Schulze P. C., Yoshioka J., Takahashi T., He Z., King G. L., Lee R. T. Hyperglycemia promotes oxidative stress through inhibition of thioredoxin function by thioredoxin-interacting protein. *The Journal of biological chemistry,* 2004;279(29):30369-74.

[114] Schulze P. C., De Keulenaer G. W., Yoshioka J., Kassik K. A., Lee R. T. Vitamin D3-upregulated protein-1 (VDUP-1) regulates redox-dependent vascular smooth muscle cell proliferation through interaction with thioredoxin. *Circulation research,* 2002;91(8):689-95.

[115] Lipton S. A. NMDA receptor activity regulates transcription of antioxidant pathways. *Nature neuroscience,* 2008;11(4):381-2.

[116] Papadia S., Soriano F. X., Leveille F., Martel M. A., Dakin K. A., Hansen H. H., et al. Synaptic NMDA receptor activity boosts intrinsic antioxidant defenses. *Nature neuroscience,* 2008;11(4):476-87.

[117] Federico A., Cardaioli E., Da Pozzo P., Formichi P., Gallus G. N., Radi E. Mitochondria, oxidative stress and neurodegeneration. *Journal of the neurological sciences,* 2012;322(1-2):254-62.

[118] Norton M., Ng A. C., Baird S., Dumoulin A., Shutt T., Mah N., et al. ROMO1 is an essential redox-dependent regulator of mitochondrial dynamics. *Science signaling,* 2014;7(310):ra10.

[119] Liot G., Bossy B., Lubitz S., Kushnareva Y., Sejbuk N., Bossy-Wetzel E. Complex II inhibition by 3-NP causes mitochondrial fragmentation and neuronal cell death via an NMDA- and ROS-dependent pathway. *Cell death and differentiation,* 2009; 16(6): 899-909.

[120] Yu T., Robotham J. L., Yoon Y. Increased production of reactive oxygen species in hyperglycemic conditions requires dynamic change of mitochondrial morphology. *Proceedings of the National Academy of Sciences of the United States of America,* 2006;103(8):2653-8.

[121] Chung Y. M., Kim J. S., Yoo Y. D. A novel protein, Romo1, induces ROS production in the mitochondria. *Biochemical and biophysical research communications,* 2006; 347(3): 649-55.

[122] Chung Y. M., Lee S. B., Kim H. J., Park S. H., Kim J. J., Chung J. S., et al. Replicative senescence induced by Romo1-derived reactive oxygen species. *The Journal of biological chemistry,* 2008;283(48):33763-71.

[123] Lee S. B., Kim J. J., Kim T. W., Kim B. S., Lee M. S., Yoo Y. D. Serum deprivation-induced reactive oxygen species production is mediated by Romo1. *Apoptosis : an international journal on programmed cell death,* 2010;15(2):204-18.

[124] Scorrano L., Ashiya M., Buttle K., Weiler S., Oakes S. A., Mannella C. A., et al. A distinct pathway remodels mitochondrial cristae and mobilizes cytochrome c during apoptosis. *Developmental cell,* 2002;2(1):55-67.

[125] Kim J. J., Lee S. B., Park J. K, Yoo Y. D. TNF-alpha-induced ROS production triggering apoptosis is directly linked to Romo1 and Bcl-X(L). *Cell death and differentiation,* 2010;17(9):1420-34.

[126] Avshalumov M. V., Chen B. T., Marshall S. P., Pena D. M., Rice M. E. Glutamate-dependent inhibition of dopamine release in striatum is mediated by a new diffusible messenger, H2O2. *The Journal of neuroscience : the official journal of the Society for Neuroscience,* 2003;23(7):2744-50.

[127] Avshalumov M. V., Patel J. C., Rice M. E. AMPA receptor-dependent H2O2 generation in striatal medium spiny neurons but not dopamine axons: one source of a retrograde signal that can inhibit dopamine release. *Journal of neurophysiology,* 2008;100(3):1590-601.

[128] Chen B. T., Avshalumov M. V., Rice M. E. H(2)O(2) is a novel, endogenous modulator of synaptic dopamine release. *Journal of neurophysiology,* 2001;85(6):2468-76.

[129] Avshalumov M. V., Chen B. T., Koos T., Tepper J. M., Rice M. E. Endogenous hydrogen peroxide regulates the excitability of midbrain dopamine neurons via ATP-sensitive potassium channels. *The Journal of neuroscience : the official journal of the Society for Neuroscience,* 2005;25(17):4222-31.

[130] Avshalumov M. V., Rice M. E. Activation of ATP-sensitive K+ (K(ATP)) channels by H2O2 underlies glutamate-dependent inhibition of striatal dopamine release.

Proceedings of the National Academy of Sciences of the United States of America, 2003;100(20):11729-34.

[131] Gruber A. J., McDonald R. J. Context, emotion, and the strategic pursuit of goals: interactions among multiple brain systems controlling motivated behavior. *Frontiers in behavioral neuroscience,* 2012;6:50.

[132] Yin H. H., Knowlton B. J. The role of the basal ganglia in habit formation. *Nature reviews Neuroscience,* 2006;7(6):464-76.

[133] Palmiter R. D. Dopamine signaling in the dorsal striatum is essential for motivated behaviors: lessons from dopamine-deficient mice. *Annals of the New York Academy of Sciences,* 2008;1129:35-46.

[134] Balleine B. W., Delgado M. R., Hikosaka O. The role of the dorsal striatum in reward and decision-making. *The Journal of neuroscience : the official journal of the Society for Neuroscience,* 2007;27(31):8161-5.

[135] Nakano K., Kayahara T., Tsutsumi T., Ushiro H. Neural circuits and functional organization of the striatum. *Journal of neurology,* 2000;247 Suppl. 5:V1-15.

[136] Hernandes M. S., Britto L. R. NADPH oxidase and neurodegeneration. *Current neuropharmacology,* 2012;10(4):321-7.

[137] Valencia A., Sapp E., Kimm J. S., McClory H., Reeves P. B., Alexander J., et al. Elevated NADPH oxidase activity contributes to oxidative stress and cell death in Huntington's disease. *Human molecular genetics,* 2013;22(6):1112-31.

[138] Stephan D., Winkler M., Kuhner P., Russ U., Quast U. Selectivity of repaglinide and glibenclamide for the pancreatic over the cardiovascular K(ATP) channels. *Diabetologia,* 2006;49(9):2039-48.

[139] Ashcroft S. J., Ashcroft F. M. Properties and functions of ATP-sensitive K-channels. *Cellular signalling,* 1990;2(3):197-214.

[140] Babenko A. P., Aguilar-Bryan L., Bryan J. A view of sur/KIR6.X, KATP channels. *Annual review of physiology,* 1998;60:667-87.

[141] Bao L., Avshalumov M. V., Patel J. C., Lee C. R., Miller E. W., Chang C. J., et al. Mitochondria are the source of hydrogen peroxide for dynamic brain-cell signaling. *The Journal of neuroscience : the official journal of the Society for Neuroscience,* 2009;29(28):9002-10.

[142] Dan Y., Poo M. M. Spike timing-dependent plasticity of neural circuits. *Neuron,* 2004;44(1):23-30.

[143] Raymond C. R. Different requirements for action potentials in the induction of different forms of long-term potentiation. *The Journal of physiology,* 2008;586(7):1859-65.

[144] Katsuki H., Nakanishi C., Saito H., Matsuki N. Biphasic effect of hydrogen peroxide on field potentials in rat hippocampal slices. *European journal of pharmacology,* 1997; 337(2-3):213-8.

[145] Auerbach J. M., Segal M. Peroxide modulation of slow onset potentiation in rat hippocampus. *The Journal of neuroscience : the official journal of the Society for Neuroscience,* 1997;17(22):8695-701.

[146] Thiels E., Urban N. N., Gonzalez-Burgos G. R., Kanterewicz B. I., Barrionuevo G., Chu C. T., et al. Impairment of long-term potentiation and associative memory in mice that overexpress extracellular superoxide dismutase. *The Journal of neuroscience : the official journal of the Society for Neuroscience,* 2000;20(20):7631-9.

[147] Klann E. Cell-permeable scavengers of superoxide prevent long-term potentiation in hippocampal area CA1. *Journal of neurophysiology,* 1998;80(1):452-7.

[148] Kishida K. T., Hoeffer C. A., Hu D., Pao M., Holland S. M., Klann E. Synaptic plasticity deficits and mild memory impairments in mouse models of chronic granulomatous disease. *Molecular and cellular biology,* 2006;26(15):5908-20.

[149] Thiels E., Klann E. Hippocampal memory and plasticity in superoxide dismutase mutant mice. *Physiology and behavior,* 2002;77(4-5):601-5.

[150] Hu D., Serrano F., Oury T. D., Klann E. Aging-dependent alterations in synaptic plasticity and memory in mice that overexpress extracellular superoxide dismutase. The *Journal of neuroscience: the official journal of the Society for Neuroscience,* 2006; 26(15):3933-41.

In: Reactive Oxygen Species, Lipid Peroxidation …
Editor: Angel Catalá

ISBN: 978-1-63321-886-4
© 2015 Nova Science Publishers, Inc.

Chapter 9

OXIDATIVE STRESS IN DIABETES AND HYPERTENSION TREATED WITH ALTERNATIVE THERAPY OF MEDICINAL PLANTS

Alfredo Saavedra-Molina, Rafael Salgado-Garciglia, Ruth Noriega-Cisneros, Edgar R. Esquivel-Gutiérrez, Salvador Manzo-Avalos, Christian Cortés-Rojo and Rocío Montoya-Pérez

Instituto de Investigaciones Químico-Biológicas,
Universidad Michoacana de San Nicolás de Hidalgo, Morelia, Mich. México

ABSTRACT

Diabetes mellitus (DM) and hypertension are the most common diseases with high risk affecting most of the worldwide adult population in both genders. DM is the first cause of death in women and ischemic heart disease becomes the leading cause of mortality in men. High blood pressure, also called hypertension, is one of the major risk factors for coronary artery disease, stroke, and is currently among the ten leading causes of death worldwide. DM is a metabolic disorder of multiple etiologies, characterized by chronic hyperglycemia caused by defects in the secretion of insulin or the action of insulin, or both. In the early stages of the disease the symptoms of DM are not severe or may be absent. Consequently, hyperglycemia may be present and cause pathological and functional changes before the diagnosis is made. Hypertension represents a major risk factor for developing other diseases such as endothelial dysfunction, metabolic syndrome, DM, congestive heart failure, coronary artery disease, stroke and renal dysfunction. In both diseases, there is a characteristic in common, the generation of oxidative stress that is an exacerbated complication when each disease increases. Generally, multiple drugs with different chemical structures and different mechanisms of action are used for the therapeutic management of both diseases, with the aim to normalize blood glucose and blood pressure levels. These are managed for a long time, which often represents a high economic cost. On the other hand, some patients have no adherence to treatment. This is ineffective, and the adverse effects are situations that require change or immediate discontinuance of medication. It is important to develop new antidiabetic or antihypertensive agents, and medicinal plants are an option. Scientific interest aimed at the search of phytotherapeutic drugs for the treatment of these diseases has led the conduct of research that validates the use of medicinal plants, or they have found new agents with antidiabetic and antihypertensive properties. Some examples of medicinal plants have described their potential effects as antidiabetic or antihypertensive on animal models. This chapter is discussed along with traditional medicine that involves the use of plant extracts to treat DM and/or hypertension.

INTRODUCTION

Ethnobotanical studies are an important activity in the area of research and development of drugs since some reports claim that approximately 40% of pharmaceuticals consumed in developed countries come from natural sources, mainly from plants. For some years the interest has become apparent by studying and seeing the effects of herbs. In spite of this, the vast majorities have not been studied, possibly on due to the great diversity of plants used in traditional medicine or the variety of uses and properties that can be attributed to each one of them. The objective of the study of medicinal plants is to ensure its efficacy and safety in their consumption. Many plants have been studied and as a consequence are published results which demonstrate a good or poor efficiency; also safety aspects of some of the most frequently used plants are now well known [1]. The growing need to find alternatives for the treatment of diabetes or hypertension justifies the study of medicinal plants used in traditional medicine [2]. In traditional medicine, for example, there are a great variety of plants with global importance of antihypertensive activity, which have isolated vasoactive compounds. The contraindications of some plants by their interactions with drugs are also being learned, but this knowledge is not yet available for all plants [3]. Currently, the reports indicate the existence of scientific literature supporting the use of plants, extracts or their active compounds against various diseases such as diabetes, hypertension and cancer, or with antibacterial, antifungal, antiprotozoal, relaxing and sedative properties [4]. The therapeutic effects of plants are due to the content of different secondary metabolites such as essential oils, tannins, phenolic acids, sesquiterpene lactones, ketones and flavonoids, among others [5].

1. COMPOUNDS OF BIOLOGICAL INTEREST PRESENT IN PLANTS

Phenols are secondary metabolites that are widely distributed in the plant Kingdom. The antioxidant property of phenols is the reactivity of the phenol group [6]. Flavonoids are polyphenols that have at least 2 phenolic subunits. Flavonoids and other polyphenols have powerful antioxidant properties *in vitro*, being able to eliminate a wide range of reactive species, including the hydroxyl and superoxide radicals. They can also inhibit biomolecular damage by peroxynitrite *in vitro*; in addition many flavonoids chelate ion transition metals decreasing reactive oxygen species (ROS) [7]. Among the plant secondary metabolites are prescribed to patients that present painful diseases and cancer, including taxol, an active principle from *Taxus brevifolia* and *Taxus cuspidata*, a compound with anticancer activity [8]; reserpine, synthesized by the species of *Rauwolfia serpentina* and *Rauwolfia vomitoria*, with antihypertensive activity and tranquilizer [9]; and morphine and noscapine, the active compounds of *Papaver somniferum*, that are analgesic and antitumor, respectively [10,11].

Essential oils of different species of plants exert antioxidant activity and anti-inflammatory effects. These effects are attributed to the terpene compounds [12,13]. Those compounds are produced by aromatic plants of some families as Apiaceae, Asteraceae, Campanulatae, Lamiaceae, Lauraceae, Magnoliaceae, Rutaceae and Verbenaceae [14]. The antioxidant activity of terpenes has been widely studied because of their potential as preservatives, cosmeceuticals and nutraceuticals in the food and cosmetics industry [15]. The essential oil of chamomile (*Matricaria chamomilla*) has been used for centuries for its anti-inflammatory effect [16]. Terpenes as eugenol, thymol, p-cymene, linalool, β-caryophyllene, thujone, 4-terpineol, components of essential oils from plants like clove (*Eugenia caryophyllus*), basil (*Ocimum basilicum*), thyme (*Thymus vulgaris*) and myrtle (*Myrtus communis*), have antioxidant and anti-inflammatory properties [15].

The inhibitory effect of these essential oils on the expression of pro-inflammatory cytokines occurs primarily at the transcriptional level [17,18]. The essential oil of thyme (*Thymus vulgaris*), mostly consisting of p-cymene and thymol, significantly inhibited the total expression of IL-1β mRNA in mouse colon, inducing colitis with TNBS (acid 2,4,6-trinitrobencen sulfonic acid) [19].

Resveratrol, another natural product, possesses multiple biological activities including anti-oxidant and anti-cancer effects. Resveratrol is a polyphenol phytoalexin (trans-3,4',5-trihydroxystilbene) found in red wine, peanuts, grapes, berries (especially mulberries), various herbs, and propolis (bee products). It mediates diverse biochemical and physiological actions that include the ability to protect the brain, kidneys, and heart from ischemic injury. Such remarkable properties have elicited a vast interest in the identification of resveratrol-inhibited enzymes and others whose activation is enhanced [20]. Resveratrol exerts its protective effects on mitochondria, including by the direct modulation of mitochondrial transmembrane potential, inhibition of state 3 respiration, increase in nitric oxide (NO) levels and protection of mitochondrial reduced glutathione loss [21]. Mitochondrial dysfunction and subsequent production of ROS are contributors to cardiac failure. Additionally, there are quantitative and qualitative changes in mitochondria during hypertension and cardiac hypertrophy [22].

Dietary polyphenols, such as curcumin derived from the spice turmeric, which comes from *Curcuma longa* of ginger (*Zingiberaceae*), have been used safely for centuries in the Hindu medicinal system [23]. A number of diseases are targeted by curcumin, including metabolic diseases such as DM, obesity, hyperlipidemia, hypoglycemia, hypothyroidism; liver diseases such as cirrhosis, alcohol-induced liver disease, fibrosis; cardiovascular diseases such as atherosclerosis, cardiomyopathy, and stroke [24].

In countries such as China, India and Thailand there have been significant advances in the articulation of integrated models of health; while in some countries in Latin America like Mexico, Nicaragua and Brazil have interesting experiences with progress towards the integration of traditional medicines in modern medicine [25].

2. DIABETES AND OXIDATIVE STRESS

Diabetes mellitus is a chronic and progressive disorder characterized by hyperglycemia due to absolute or relative deficiency of insulin. Metabolic disturbances of lipids and increased oxidative stress are present, which leads to the development of complications and diabetic conditions worsen [2]. The alarming increase of the diabetic population is making it necessary to find a safe alternative effective treatment. Complications of DM are usually classified in macrovascular and microvascular; both occurring in the majority of people with diabetes both type I and type II. Next to these oxidative stress complications there is the development of abnormalities that appears to have chronic hyperglycemia as a common and triggering factor. Major macrovascular complications that diabetics present include: cardiovascular disease, resulting in heart attack, myocardial and cerebrovascular disease, manifesting as stroke [26]. In addition, there is an increased frequency of cardiovascular diseases related to atherosclerosis, vascular cerebral insufficiency, heart failure and peripheral arterial insufficiency depending on the location of the blocked arteries caused by atherosclerosis [2,27]. It is frequent that diabetic patients present a combined appearance of hyperglycemia and dyslipidemia (28). Diabetic dyslipidemia encompasses a set of abnormalities in lipoprotein and lipid potentially atherogenic [27]. The most common microvascular complications that arise in diabetics include nephropathy, retinopathy and peripheral neuropathy resulting in amputations [25].

Diabetic nephropathy is one of the most severe microvascular complications and the leading cause of terminal kidney failure [25]. It is known that in the pathogenesis of diabetic nephropathy, the high generation of reactive oxygen species caused by hyperglycemia and subsequent oxidative stress occupies an important place [28]. The mechanism that related hyperglycemia with oxidative stress and diabetic nephropathy is not fully known. Studies have shown that oxidative stress may affect nucleic acids and trigger processes of cell death by apoptosis in the podocytes, also the elevation of antioxidant enzymes such as heme oxygenase 1 has been reported to reduce the apoptosis of podocytes under conditions of diabetes [29]. Hyperglycemia can stimulate the generation of ROS from different sources such as oxidative phosphorylation, auto oxidation of glucose, NADPH oxidase, xanthine oxidase, among others. However, the main generating source of reactive oxygen species is located within the mitochondria electrons transport chain, which produces anion superoxide (O_2^-) due to the partial reduction of oxygen [30].

Elevated levels of glucose in diabetes produce anion superoxide and hydroxyl radicals (OH) in the presence of transition metal ions which cause oxidative damage to lipids in the cell membranes, however, the extent of the damage appears to be tissue specific, being more susceptible to cardiac tissue to liver tissue or renal tissue [31]. The harmful effect of O_2^- and ·OH that cause oxidative stress can be countered by the antioxidant enzymes superoxide dismutase (SOD) and catalase (CAT). There has been an increase in these antioxidant enzymes as a possible mechanism of response in the early stages of diabetes [31].A decrease of ROS in the plasma of patients with DM [32] was observed with non-enzymatic antioxidants like vitamins E and C Nitric oxide (NO), produced by nitric oxide synthase (NOS), is also associated with several disorders in diabetes. In biological systems where several reactive species generation is harnessed, interaction is given as in the case of ROS and NO, resulting in the formation of even more harmful reactive species such as peroxynitrite. It is reported that there is an increase in the levels of final products of the metabolism of the NO in kidneys of diabetic rats by alloxan [33].

3. DIABETES AND MEDICINAL PLANTS

For some years, interest has become apparent by studying and seeing the effects of herbs. In spite of this, the vast majority have not been studied, possibly on the one hand due to the great diversity of plants used in traditional medicine and on the other hand, the variety of uses and properties that can be attributed to each one of them. Many plants used in traditional medicine for people with diabetes have been studied, tested and probed as to their effects, such as: *Capparis decidua*, which has hypoglycemic and antioxidant activity in diabetic rats by alloxan [31], *Zaleya decandra,* which also has hypoglycemic activity in diabetic rats by alloxan [34], and *Orostachys japonicas,* which has hypoglycemic and hypolipidemic effects in diabetic rats by streptozotocin (STZ), just to name a few [35].

Figure 1. Plants of *Eryngium carlinae*. Apiaceae, perennial, of 5 to 50 cm tall plant, one stem or several, basal leaves in dense rosette, spinulous, caulinar, cymose inflorescence, stalked flower heads leaves, blue, violet or white, ovoid, with spatulate petals.

Eryngium carlinae F. Delaroche is a perennial herb plant considered a weed belonging to the family of *Umbelliferae* (Fig. 1). It is distributed in forests of fir, pine, pine-oak, hillsides and canyons, and deep soils rich in organic matter. It is distributed from 2020-2590 meters above sea level [2]. It is commonly known as "Frog herb". Decoctions of the aerial parts of the plant are used to treat coughs, indigestion, diseases of the prostate, lipid disorders, and diabetes [36]. It has been attributed to healing and diuretic properties to extracts from the plant. Other species of *Eryngium sp.* (*Eryngium columnare*) have been used to treat kidney disease, diarrhea, allergy, cough, and cancer [36]. Results from our laboratory using the whole ethanol extract of *E. carlinae* show higher antioxidant capacity than any of its fractions or aqueous preparations by eliminating DPPH$^.$ (2,2-diphenyl-1-picrylhydrazyl) and ABTS$^{.+}$ (2,2'-azino-bis(3-ethylbenzothiazoline-6-sulphonic acid) radicals; this is probably due to the content of flavonoids and phenols found in the preparations.

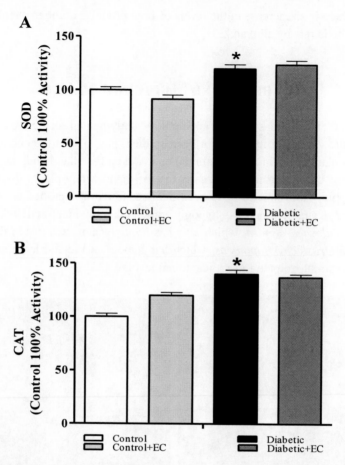

Figure 2. Effect of ethanol extract of *E. carlinae* on the activity of antioxidant enzymes SOD and CAT in kidney mitochondria. (A) SOD activity; (B) CAT activity. Values represent the mean ± SE. Group controls n=4; diabetic groups n=5. P<0.05 vs. Control.

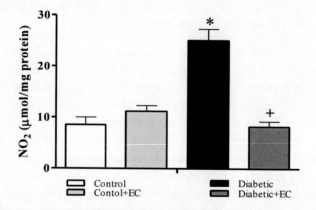

Figure 3. Effects of ethanol extract of *E. carlinae* on NO levels in kidney mitochondria. Values represent the mean ± SE. Control groups n=4; diabetics groups n=5. *P<0.05 vs. Control; $^+$P<0.05 vs. Diabetic. Nitrite levels were measured as an indirect determination of the NO levels. Kidney mitochondria of rats (0.5 mg) of the different groups were incubated with 100 µl of Griess reagent by 10 min and absorbance read at 546 nm using Perkin Elmer Lamda 18. Nitrite concentration in the samples was calculated based on sodium nitrite (1 mM) standard curve.

On the other hand, oral administration of the ethanol extract of *E. carlinae* to STZ-induced diabetic rats does not affect the activity of the antioxidant enzymes superoxide dismutase (SOD) and catalase (CAT) (Figure 2) or the levels of lipid peroxidation in mitochondria of kidney. Also, it is observed that the extract is capable of reducing the nitric oxide levels (NO) (Figure 3) elevated in diabetic rats in the early stages of kidney damage (in preparation). Hyperglycemia is the main feature of diabetes and is directly associated with the development of its complications. The mechanism of damage by hyperglycemia is closely related to the high production of reactive species at the mitochondrial level [37].

4. HYPERTENSION AND OXIDATIVE STRESS

Arterial hypertension (AHT) is one of the major risk factors for cardiovascular disease, stroke and kidney disease, which are major causes of mortality worldwide. Its prevalence increases with age and is higher after the age of 70 [38-40]. The economic costs associated with the treatment of this disease and its complications represent a burden for patients and health [38-40]. AHT is classified in primary hypertension and secondary hypertension and is highly prevalent in the world due to increased longevity and factors contributing to its development, such as obesity [41] and diabetes [42]. Hypertension is defined as a sustained blood pressure $\geq$ 140/90mmHg increase. The risk of cardiovascular disease is lower with arterial systolic pressure less than 120 mmHg and less than 80 mmHg for diastolic pressure; these risks increase progressively with highest systolic and diastolic pressures [42].

The administration of N^G-nitro-L-arginine methyl ester (L-NAME), causes an imbalance between nitric oxide (NO) and Angiotensin II (Ang II), and changed the balance in favor of vasoconstriction [42]. The L-NAME is water soluble and active orally. As well as increasing the arterial pressure (AP), it has been observed that NO is chronically maintained, then the glomerular damage appears due to glomerular capillary hypertension, which has been involved in the pathogenesis of primary glomerular disease [42]. The acute administration of analogues of L-arginine, as L-NAME, causes marked hypertension and renal vasoconstriction, presumably as a result of inhibition of the biosynthesis of the NO.

New animal models of hypertension are being developed as new perspectives for understanding the pathogenesis. These animal models also are being used in the selection of antihypertensive agents since a host of new molecules have been isolated and synthesized; mainly from plants, so the use of animal models has increased to test their therapeutic effects. Endothelial dysfunction is associated with hypertension and vascular tone plays an important role in regulating the AP.

High blood pressure (HBP) causes a series of complications at the level of blood vessels coming to affect major organs such as the kidney and heart. An attenuated bioavailability of NO, the main characteristic of endothelial dysfunction is present in the AHT. Patients with hypertension have increased levels of ROS, which abduct the NO, recognizing its availability. In addition, it has been observed that the treatment or management of endogenous antioxidant sources (enzymatic) or exogenous, which interact with the endothelial cells; reduce blood pressure [43]. These antioxidant actions are particularly important since oxidative stress and the resulting removal of NO by excessive production of ROS, is believed to be one of the main causes of alteration of the bioactivity of the NO.

The integral role of oxidative stress in the deterioration of NO in hypertension has been demonstrated in studies *in vivo* and *in vitro* showing that substances that protect against the damage produced by the anion superoxide (main ROS), such as SOD, and vitamin C, restored both in animal models and in human the endothelium-dependent vasodilation [43]. Superoxide reacts directly with the NO to form peroxynitrite (ONOO$^-$) [44] and in this way inactive it. ONOO$^-$ is extremely reactive, also oxidizes to the tetrahydrobiopterin (BH$_4$); an important cofactor for the nitric oxide synthase (NOS). In the absence of BH$_4$, the NOS produces O$_2^-$ rather than NO, a process called decoupling of the NOS, managing to increase oxidative stress [45].

5. HYPERTENSION AND MEDICINAL PLANTS

For the treatment of hypertension there is a variety of antihypertensive drugs such as calcium channel blockers, angiotensin-converting enzyme inhibitors, and β blockers with or without vasodilator properties giving them alone or in combination with diuretics, suggesting that this is the consequence of the decrease of the AP [46].

In traditional medicine, there are a great variety of plants with global importance antihypertensive activity of which have isolated vasoactive compounds. The therapeutic effects of plants are due to in particular to the content of different secondary metabolites, which have been tested in *in vivo* and *in vitro* tests [5], for example, *Agastache mexicana* have their antihypertensive effects through the opening of potassium channels as well as via the NO/cGMP pathway and these effects are attributed to tilianin compound isolated from this plant [47]. Currently, studies with isolated or synthetic metabolites are tested by its vasorelaxants or antihypertensive effects, for example, the cinnamic acid (derived from *Cinnamomum* spp.*)*, it has been involved in a range of therapeutic effects including: antimicrobial, antifungal and anti-tumoral; but recently, it was probed its vasorelaxing effect via NO/cGMP in rat thoracic aorta [48]. Some of the plants with global importance antihypertensive activity are *Rauwolfia serpentine* [49], *Veratrum album* [50] and *Rhododendrom molle* [51]. Ajmalicine, reserpine and rescinamamine are antihypertensive metabolites, isolated from *R. serpentine*; the protoveratrines A and B are the active principles of *V. album*; and the romitoxine is the agent antihypertensive of *R. molle* [52].

Justicia spicigera is a medicinal plant member of the family of the Acanthaceae family (*Acanthaceae*). Traditionally the aerial parts of this plant are used as herbal teas and are indicated in the treatment of intestinal disorders, headache, chronic headache, epilepsy, cancer, DM and hypertension [53]. In 2012, Ortiz-Andrade and colleagues evaluated the anti-diabetic property of muicle, finding that the ethanol extract of *Justicia spicigera* has an antidiabetic effect that is related to the stimulation of glucose intake by of human and murine adipose cells [54]. It is the first study that supports its therapeutic use in a disease linked to hypertension.

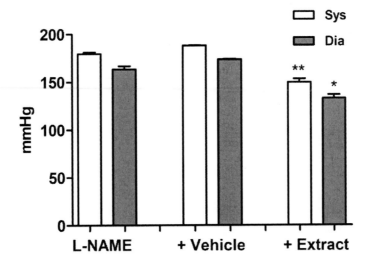

Figure 4. Effects of chloroform extract (150 mg/kg/w) on blood pressure L-NAME-rats. Blood pressure was measured 3 h after administration orally through oropharyngeal probe. Vehicle employed was DMSO 0.5%. The results show the mean (n=5) and SE with P values 0.0098 (systolic, Sys,**) and 0.0184 (diastolic, Dia,*) compared with hypertensive animals. DMSO 0.5 % does not modify the blood pressure.

In our laboratory we demonstrated that L-NAME ingestion caused a large rise in the resting mean arterial pressure (MAP) (175 ± 5mmHg) and heart rate (HR) (440 ± 17 beats per minute), compared to the untreated control rats (resting MAP: 112 ± 2 mm Hg and HR: 345 ± 8 beats per minute), as has been reported [53]. The hypertension model of chronic L-NAME administration is characterized by endothelial dysfunction, thereby causing vasoconstriction. Furthermore, this model is also characterized by the development of cardiac hypertrophy and renal damage [42]. When we evaluated the antihypertensive effect of *J. spicigera* in a single dose (150 mg/kg/w), it lowered the blood pressure in L-NAME rats that had values of $180/164\pm 1.7/3.2$ mmHg (systolic/diastolic) to values of $149/133 \pm 4.0/3.7$ mmHg (systolic/diastolic) with $P < 0.05$ (Figure 4). In addition to the antihypertensive effect of *J. spicigera*, also possesses the ability to relax phenylephrine aorta artery rings. However, this property is independent of the endothelium, this makes it a good candidate in the search for chemical compounds similar to those used for hypertension therapy not related to the way of NO. NO is the main component released in the arteries and helps reduce the arterial pressure between 20% and 30% of the maximum response to acetylcholine, and has the ability to modulate the bioavailability of NO from the endothelium, an open window towards the therapeutic of hypertension [55]. However, a blood arterial level, *J. spicigera* does not involve NO as relaxation mechanism. But to kidney mitochondrial level, *J. spicigera* contains a component that has antioxidant function, thus improving bioavailability and/or as NO donor agent. Other studies show that the antihypertensive effects are due to metabolites isolated from medicinal plants to mediate its effects through calcium channel antagonism (*Laelia anceps*) [56], in the case of *Persea americana* Mill. (Avocado), the reduction of the AP is presumed to be due to its high content of oleic acid [57], which is credited as cardioprotective to mediate stress.

CONCLUSION

Wild plants used in traditional medicine, have been evaluated to identify the major chemical components to determine its pharmacological effects, the stability of its products and its clinical behavior, in order to find new compounds with medicinal properties or validate its folk medicinal use, as for *Eryngium carlinae* and *Justicia spicigera* for diabetes mellitus or hypertension, respectively. Most particularly, it requires additional studies that allow you to elucidate the mechanism of action for both antidiabetic and antihypertensive effects.

ACKNOWLEDGMENTS

The authors appreciate the partial economic support from CONACYT grants (169093 to ASM; 130638 to CCR), CIC-UMSNH (2.10 to RSG; 2.16, to ASM; 2.37 to SMA). RNC and EREG are CONACYT Postdoctoral fellows. RNC and EREG contributed equally to the manuscript.

REFERENCES

[1]   Croteau, R; Kutcher, TM; Lewis, NG. Natural products (secondary metabolites). In: *Biochemistry & Molecular Biology of Plants*. Buchanan W, Gruisserm W, Jones R. (Eds.) 2002; pp 1250-1318.

[2]   Noriega-Cisneros, R; Ortiz-Avila, O; Esquivel-Gutiérrez, E; Clemente-Guerrero, M; Manzo-Avalos, S; Salgado-Garciglia, R; Cortés-Rojo, C; Boldogh, I; Saavedra-Molina, A. (2012). Hypolipidemic activity of *Eryngium carlinae* on Streptozotocin-induced diabetic rats. *Biochem Res Int,* 2012, 603501.

[3]   Kumar, Tyagi, A; Bukvicki, D; Gottardi, D; Veljic, M; Guerzoni, ME; Malik, A; Marin, PD. (2013). Antimicrobial Potential and Chemical Characterization of Serbian Liverwort (Porella arboris-vitae): SEM and TEM Observations. *Evid Based Complement Alternat Med*, 2013, 382927.

[4]   Huerta, C. (1997). La herbolaria: mito o realidad. CONABIO. *Biodiversitas,* 12, 1-7.

[5]   Esquivel-Gutiérrez, ER; Noriega-Cisneros, R; Saavedra-Molina, A; Salgado-Garciglia, R. (2013). Plants used in Mexican folk medicine with antidiabetic and antihypertensive properties. *PharmacologyOnline*, 2, 15-23.

[6]   Hegsted, DM; McGandy, RB; Myers, ML; Stare, FJ. (1965). Quantitative effects of dietary fat on serum cholesterol in man. *Am J Clin Nutr,* 17(5), 281-295.

[7]   Bonanome, A; Grundy, SM. (1998). Effect of dietary stearic acid on plasma cholesterol and lipoprotein levels. *N Engl J Med,* 318(19), 1244-1248.

[8]   Wani, MC; Taylor, HL; Wall, ME; Coggon, P; McPhail, AT. (1971). Plant antitumor agents. VI. The isolation and structure of taxol, a novel antileukemic and antitumor agent from *Taxus brevifolia. J Amer Chem Soc*, 93, 2325-2327.

[9]   Vakil, RJ. (1955). *Rauwolfia serpentina* in the treatment of high blood pressure: A review of the literature. *Circulation*, 12, 220-229.

[10] Duke, JA. (1973). Utilization of papaver. *Econ Bot*, 27, 390-391.

[11] Bulduk, B; Taktak, F. (2013). Isolation and characterization of antitumor alkaloids from poppy capsules (*Papaver somniferum*). *J Chem*, 2013, 1-4.

[12] Cardona, LEH; Mejía, LFG. (2009). Evaluación del efecto antioxidante de aceites esenciales y extractos de *Eugenia caryophyllata*, *Origanum vulgare* y *Thymus vulgaris*. *Biosalud*, 8, 58-70.

[13] Daniel, AN; Sartoretto, SM; Schmidt, G; Caparroz-Assef, SM; Bersani-Amado, CA; Cuman, RKN. (2009). Anti-inflammatory and antinociceptive activities of eugenol essential oil in experimental animal models. *Brazilian J Pharmacognosy*, 19(1B), 212-217.

[14] Dewick, PM. Medicinal natural products (Third Edition). *John Wiley & Sons Ltd*, England; (2009), p 550.

[15] Miguel, MG. (2010). Antioxidant activity of medicinal and aromatic plants. *Flavour Fragr J*, 25, 291-312.

[16] Kamatou, GPP; Viljoen, AM. (2010). A review of the application and pharmacological properties of α-bisabolol and α-bisabolol-rich oils. *J Am Oil Chem Soc*, 87, 1-7.

[17] Dutra, RC; Fava, MB; Alves, CSC; Ferreira, AP; Barbosa, NR. (2009). Antiulcerogenic and anti-inflammatory activities of the essential oil from *Pterodon emarginatus* seeds. *J Pharm Pharmacol*, 61, 243-250.

[18] Yoon, WJ; Kim, SS; Oh, TH; Lee, NH; Hyun, CG. (2010). *Abies koreana* essential oil inhibits drug-resistant skin pathogen growth and LPS-induced inflammatory effects of murine macrophage. *Lipids*, 44, 471-476.

[19] Juhás, Š; Bujňáková, D; Rehák, P; Cikoš, Š; Czikková, S; Veselá, J; Il'ková, G; Koppel, J. (2008). Anti-inflammatory effects of thyme essential oil in mice. *Acta Vet Brno*, 77, 327-334.

[20] Pirola, L; Fröjdo, S. (2008). Resveratrol: one molecule, many targets. *IUBMB Life*, 60, 323–332.

[21] Gutiérrez-Pérez, A; Cortés-Rojo, C; Noriega-Cisneros, R; Calderón-Cortés, E; Manzo-Avalos, S; Clemente-Guerrero, M; Godínez-Hernández, D; Boldogh, I; Saavedra-Molina, A. (2011). Protective effects of resveratrol on calcium-induced oxidative stress in rat heart mitochondria. *J Bioenereg Biomembr*, 43, 101-107.

[22] Leary, SC; Michaud, D; Lyons, CN; Hale, TM; Bushfield, TL; Adams, MA; Moyes, CD. (2002). Bioenergetic remodeling of heart during treatment of spontaneously hypertensive rats with enalapril. *Am J Physiol Heart Circ Physiol*, 283, H540-H548.

[23] Zhou H, Beevers CS, Huang S. 2011. The targets of curcumin. *Curr Drug Targets*, 12(3), 332-347.

[24] Prasad, S; Gupta, SC; Tyagi, AK; Aggarwal, BB. (2014). Curcumin, a component of golden spice: From bedside to bench and back. *Biotechnol Adv*, http://dx.doi.org/10.1016/j.biotechadv.2014.04.004.

[25] OMS. Estrategia de la OMS sobre Medicina Tradicional 2002-2005. *Organización mundial de la salud*, Ginebra, Suiza 2002, pp 65.

[26] Grundy, SM; Benjamin, IJ; Burke, GL; Chait, A; Eckel, RH; Howard, BW; Mitch, W; Smith, SC Jr.; Sowers, JR. (1999). Diabetes and Cardiovascular Disease: A Statement for Healthcare Professionals From the American Heart Association. *Circulation*, 100, 1134-1146.

[27]   Andrade-Cetto, A; Heinrich, M. (2011). From the field into the lab: useful approaches to selecting species based on local knowledge. *Front Pharmacol, 2*, 20.

[28]   Barham, D; Trinder, P. (1972). An improved color reagent for the determination of blood glucose by the oxidase system. *The Analyst,* 97(1151), 142-145.

[29]   Zhan, YH; Liu, J; Qu, XJ; Hou, KZ; Wang, KF; Liu, YP; Wu, B. (2012). β-Elemene induces apoptosis in human renal-cell carcinoma 786-0 cells through inhibition of MAPK/ERK and PI3K/Akt/mTOR signalling pathways. *Asian Pac J Cancer Prev,* 13(6), 2739-2744.

[30]   Chen, M; Zhang, J; Yu, S; Wang, S; Zhang, Z; Chen, J; Xiao, J; Wang, Y. (2012). Anti-Lung-Cancer Activity and Liposome-Based Delivery Systems of *β*-Elemene. *Evid Based Complement Alternat Med,* 2012, 259523.

[31]   Chung, IM; Kim, MY; Park, WH; Moon, HI. (2009). Antiatherogenic activity of *Dendropanax morbifera* essential oil in rats. *Pharmazie,* 64(8), 547-549.

[32]   Fernandes, ES; Passos, GF; Medeiros, R; da Cunha, FM; Ferreira, J; Campos, MM; Pianowski, LF; Calixto, JB. (2007). Anti-inflammatory effects of compounds alpha-humulene and (-)-trans-caryophyllene isolated from the essential oil of *Cordia verbenacea*. *Eur J Pharmacol*, 569(3), 228-236.

[33]   Rogerio, AP; Andrade, EL; Leite, DF; Figueiredo, CP; Calixto, JB. (2009). Preventive and therapeutic anti-inflammatory properties of the sesquiterpene alpha-humulene in experimental airways allergic inflammation. *Br J Pharmacol*, 158(4), 1074-1087.

[34]   Hsouna, AB; Hamdi, N. (2012). Phytochemical composition and antimicrobial activities of the essential oils and organic extracts from *Pelargonium graveolens* growing in Tunisia. *Lipids Health Dis*, 11, 167.

[35]   Cárdenas, J; Rojas, J; Rojas-Fermin, L; Lucena, M; Buitrago, A. (2012). Essential oil composition and antibacterial activity of *Monticalia greenmaniana* (Asteraceae). *Nat Prod Commun,* 7(2), 243-244.

[36]   Bello, GMA. (2006). Catálogo de Plantas Medicinales de la Comunidad Indígena Nuevo San Juan Parangaricutiro, *Libro Técnico no. 4.* Campo Experimental Uruapan. CIRPAC. INIFAP, Michoacán, México.

[37]   Brownlee, M. (2005). The Pathobiology of Diabetic Complications. A Unifying Mechanism. *Diabetes,* 54(6), 1615-1625.

[38]   ENSANUT. (2012). Evidence for public health policy. Hypertension in Mexican adults: importance of improving early diagnosis and control. Retrieved from http://ensanut.insp.mx.

[39]   Hall, JE. (2002). The kidney, hypertension and obesity. *Hypertension*, 41, 625-633.

[40]   WHO. (2012). Hypertension guidelines. Retrieved from www.who.org

[41]   Moncada, S; Palmer, RM; Higgs, EA. (1991). Nitric oxide: physiology, pathophysiology, and pharmacology. *Pharmacol Rev,* 43, 109-142.

[42]   Baylis, C; Mitruka, B; Deng, A. (1992). Chronic blockade of nitric oxide synthesis in the rat produces systemic hypertension and glomerular damage. *J Clin Invest*, 1, 278-281.

[43]   Hermann, M; Flammer, A; Lüscher, TF. (2007). Nitric Oxide in Hypertension. *J Clin Hypertension,* 8(12), 17-29.

[44]   Beckman, JS; Beckman, TW; Chen, J; Marshall, PA; Freeman, BA. (1990). Apparent hydroxyl radical production by peroxynitrite: Implications for endothelial injury from nitric oxide and superoxide. *Proc Natl Acad Sci USA,* 87, 1620-1624.

[45]   Ghafourifar, P; Saavedra-Molina, A. (2006). Functions of mitochondrial nitric oxide synthase. In: Lamas S and Cadenas E. *Nitric Oxide, Cell Signaling and Gene Expression. Taylor and Francis.* USA, 4, 77-98.

[46]   Mancia, G. (2012). Short- and Long-Term Blood Pressure Variability. Present and Future. *Hypertension*, 60, 512-517.

[47]   Hernández-Abreu, O; Castillo-España, P; León-Rivera, I; Ibarra-Barajas, M; Villalobos-Molina, R; González-Christen, J; Vergara-Galicia, J; Estrada-Soto, S. (2009). Antihypertensive and vasorelaxant effects of Tilianin isolated from *Agastache mexicana* are mediated by NO/cGMP pathway and potassium channel opening. *Biochem Pharmacol,* 78, 54-61.

[48]   Kang, YH; Kang, JS; Shin, HM. (2013). Vasodilatory Effects of Cinnamic Acid via the Nitric Oxide–cGMP–PKG Pathway in Rat Thoracic Aorta. *Phytother Res,* 27, 205–211.

[49]   Vakil, RJ. (1955). *Rauwolfia serpentina* in the treatment of high blood pressure: A review of the literature. *Circulation,* 12, 220-229.

[50]   Nash, HA; Brooker, RM. (1952). Hypotensive alkaloids from *Veratrum album* protoveratrine A, protoveratrine B and germitetrine B. *J Am Chem Soc,* 75, 1942-1948.

[51]   Mao, HY; Tu, YS; Nei, FD; Liang, GF; Feng, YB. (1981). Rapid antihypertensive effect of rhomotoxin in 105 hypertension cases. *Chin Med J (Engl),* 94(11), 733-736.

[52]   Fabricant, DS; Farnsworth, NR. (2001). The value of plants used in traditional medicine for drug discovery. *Environ Health Perspect,* 101, 69-75.

[53]   Esquivel-Gutiérrez, ER; Noriega-Cisneros, R; Arellano-Plaza, M; Ibarra-Barajas, M; Salgado-Garciglia, R; Saavedra-Molina, A. (2013). Antihypertensive effect of *Justicia spicigera* in L-NAME-induced hypertensive rats. *PharmacologyOnline,* 2, 120-127.

[54]   Ortiz-Andrade, R; Cabañas-Wuan, A; Arana-Argáez, VE; Alonso-Castro, AJ; Zapata-Bustos, R; Salazar-Olivo, L; Domínguez, F; Chávez, M; Carranza-Álvarez, C; García-Carrancá, A. (2012). Antidiabetic effects of *Justicia spicigera* Schltdl (Acanthaceae). *J Ethnopharm,* 143, 455-462.

[55]   Greenstein, AS. (2012). New Targets and Opportunities at the Level of the Endothelium. *Hypertension,* 60, 896-897.

[56]   Vergara-Galicia, J1; Ortiz-Andrade, R; Rivera-Leyva, J; Castillo-España, P; Villalobos-Molina, R; Ibarra-Barajas, M; Gallardo-Ortiz, I; Estrada-Soto, S. (2010). Vasorelaxant and antihypertensive effects of methanolic extract from roots of *Laelia anceps* are mediated by calcium-channel antagonism. *Fitoterapia,* 81(5), 350-357.

[57]   Ortiz-Avila, O; Sámano-García, CA; Calderón-Cortés, E; Pérez-Hernández, IH; Mejía-Zepeda R; Rodríguez-Orozco, AR; Saavedra-Molina, A; Cortés-Rojo, C. (2013). Dietary avocado oil supplementation attenuates the alterations induced by type I diabetes and oxidative stress in electron transfer at the complex II-complex III segment of the electron transport chain in rat kidney mitochondria. *J Bioenerg Biomembr,* 45(3), 271-287.

In: Reactive Oxygen Species, Lipid Peroxidation …
Editor: Angel Catalá

ISBN: 978-1-63321-886-4
© 2015 Nova Science Publishers, Inc.

Chapter 10

REDOX HOMEOSTASIS IMPAIRMENT AS AN IMPORTANT PATHOMECHANISM OF TISSUE DAMAGE IN INBORN ERRORS OF METABOLISM WITH INTOXICATION: INSIGHTS FROM HUMAN AND ANIMAL STUDIES

Guilhian Leipnitz[1], Bianca Seminotti[1], César Augusto João Ribeiro[1] and Moacir Wajner[1,2]

[1]Departamento de Bioquímica, Instituto de Ciências Básicas da Saúde,
Universidade Federal do Rio Grande do Sul, Porto Alegre, RS, Brazil
[2]Serviço de Genética Médica, Hospital de Clínicas de Porto Alegre,
Porto Alegre, RS, Brazil

ABSTRACT

Aminoacidopathies and organic acidemias are inherited metabolic disorders caused by defects in proteins, generally enzymes, resulting in tissue accumulation and elevated urinary excretion of potentially toxic compounds. Affected individuals present predominantly neurological symptoms and brain abnormalities that may be accompanied by liver, heart and skeletal muscle alterations. The pathogenesis of the tissue damage observed in these disorders is not yet fully established, but oxidative stress has been suggested to be involved in this injury. This chapter focuses on the role of oxidative stress in the pathophysiology of four prevalent IEM, namely phenylketonuria, maple syrup urine disease, methylmalonic acidemia and homocystinuria. The discussion will be concentrated more particularly on the brain pathomechanisms because of its vulnerability to reactive species due to its high oxygen demand, low antioxidant content and abundance of highly oxidizable polyunsaturated fatty acids. In the last few decades, several findings in animal models and patients affected by these disorders indicate that the accumulating metabolites (amino acids and organic acids) may cause mitochondrial dysfunction and/or increase free radical formation leading to oxidative damage to biomolecules (lipids, proteins and DNA) and to a decrease of antioxidant defenses. It is also important to emphasize that a dietary restriction of nutrients with antioxidant properties generally employed for the treatment of these diseases may contribute to the altered antioxidant status. These findings offer new perspectives for potential therapeutic strategies, which may include the early use of appropriate antioxidants with the ability to easily cross the blood-brain barrier, besides the usual therapies based on preventing metabolite accumulation and accelerating their removal through special diets and pharmacological agents.

LIST OF ABBREVIATIONS

AdoCbl	5-deoxyadenosyl cobalamin
BCAA	branched-chain amino acids
BCKA	branched-chain α-keto acids
BCKD	branched-chain α-keto acid dehydrogenase
BH_4	tetrahydrobiopterin
CAT	catalase
CBS	cystathionine β-synthase
CNS	central nervous system
CSF	cerebrospinal fluid
eNOS	endothelial nitric oxide synthase
G6PDH	glucose-6-phosphate dehydrogenase
GPx	glutathione peroxidase
GR	glutathione reductase
Hcy	homocysteine
HPA	hyperphenylalaninemia
IEM	inborn errors of metabolism
Ile	isoleucine
iNOS	inducible nitric oxide synthase
KIC	α-ketoisocaproic acid
KIV	α-ketoisovaleric acid
KMV	α-keto-β-methylvaleric acid
Leu	leucine
MAPK1/2	mitogen-activated protein kinase 1/2
MCM	methylmalonyl-CoA mutase
MDA	malondialdehyde
mGPDH	mitochondrial glycerophosphate dehydrogenase
MMAcidemia	methylmalonic acidemia
MSUD	maple syrup urine disease
MTHFR	5,10-methylenetetrahydrofolate reductase
Mut^-	partial methylmalonyl-CoA mutase deficiency
Mut°	complete methylmalonyl-CoA mutase deficiency
PAA	phenylacetate
PAH	phenylalanine hydroxylase
Phe	phenylalanine
PKU	phenylketonuria
PLA	phenyllactate

PPA   phenylpyruvate
ROS   reactive oxygen species
SOD   superoxide dismutase
Val   valine

INTRODUCTION

Inborn errors of metabolism (IEM) constitute a phenotypically and genetically heterogeneous group of disorders caused by defects in specific proteins, usually enzymes. The enzyme deficiency leads to the blockage of a metabolic pathway resulting in accumulation of intermediate metabolites. To date, the biochemical defect of over 600 IEM has been identified [1]. Although the IEM are individually rare, the cumulative incidence has been shown to be approximately 1 in 800 births. The clinical presentation is heterogeneous, but is generally characterized by early symptoms in the neonatal period, although chronic and progressive symptomatology or recurrent attacks of metabolic decompensation with acute manifestations also occur [2]. The most common clinical findings are neurological, such as developmental delay, hypotonia, failure to thrive, lethargy, convulsions and coma that can progress to death. However, dysfunction of other organs, such as heart and liver, may also be observed [1-3].

The key to successful treatment of IEM is the initial suspicion and diagnosis followed by prompt management. The clinical history and physical examination may help to suggest the diagnosis of an IEM, but the identification of the accumulating metabolites in biological fluids and complex molecule storage in tissues by a large spectrum of techniques is usually necessary to establish a definite diagnosis. In some cases, the enzyme activity measurement and mutational analysis are performed to confirm the diagnosis [4-6].

The treatment is usually based in avoiding the accumulation of specific metabolites by dietary restriction of the substrates of the involved pathway, removal of these intermediates by pharmaceutical therapy and/or to replace the crucial deficient metabolic products that are essential for the body. For many IEM, the treatment strategies rely on the provision of specialized medical foods and dietary supplements [7]. However, the long-term consequences of artificial diets on the offspring have to be evaluated throughout life. Other strategies to decrease the concentration of toxic substrates or their precursors involve the administration of a variety of cleansing drugs that bind to the metabolites facilitating their excretion. The administration of vitamins also shows remarkable efficiency in vitamin-responsive disorders.

The pathophysiology of IEM has been object of intense investigation since, despite some exceptions, there is no clear genotype-phenotype correlation. From a pathophysiological point of view, the IEM can be divided into disorders which give rise to intoxication, disorders involving bioenergetics dysfunction and disorders involving complex molecules [2]. The IEM that give rise to intoxication are the most prevalent disorders and include aminoacidopathies, organic acidemias, urea cycle defects, sugar intolerances, metal intoxication and porphyrias [2].

In this chapter we review the pathophysiology of four intoxication disorders, namely phenylketonuria (PKU), maple syrup urine disease (MSUD), methylmalonic acidemia (MMAcidemia) and homocystinuria, whose pathophysiology and clinical phenotype have been extensively linked to a possible toxicity of the accumulating compounds. However, it should be emphasized here that the plasma levels of these intermediates do not predict the clinical picture of these disorders [8, 9]. The present knowledge suggests various mechanisms for the toxicity of these compounds, including bioenergetics dysfunction, excitotoxicity and oxidative stress. We focus here on the role of oxidative stress as a pathomechanism involved in the pathophysiology of PKU, MSUD, MMAcidemia and homocystinuria.

PHENYLKETONURIA

Phenylketonuria (PKU) is the most prevalent autosomal recessive disorder of amino acid metabolism, with an incidence of about 1:10,000 in populations of European descent. PKU is caused by mutations in the gene encoding the rate-limiting enzyme phenylalanine hydroxylase (PAH; EC 1.14.16.1), that converts phenylalanine (Phe) to tyrosine (Figure 1), leading to high plasma Phe concentrations (400-1,800 μmol/L). The excess of Phe is metabolized by alternative pathways producing phenylpyruvate (PPA), phenyllactate (PLA) and phenylacetate (PAA). More than 500 mutations have been described at the *PAH* locus. Other cases of hyperphenylalaninemia (HPA) occur due to mutations in enzymes involved in the synthesis or recycling of tetrahydrobiopterin (BH$_4$), the cofactor of PAH [10, 11].

PKU is clinically characterized by severe mental retardation, epilepsy, microcephaly, cerebral white matter abnormalities and progressive supranuclear motor disturbances. Lack of myelin, and altered axonal conduction and synaptic transmission velocity have also been reported [10-12]. Affected patients also present neurotransmission impairment since high plasma levels of Phe inhibit the transport of neutral amino acids into the brain, reducing their availability for the synthesis of proteins and of the neurotransmitters noradrenaline and dopamine [13, 14].

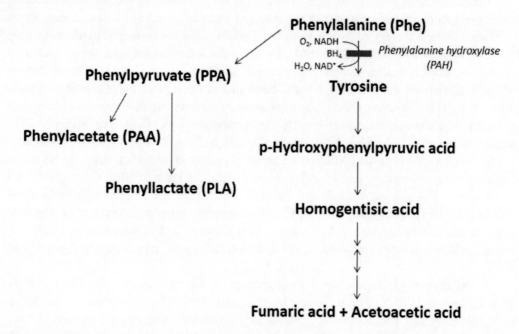

Figure 1. Catabolic pathway of phenylalanine (Phe) with phenylalanine hydroxylase (PAH) deficiency.

Mass newborn screening programs for PKU occurs in most developed countries since the late 1960s and also in many developing countries [12]. Initially, PKU screening was performed by the Guthrie test [15], which detects blood Phe in infants using blood spots dried on filter paper combined with a bacterial inhibition assay. More recently, PKU screening has been performed with greater accuracy by tandem mass spectrometry.

Treatment of PKU patients is basically carried out by Phe/protein dietary restriction. The newborn PKU child must avoid ingesting large amounts of proteins and Phe to maintain Phe levels at a normal range. For this purpose, commercial Phe-free formulas have been developed. On the other hand, HPA patients that are BH_4-responsive may require only pharmacologic therapy with this pterin. Alternative treatments include the possibility of enzyme substitution with engineered recombinant phenylalanine ammonia lyase and gene therapy [11, 12].

We will focus here on the results obtained from animal studies and from biological fluid samples of PKU patients that support the implication of oxidative stress in the pathophysiology of this disease.

Oxidative Stress in PKU: Insights from *in Vitro* Studies and *in Vivo* Animal Models

In vitro studies performed in rat brain homogenates exposed to Phe evidenced that this amino acid induces lipid and protein oxidative damage, and diminishes non-enzymatic and enzymatic antioxidant defenses [16, 17]. The major Phe derivatives PPA, PLA and PAA are also capable of causing lipid damage in rat brain [17]. Furthermore, it was verified that PPA inhibits glucose-6-phosphate dehydrogenase (G6PDH) activity in rat brain homogenates [18], causing a decrease of NADPH production and a consequent failure in the elimination of hydrogen peroxide and lipid peroxides because NADPH is the cofactor of glutathione peroxidase (GPx). PLA and PAA were also shown to increase the activity of purified superoxide dismutase (SOD) [19], although the mechanism involved in this effect has not been established. Another study carried out in primary cultured cortical neurons demonstrated that Phe elicits superoxide production, which is abrogated by the inhibitors of NADPH oxidase apocynin and diphenylene iodonium, indicating that this enzyme is the source of superoxide when these cells are exposed to Phe. The same study further verified that the increase of NADPH oxidase activity is due to the up regulation of the subunits p47phox and p67phox [20].

Observations drawn from rats subjected to an HPA model based on the administration of Phe plus α-methyl-DL-phenylalanine, a PAH inhibitor, evidenced lipid peroxidation and impairment of antioxidant defenses in the brain of these animals [16]. A strong correlation was observed between lipid oxidative damage and decreased antioxidant defenses, implying that the consumption of antioxidants in rat brain occurred due to the reactive species generated during the lipid peroxidation process. It was also verified an increase of SOD activity and a decrease of catalase (CAT), GPx and G6PDH activities in the HPA model [16, 21]. These alterations were prevented by physical training (2-week aerobic exercise for 20 min/day) and lipoic acid supplementation [19, 21]. On the other hand, Berti and collaborators [22] showed that a single Phe intrahippocampal administration causes learning/memory deficit and alterations of oxidative stress parameters similarly to those observed in the HPA model, and that these changes were prevented by the administration of pyruvate and creatine.

Moreover, Martinez-Cruz and collaborators [23] demonstrated that a maternal HPA model induced with injections of Phe and *p*-chlorophenylalanine provokes oxidative injury and morphological alterations in the brain and cerebellum of pup rats. The pups also presented decreased activities of GPx and glutathione reductase (GR), as well as of mitogen-activated protein kinase 1/2 (MAPK1/2). Mitochondrial dysfunction was further observed in the brain and liver of the pup rats, as reflected by increased levels of malondialdehyde (MDA) and 4-hydroxy-2-nonenal in this organelle [23, 24]. These effects were prevented by treatment with melatonin, vitamin E and vitamin C from the period of rat mating until delivery [23, 24]. Other studies performed in BTBR-Pahenu2 mice, a genetic animal model for PKU, reported augmented levels of lipid peroxidation products and decreased GSH/glutathione disulfide ratio in the brain, blood and red blood cells of these animals [25]. Furthermore, CAT and G6PDH activities were also increased in the red blood cells of these PKU mice [25]. It was suggested that these alterations in BTBR-Pahenu2 mice were mediated by increased production of superoxide by NADPH oxidase, which was up regulated in mononuclear cells of these animals [26].

Oxidative Stress Biomarkers in PKU Patients

Studies investigating the involvement of oxidative injury in the pathophysiology of PKU verified induction of lipid and protein oxidative damage in plasma and erythrocytes from PKU patients [27-29]. Lipid oxidative damage was inferred by increased levels of MDA and oxidized LDL in plasma, and acrolein lysine in urine, and protein damage by the augmented carbonyl group content in plasma [28]. These observations were found even in treated PKU patients with normal Phe plasma levels, implying that oxidative stress occurs in patients under protein dietary restriction therapy [30]. Furthermore, DNA damage was also verified in PKU patients and in normal individuals exposed to Phe [30, 31]. This is in accordance with another study showing high levels of 8-hydroxy-2-deoxyguanosine in serum of poorly controlled PKU patients [32]. It is noteworthy that DNA damage index is lower in treated PKU patients as compared to individuals with high Phe levels, indicating that this parameter correlates with Phe blood levels [31].

Impairment of antioxidant status was also found in affected PKU patients. GSH concentrations decrease was seen in serum, that could be attributed to selenium deficiency due to protein restricted diet [33, 34] or secondary to an inhibition caused by Phe on the amino acid transport system for cysteine and glycine, which are substrates for the production of GSH [29]. Furthermore, it was verified that the deficiency of selenium leads to a decrease of erythrocyte GPx activity and that neuropsychological symptoms are more frequent in these patients [35]. In addition to selenium deprivation, low levels of α-tocopherol, uric acid, coenzyme Q10, beta-carotene and L-carnitine were detected in PKU patients strictly adherent to the treatment, probably as a consequence of the low protein diet [28, 29, 35-37]. In this context, it was shown that supplementation of L-carnitine and of selenium was able to revert the lipid and protein oxidative damage, as well as the reduction of GPx activity observed in PKU affected individuals [37].

MAPLE SYRUP URINE DISEASE

Maple syrup urine disease (MSUD), also called branched-chain ketoaciduria, is an inherited metabolic disorder caused by a severe deficiency of the branched-chain α-keto acid dehydrogenase (BCKD) complex activity. This human multienzyme complex, associated with the mitochondrial inner membrane, catalyzes the oxidative decarboxylation of the branched-chain α-keto acids (BCKA), namely α-ketoisocaproic acid (KIC), α-keto-β-methylvaleric acid (KMV) and α-ketoisovaleric acid (KIV), that are derived from their corresponding branched-chain amino acids (BCAA) leucine (Leu), isoleucine (Ile) and valine (Val). The reaction products of the BCKA complex are isovaleryl-CoA, α-methylbutyryl-CoA and isobutyryl-CoA [38] (Figure 2). The BCAA catabolic pathway blockage at the step of BCKD complex leads to the tissue accumulation of the amino acids Leu, Ile and Val and their corresponding BCKA, as well as their hydroxy byproducts [39]. MSUD has a worldwide frequency of approximately 1 in 185,000 newborns, including both the classic and certain variant forms of the disorder, whereas at locations where consanguinity is usual, such as in Saudi Arabia, Turkey, Spain and India, MSUD is highly prevalent [40].

MSUD affected individuals can be separated into the distinctive groups classic, intermediate, intermittent, thiamine-responsive and dihydrolipoyl dehydrogenase (E3)-deficient, according to clinical and biochemical phenotypes. These clinical phenotypes range from a severe classic form with neonatal onset to milder variant forms with later onset, showing different residual enzyme activity 38, 41]. The most relevant laboratorial and clinical findings include poor feeding, hypoglycemia, ketoacidosis, apnea, ataxia, convulsions, coma, psychomotor delay and mental retardation [38]. Neuroradiological studies reveal generalized edema and hypomyelination/demyelination in the central nervous system (CNS), characterizing MSUD as a white-matter disease [39, 42-44].

The treatment of this disorder requires limited intake of BCAA with the purpose to minimize the accumulation of intermediates that can lead to organ injury, especially the CNS.

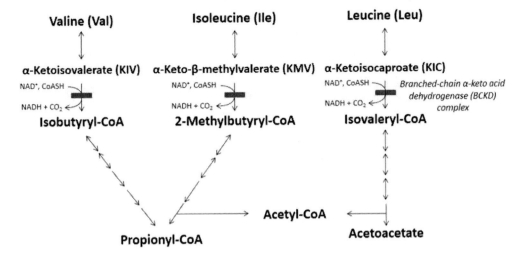

Figure 2. Catabolic pathway of the branched-chain amino acids valine (Val), isoleucine (Ile) and leucine (Leu) with branched-chain α –keto acid dehydrogenase (BCKD) complex deficiency.

Taken into account that increased Leu is associated with the appearance and worsening of neurological symptoms in MSUD patients, this amino acid and/or its keto acid are considered the main neurotoxic metabolites, and detection of their plasma concentrations is important for monitoring the treatment. The long-term dietary management is fundamental to provide an adequate nutrition, maintaining normal growth and development, and avoiding the appearance of neurological symptoms. A specific formula containing essential amino acids (except BCAA) and micronutrients was developed and is used as supplementation [45].

Although the exact mechanisms involved in the pathophysiology of MSUD remain to be elucidated, oxidative stress induced by the accumulating metabolites is suggested to play an important role in the brain damage observed in MSUD patients.

Oxidative Stress in MSUD: Insights from *in Vitro* Studies and *in Vivo* Animal Models

In vitro reports showed that BCAA, BCKA and the corresponding hydroxy acids induce lipid peroxidation in rat brain homogenates [46, 47], whereas Leu and BCKA also compromise enzymatic and non-enzymatic antioxidant defenses [47, 48]. These pro-oxidant effects exerted by Leu were prevented by the free radical scavengers ascorbic acid, α-tocopherol and GSH [48]. Observations in C6 cells revealed that the exposition of these cells to BCKA results in alterations of antioxidant status and increased nitric oxide production, whereas KIC and KIV also enhance S100B secretion. It was further verified that the BCKA cause morphological changes and cell death, which were prevented by free radical scavengers [49, 50]. Another study conducted in C6 cells evidenced that BCAA, similarly to BCKA, induce morphological alterations and oxidative injury, as well as changes in the organization of glial fibrillary acidic protein (GFAP) filaments [51].

There are also *in vivo* studies demonstrating the involvement of free radicals in MSUD pathogenesis. Mescka and collaborators [52] showed that an acute model of MSUD induced by the injection of BCAA pool in rats causes lipid and protein oxidative damage and alters the activities of CAT and GPx in the brain, while L-carnitine treatment prevents all these changes. Other works using the same MSUD model found that administration of N-acetylcysteine (NAC) and deferoxamine prevents the memory impairment observed in rats injected with the pool of BCAA [53 ,54]. The antioxidants NAC and deferoxamine also diminish the frequency and index of DNA damage and the induction of acetylcholinesterase activity in brain of rats receiving BCAA [55, 56]. These findings suggest that a disturbance of redox homeostasis is associated to memory impairment induced by BCAA administration.

Another relevant study showed that Leu, when administered to female Wistar rats during pregnancy and lactation, induces oxidative stress and bioenergetic dysfunction in the brain of the offspring [57]. These findings indicate that non-treated maternal hyperleucinemia is toxic to the brain of the offspring.

Oxidative Stress Biomarkers in MSUD Patients

Studies using biological samples from MSUD diagnosed individuals also support that oxidative stress is closely associated with MSUD pathophysiology. MDA levels increase and changes in antioxidant defenses were detected in plasma from untreated patients with the classic form of the disease. Similar results were reported in plasma from MSUD patients treated with BCAA-restricted diet and supplemented with a specific formula (essential amino acids, vitamins and minerals) [58], implying that the treatment does not revert oxidative damage.

It is also interesting that the low protein diet used for MSUD treatment led to significant alterations in antioxidant defenses by reducing vitamin and mineral absorption [45]. In this context, samples from MSUD patients showed reduced selenium levels, being more evident during treatment [59-61], that caused a decrease of erythrocyte GPx activity [61]. According to these findings, activity of GPx was restored after selenium supplementation. In addition, it was suggested that the low protein diet provokes L-carnitine deficiency, since the supplementation with this compound reverted the oxidative damage in plasma from MSUD patients treated with this special diet [62].

METHYLMALONIC ACIDEMIA

Methylmalonic acidemia (MMAcidemia) comprises a group of autosomal recessive genetic disorders affecting the catabolic pathways of the amino acids Ile, Val, methionine and threonine, as well as of thymine, odd carbon number fatty acids and the side chain of cholesterol. All these compounds have propionyl-CoA as a common product of their catabolism. MMAcidemia has an estimated incidence of 1 in 50,000 newborns [63-65] and is most commonly caused by mutations in the gene *MUT* encoding methylmalonyl-CoA mutase (MCM, EC 5.4.99.2), a mitochondrial matrix enzyme that catalyses the conversion of L-methylmalonyl-CoA, which is synthesized from propionyl-CoA, to succinyl-CoA [64-66] (Figure 3). Furthermore, MMAcidemia can also result from defects of 5-deoxyadenosyl cobalamin (AdoCbl) synthesis, a vitamin B_{12}-derived cofactor required for MCM activity, as well as from failure in the metabolism of cobalamin itself that can promote a functional deficiency of MCM. The deficiency of MCM leads to the primary accumulation of methylmalonic acid (MMA) and to secondary elevation of the levels of other metabolites, such as propionate, 3-hydroxypropionate and 2-methylcitrate [65].

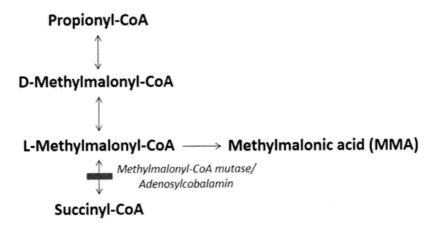

Figure 3. Catabolic pathway of propionyl-CoA with methylmalonyl-CoA mutase deficiency.

Mutations in *MUT* may cause partial (Mut⁻) or complete (Mut°) enzyme deficiency, and there is a good correlation between MCM activity and the severity of the clinical phenotype [67, 68]. Mut° patients have an earlier symptom onset, higher mortality rate and poorer neurological outcome than Mut⁻ individuals, who become symptomatic later in infancy and have a better prognostic. The most common signs and symptoms include lethargy, failure to thrive, recurrent vomiting, respiratory distress, hypotonia, mental retardation and seizures, although hepatomegaly and coma are relatively frequent [64, 65, 67]. Neuropathological findings include demyelination, ventricular dilation, cortical atrophy, white matter abnormalities, thinning of the corpus callosum, cerebellar atrophy and basal ganglionic calcification [65, 69, 70].

MMA is considered the main neurotoxin in this disease, although propionate and 2-methylcitrate also exert toxic effects [71]. The neurodegeneration in MMAcidemia possibly results from intracerebral trapping of these metabolites within the CNS due to the limited transport capacity of blood brain barrier for dicarboxylates [72]. A large body of evidence has emerged demonstrating that accumulation of MMA causes impairment of energy metabolism and redox imbalance in the brain [65, 71, 73]. The effects of MMA on energy metabolism are primarily related to the inhibition of enzymatic activities of the tricarboxylic acid cycle and the mitochondrial electron transport chain [71, 74-76]. We emphasize the role of oxidative stress in MMAcidemia as discussed below.

Oxidative Stress in MMacidemia: Insights from *in Vitro* Studies and *in Vivo* Animal Models

In vitro findings evidenced that MMA induces lipid peroxidation, protein damage and decreases the quantity of non-enzymatic antioxidant defenses in rat brain [77-79]. It was also observed that MMA inhibits the activity of creatine kinase via oxidation of crucial sulfhydryl groups of this enzyme, suggesting the involvement of reactive species in this effect [80].

Several *in vivo* findings have also been reported showing that MMA induces oxidative stress. Chronic MMA treatment causes behavioral alterations and inhibits Na^+,K^+-ATPase activity in brain of rats, which were prevented by free radical scavengers, implying that reactive species overproduction is involved in the cognitive deficit and neurotransmission impairment caused by this metabolite [78, 81]. Furthermore, Ribeiro and colleagues [82] found that chronic treatment with MMA increases the levels of pro-inflammatory cytokines, as well as the expression of inducible nitric oxide synthase (iNOS) and 3-nitrotyrosine content, causing nitrosative stress in cerebral cortex of rats. In addition, acute intracerebral administration of MMA elicits reactive species generation and induces oxidative damage in rat striatum, besides provoking convulsions [79, 83]. These effects were exacerbated in rat cerebral cortex when MMA was associated to hyperammonemia [84], which is a common laboratorial finding in MMAcidemia [65]. Histological alterations including vacuolization, ischemic neurons and pericellular edema could also be observed in brain of hyperammonemic rats treated with MMA [84]. Most of the effects caused by MMA were prevented by neuroprotective agents that included L-NAME and free radical scavengers, such as creatine, ascorbic acid and α-tocopherol, suggesting the involvement of nitric oxide and reactive oxygen species (ROS) in MMA pro-oxidant action [83, 85-88]. MMA-induced oxidative injury via nitric oxide generation was reinforced by experiments in iNOS knockout (iNOS⁻/⁻)

mice intrastriatally injected with MMA demonstrating a decrease of time of convulsions in iNOS$^{-/-}$ mice compared to iNOS$^{+/+}$ animals. The same study evidenced that MMA increases the concentrations of nitric oxide derivatives and 3-nitrotyrosine, as well as inhibits Na$^+$,K$^+$-ATPase activity in a greater level in iNOS$^{+/+}$ mice than in iNOS$^{-/-}$ mice [89].

It has been observed that other organs besides CNS are affected by MMA. In this context, Schuck and collaborators [90, 91] verified that acute subcutaneous administration of MMA alters the redox status in rat kidney.

Oxidative Stress Biomarkers in MMAcidemia Patients

Oxidative stress parameters are also altered in patients affected by MMAcidemia. Some studies reported augmented ROS production and MnSOD expression in fibroblasts [92-94], as well as a reduction of GSH levels in plasma of these patients [95]. Another study verified that the mitochondrial glycerophosphate dehydrogenase (mGPDH) is an important source of superoxide in fibroblasts of affected patients, since mGPDH was found to be over expressed in these cells and the knock-down of this enzyme reverted the increased production of ROS [93]. Further observations in plasma of patients revealed elevated MDA and carbonyl content, and reduced levels of sulfhydryl groups [96].

HOMOCYSTINURIA

Homocysteine (Hcy) is a thiol amino acid formed during the metabolism of methionine. Under normal conditions, plasma Hcy concentrations do not exceed 15 µM [97], whereas in cerebrospinal fluid (CSF) and brain tissue they are reported to range from 0.5 to 10 µM [98].

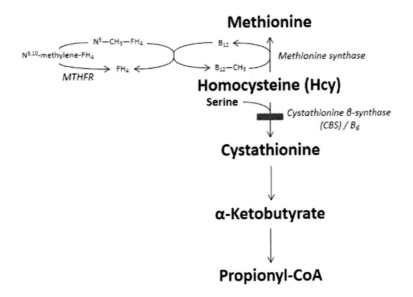

Figure 4. Metabolic pathway of homocysteine (Hcy) with cystathionine β –synthase (CBS) deficiency. FH4-Tetrahydrofolate; MTHFR-5,10-methylenetetrahydrofolate reductase.

Several genetic disorders have been associated with elevated plasma levels of Hcy (hyperhomocysteinemia), including cystathionine β-synthase (CBS) (EC 4.2.1.22) deficiency (classical homocystinuria), and the deficiencies of 5,10-methylenetetrahydrofolate reductase (MTHFR) and methionine synthase (Figure 4). The deficiencies of the vitamin cofactors folate, cobalamin or pyridoxine, that are essential for Hcy metabolism, may also cause hyperhomocysteinemia.

CBS deficiency is the most common and severe disorder biochemically characterized by hyperhomocysteinemia [99]. In normal human plasma, the majority of homocysteinyl moieties are bound to proteins as mixed disulfides with cysteines, whereas the remaining part occurs as free Hcy or free disulfides, homocystine and cysteine-homocysteine disulfide. In CBS-deficient individuals with elevation of total Hcy (free and conjugated Hcy), the percentage of the free Hcy rises, reaching 10-25% of total Hcy (150-400 mM) [100]. In addition to Hcy, methionine, due to excessive remethylation of Hcy, and a variety of other derivatives of Hcy accumulate in the body and are excreted in the urine of CBS-deficient patients.

Homocystinuria due to CBS deficiency is accompanied by a variety of clinical and pathologic abnormalities. Four organ systems present major involvement: the ocular, the skeletal, the vascular and the central nervous systems. Affected individuals commonly present ectopia lentis, myopia, osteoporosis, biconcave ("codfish") vertebrae, scoliosis, increased length of long bones, mental retardation, psychiatric disturbances and vascular occlusions. It has been reported that thromboembolism is the most common cause of death of affected patients [2].

CBS deficiency treatment is based on dietary protein restriction and supplementation with vitamin B_6. Although the administration of vitamin B_6 is not always successful, data indicate that the risk of developing clinical symptoms of the disease increases with age and that B_6-responsive patients are usually more mildly affected than B_6-non responsive patients [101].

Hyperhomocysteinemia resulting either from mutations in genes encoding Hcy-metabolizing enzymes or from deficiencies of folic acid also induces toxicity. In this context, increased Hcy levels has been demonstrated to be a risk factor for cardiovascular diseases, stroke and neurodegenerative disorders [102], such as epilepsy [103], dementia [97, 104] and Alzheimer's disease [102, 105-107]. In these pathological situations plasma Hcy levels may reach millimolar concentrations [108].

Hcy is a redox active molecule, and a large body of evidence has shown impairment of redox homeostasis. Hcy readily auto oxidizes in solution, leading to the formation of homocystine, homocysteine-mixed disulfides or homocysteine thiolactone, as well as superoxide and hydrogen peroxide [109], which cause biomolecule damage and citotoxicity in several cell lines and tissues.

Oxidative Stress in Homocystinuria: Insights from *in Vitro* Studies and *in Vivo* Animal Models

Several experimental *in vitro* and *in vivo* works have indicated the involvement of oxidative stress in homocystinuria. Upchurch and collaborators [110] showed that Hcy induces endothelial nitric oxide synthase (eNOS) expression, leading to increased production of S-nitroso-Hcy in bovine aortic endothelial cells. Moreover, Hcy impairs the activity of intracellular GPx in endothelial cells, contributing to the maintenance of increased hydrogen peroxide generated through Hcy auto-oxidation reactions [111]. Hcy also increases the production of reactive oxygen and nitrogen species, and reduces viability of rat thoracic aortic smooth muscle cells. These alterations were reverted by hydrogen sulfide, an antioxidant and anti-inflammatory agent [112].

Studies in other cell lines, such as cultured cortical neurons, neuroblastoma cells and dorsal root ganglion neurons, evidenced that elevated levels of Hcy induced by deficiency of folate diminishes GSH and increases intracellular calcium influx, reactive species production and phospho tau content, leading to apoptosis [113-115]. These alterations were prevented by NAC, vitamin E, nimodipine (an L-voltage-sensitive calcium channel antagonist) and MK-801 (a NMDA receptor antagonist). Folate deprivation also potentiates the neurotoxic effects of amyloid-β, indicating that the deficiency of folate leading to increased Hcy levels may worse AD neuropathology by eliciting ROS generation and excitotoxicity [113]. Furthermore, it was reported that Aβ increases hydrogen peroxide production and induces neurotoxicity in the presence of Cu (II) and Hcy in primary neuronal cultures [116].

Kruman and colleagues [117] verified that Hcy induces DNA strand breaks, activation of poly-ADP-ribose polymerase and NAD^+ depletion followed by mitochondrial dysfunction, oxidative stress and caspase activation in rat hippocampal neurons. It was also found that Hcy acts as a NMDA receptor agonist in cultured neurons and rat brain synaptosomes, provoking oxidative damage through this receptor activation [118-120]. On the other hand, cortical astrocytes reorganize their cytoskeleton in response to Hcy-induced reactive species generation in order to survive and protect neurons from damage. It was further demonstrated that Hcy induces lipid peroxidation and decreases non enzymatic antioxidant defenses in rat brain homogenates [121-123]. These observations support the view that Hcy induces oxidative stress *in vitro*.

In vivo reports conducted in rodents also showed that Hcy has strong pro-oxidant properties [122, 124-126]. Thus, acute subcutaneous injection of Hcy induces oxidative stress in rat brain and erythrocytes, and increases platelet count and plasma fibrinogen levels, suggesting that hypercoagulability and oxidative stress occur in association due to high Hcy plasma levels, which possibly contributes to the vascular dysfunction and thromboembolic complications observed in hyperhomocysteinemia 124. Similarly, acute intracerebral Hcy injection provokes oxidative damage to cell components and increases mRNA and protein expression of iNOS and eNOS in rat brain. Intracerebral Hcy administration also leads to neuroinflammation, apoptosis and cerebrovascular remodeling that may be reverted by treatment with hydrogen sulfide [127].

Chronic hyperhomocysteinemia provoked by Hcy injection or methionine causes lipid peroxidation and DNA damage, and decreases antioxidant defenses in brain and blood of Wistar rats that were prevented by folic acid and melatonin administration [122, 125, 126, 128-130, 132]. Hcy also augments NF-κB immunocontent and pro-inflammatory cytokines levels, as well as modulates nitrite levels in hippocampus and serum from Wistar rats [131]. Another study using hyperhomocysteinemic Sprague-Dawley rats similarly verified that Hcy increases NF-κB and superoxide production in the endothelium of aortas of these animals, as well as in cultured human umbilical cord vein endothelial cells and aortic endothelial cells [132]. These data indicate that Hcy-induced NF-κB activation via reactive species production is probably involved in vascular and cerebrovascular damage.

Otherwise, observations in ApoE knockout mice submitted to folate deficiency showed a diminished oxidative buffering capacity against iron challenge in these animals. This is of particular interest since the apolipoprotein E4 allele is linked to Alzheimer's disease, implying that high Hcy levels may modulate the impact of genetic and environmental factors on the neurodegeneration characteristic of Alzheimer's disease [133].

Finally, there is also evidence that chronic treatment with Hcy elicits oxidative stress in lungs of rats, which could explain the chronic obstructive pulmonary disease observed in some patients with hyperhomocysteinemia [134].

Oxidative Stress Biomarkers in Homocystinuric Patients

Studies in humans have been performed focusing on the role of hyperhomocysteinemia on atherosclerosis and cardiovascular dysfunction. It was evidenced that moderate hyperhomocysteinemia induced by methionine overload in healthy humans induces endothelial dysfunction in conduit and resistance vessels that was prevented by ascorbic acid administration [135]. Furthermore, hyperhomocysteinemic patients who suffered surgery for peripheral arterial disease showed increased levels of free Hcy and protein-bound Hcy, as well as decreased cysteine levels in plasma [100]. Taken together, these data suggest that altered redox status in plasma may be involved in arteriosclerosis found in hyperhomocysteinemic patients.

Garcia and colleagues [136] also observed a correlation between elevated Hcy plasma levels with increased lipid peroxidation and methahaemoglobin levels, as well as with decreased δ-aminolevulinic acid dehydratase in cardiac patients, indicating that high Hcy levels are involved in the pathophysiology of cardiovascular diseases.

Other reports evidenced augmented MDA levels, carbonyl formation, DNA damage and a reduction of total antioxidant status in plasma and leukocytes of homocystinuric patients at diagnosis. However, the treatment with a protein restricted diet supplemented with pyridoxine, folate, betaine and vitamin B_{12} reverted lipid peroxidation and protein carbonylation, as well as the elevated levels of Hcy and methionine in plasma [137, 138].

CONCLUSION AND FUTURE DIRECTIONS

Several reports have shown a role for oxidative stress in the pathophysiology of the tissue damage, particularly the CNS abnormalities, in various IEM. These observations were mainly drawn from experimental animal *in vitro* and *in vivo* studies performed in rodent models, although there is a growing body of evidence obtained from biological fluids (in blood and urine) and tissues from affected patients. It is expected that more human studies conducted in plasma, urine and other tissues from these patients, such as fibroblasts and muscle biopsies, clarify the involvement of free radicals in the pathophysiology of IEM, as well as the underlying mechanisms of redox signaling implicated in the generation of reactive species observed in these diseases. We hope that in the near future new adjuvant therapies based on antioxidants or compounds targeted to specific molecules or signaling pathways may improve the treatments for these disorders ameliorating or preventing symptoms.

REFERENCES

[1]   Childs B, Valle D, Jimenez-Sanchez G. The Inborn Error and Biochemical Individuality. In: Scriver CR, Beaudet AL, Sly WS, Valle D, eds. *The Metabolic and Molecular Basis of Inherited Disease*. 8th ed: McGraw-Hill Professional; 2001.

[2]   Saudubray JM, Desguerre I, Sedel F, Charpentier C. A Clinical Approach to Inherited Metabolic Diseases. In: Fernandes J, Saudubray JM, van den Berghe G, Walter JH, eds. *Inborn Metabolic Diseases Dignosis and Treatment*. 4th ed2006:3-48.

[3]   Saudubray JM, Sedel F, Walter JH. Clinical approach to treatable inborn metabolic diseases: an introduction. *Journal of Inherited Metabolic Disease* 2006; 29:261-74.

[4]   Wilcken B. Newborn screening: how are we travelling, and where should we be going? *Journal of Inherited Metabolic Disease* 2011; 34:569-74.

[5]   Wilcken B, Wiley V, Hammond J, Carpenter K. Screening newborns for inborn errors of metabolism by tandem mass spectrometry. *The New England Journal of Medicine* 2003; 348:2304-12.

[6]   Schwartz IV, Souza CF, Giugliani R. Treatment of inborn errors of metabolism. *Jornal de Pediatria* 2008; 84:S8-19.

[7]   Camp KM, Lloyd-Puryear MA, Huntington KL. Nutritional treatment for inborn errors of metabolism: indications, regulations, and availability of medical foods and dietary supplements using phenylketonuria as an example. *Molecular Genetics and Metabolism* 2012; 107:3-9.

[8]   Kolker S, Sauer SW, Surtees RA, Leonard JV. The aetiology of neurological complications of organic acidaemias--a role for the blood-brain barrier. *Journal of Inherited Metabolic Disease* 2006; 29:701-4; discussion 5-6.

[9]   Salmi H, Leonard JV, Lapatto R. Patients with organic acidaemias have an altered thiol status. *Acta Paediatrica* 2012; 101:e505-8.

[10]   Mitchell JJ, Trakadis YJ, Scriver CR. Phenylalanine hydroxylase deficiency. *Genetics in medicine : official journal of the American College of Medical Genetics* 2011; 13: 697-707.

[11]   Donlon J, Levy H, Scriver CR. Hyperphenylalaninemia: Phenylalanine Hydroxylase Deficiency. In: Scriver CR, Beaudet AL, Sly WS, Valle D, eds. *The Metabolic and Molecular Bases of Inherited Disease*: McGraw-Hill Professional; 2001.

[12]   Camp KM, Parisi MA, Acosta PB, et al. Phenylketonuria Scientific Review Conference: State of the science and future research needs. *Molecular Genetics and Metabolism* 2014.

[13]   Araujo GC, Christ SE, Steiner RD, et al. Response monitoring in children with phenylketonuria. *Neuropsychology* 2009; 23:130-4.

[14]   Hanley WB, Lee AW, Hanley AJ, et al. "Hypotyrosinemia" in phenylketonuria. *Molecular Genetics and Metabolism* 2000; 69:286-94.

[15]   Guthrie R, Susi A. A Simple Phenylalanine Method for Detecting Phenylketonuria in Large Populations of Newborn Infants. *Pediatrics* 1963; 32:338-43.

[16]   Kienzle Hagen ME, Pederzolli CD, Sgaravatti AM, et al. Experimental hyperphenylalaninemia provokes oxidative stress in rat brain. *Biochimica et Biophysica Acta* 2002; 1586:344-52.

[17] Fernandes CG, Leipnitz G, Seminotti B, et al. Experimental evidence that phenylalanine provokes oxidative stress in hippocampus and cerebral cortex of developing rats. *Cellular and Molecular Neurobiology* 2010; 30:317-26.

[18] Rosa AP, Jacques CE, Moraes TB, Wannmacher CM, Dutra Ade M, Dutra-Filho CS. Phenylpyruvic acid decreases glucose-6-phosphate dehydrogenase activity in rat brain. *Cellular and Molecular Neurobiology* 2012; 32:1113-8.

[19] Moraes TB, Jacques CE, Rosa AP, et al. Role of catalase and superoxide dismutase activities on oxidative stress in the brain of a phenylketonuria animal model and the effect of lipoic acid. *Cellular and Molecular Neurobiology* 2013; 33:253-60.

[20] Lu L, Gu X, Li D, Liang L, Zhao Z, Gao J. Mechanisms regulating superoxide generation in experimental models of phenylketonuria: an essential role of NADPH oxidase. *Molecular Genetics and Metabolism* 2011; 104:241-8.

[21] Mazzola PN, Terra M, Rosa AP, et al. Regular exercise prevents oxidative stress in the brain of hyperphenylalaninemic rats. *Metabolic Brain Disease* 2011; 26:291-7.

[22] Berti SL, Nasi GM, Garcia C, et al. Pyruvate and creatine prevent oxidative stress and behavioral alterations caused by phenylalanine administration into hippocampus of rats. *Metabolic Brain Disease* 2012; 27:79-89.

[23] Martinez-Cruz F, Pozo D, Osuna C, Espinar A, Marchante C, Guerrero JM. Oxidative stress induced by phenylketonuria in the rat: Prevention by melatonin, vitamin E, and vitamin C. *Journal of Neuroscience Research* 2002; 69:550-8.

[24] Martinez-Cruz F, Osuna C, Guerrero JM. Mitochondrial damage induced by fetal hyperphenylalaninemia in the rat brain and liver: its prevention by melatonin, Vitamin E, and Vitamin C. *Neuroscience Letters* 2006; 392:1-4.

[25] Ercal N, Aykin-Burns N, Gurer-Orhan H, McDonald JD. Oxidative stress in a phenylketonuria animal model. *Free Radical Biology & Medicine* 2002; 32:906-11.

[26] He Y, Gu X, Lu L, Liang L, Gao J, Zhang X. NOX, the main regulator in oxidative stress in experimental models of phenylketonuria? *Journal of Pediatric Endocrinology & Metabolism* 2013; 26:675-82.

[27] Sirtori LR, Dutra-Filho CS, Fitarelli D, et al. Oxidative stress in patients with phenylketonuria. *Biochimica et Biophysica Acta* 2005; 1740:68-73.

[28] Sanayama Y, Nagasaka H, Takayanagi M, et al. Experimental evidence that phenylalanine is strongly associated to oxidative stress in adolescents and adults with phenylketonuria. *Molecular Genetics and Metabolism* 2011; 103:220-5.

[29] van Bakel MM, Printzen G, Wermuth B, Wiesmann UN. Antioxidant and thyroid hormone status in selenium-deficient phenylketonuric and hyperphenylalaninemic patients. *The Journal of Clinical Nutrition* 2000; 72:976-81.

[30] Sitta A, Barschak AG, Deon M, et al. Investigation of oxidative stress parameters in treated phenylketonuric patients. *Metabolic Brain Disease* 2006; 21:287-96.

[31] Sitta A, Manfredini V, Biasi L, et al. Evidence that DNA damage is associated to phenylalanine blood levels in leukocytes from phenylketonuric patients. *Mutation Research* 2009; 679:13-6.

[32] Schulpis KH, Papastamataki M, Stamou H, Papassotiriou I, Margeli A. The effect of diet on total antioxidant status, ceruloplasmin, transferrin and ferritin serum levels in phenylketonuric children. *Acta Paediatrica* 2010; 99:1565-70.

[33] Rottoli A, Lista G, Zecchini G, Butte C, Longhi R. Plasma selenium levels in treated phenylketonuric patients. *Journal of Inherited Metabolic Disease* 1985;8 Suppl 2: 127-8.

[34] Darling G, Mathias P, O'Regan M, Naughten E. Serum selenium levels in individuals on PKU diets. *Journal of Inherited Metabolic Disease* 1992; 15:769-73.

[35] Sierra C, Vilaseca MA, Moyano D, et al. Antioxidant status in hyperphenylalaninemia. *Clinica Chimica Acta* 1998; 276:1-9.

[36] Colome C, Artuch R, Vilaseca MA, et al. Lipophilic antioxidants in patients with phenylketonuria. *The Journal of Clinical Nutrition* 2003; 77:185-8.

[37] Sitta A, Vanzin CS, Biancini GB, et al. Evidence that L-carnitine and selenium supplementation reduces oxidative stress in phenylketonuric patients. *Cellular and Molecular Neurobiology* 2011; 31:429-36.

[38] Chuang DT, Max Wynn R, Shih VE. Maple Syrup Urine Disease. In: Scriver CR, Beaudet AL, Sly WS, Valle D, eds. *The Metabolic and Molecular Bases of Inherited Disease.* 8th ed: McGraw-Hill Professional; 2001.

[39] Treacy E, Clow CL, Reade TR, Chitayat D, Mamer OA, Scriver CR. Maple syrup urine disease: interrelations between branched-chain amino-, oxo- and hydroxyacids; implications for treatment; associations with CNS dysmyelination. *Journal of Inherited Metabolic Disease* 1992;15:121-35.

[40] Quental S, Vilarinho L, Martins E, et al. Incidence of maple syrup urine disease in Portugal. *Molecular Genetics and Metabolism* 2010;100:385-7.

[41] Schadewaldt P, Wendel U. Metabolism of branched-chain amino acids in maple syrup urine disease. *European Journal of Pediatrics* 1997;156 Suppl 1:S62-6.

[42] Schonberger S, Schweiger B, Schwahn B, Schwarz M, Wendel U. Dysmyelination in the brain of adolescents and young adults with maple syrup urine disease. *Molecular Genetics and Metabolism* 2004;82:69-75.

[43] Brismar J, Aqeel A, Brismar G, Coates R, Gascon G, Ozand P. Maple syrup urine disease: findings on CT and MR scans of the brain in 10 infants. *AJNR American Journal of Neuroradiology* 1990;11:1219-28.

[44] Kamei A, Takashima S, Chan F, Becker LE. Abnormal dendritic development in maple syrup urine disease. *Pediatric Neurology* 1992;8:145-7.

[45] Sitta A, Ribas GS, Mescka CP, Barschak AG, Wajner M, Vargas CR. Neurological damage in MSUD: the role of oxidative stress. *Cellular and Molecular Neurobiology* 2014;34:157-65.

[46] Fontella FU, Gassen E, Pulrolnik V, et al. Stimulation of lipid peroxidation *in vitro* in rat brain by the metabolites accumulating in maple syrup urine disease. *Metabolic Brain Disease* 2002;17:47-54.

[47] Bridi R, Araldi J, Sgarbi MB, et al. Induction of oxidative stress in rat brain by the metabolites accumulating in maple syrup urine disease. *International Journal of Developmental Neuroscience* 2003;21:327-32.

[48] Bridi R, Braun CA, Zorzi GK, et al. alpha-keto acids accumulating in maple syrup urine disease stimulate lipid peroxidation and reduce antioxidant defences in cerebral cortex from young rats. *Metabolic Brain Disease* 2005;20:155-67.

[49] Funchal C, Latini A, Jacques-Silva MC, et al. Morphological alterations and induction of oxidative stress in glial cells caused by the branched-chain alpha-keto acids

accumulating in maple syrup urine disease. *Neurochemistry International* 2006;49:640-50.

[50] Funchal C, Tramontina F, Quincozes dos Santos A, et al. Effect of the branched-chain alpha-keto acids accumulating in maple syrup urine disease on S100B release from glial cells. *Journal of the Neurological Sciences* 2007;260:87-94.

[51] de Lima Pelaez P, Funchal C, Loureiro SO, et al. Branched-chain amino acids accumulating in maple syrup urine disease induce morphological alterations in C6 glioma cells probably through reactive species. *International Journal of Developmental Neuroscience* 2007;25:181-9.

[52] Mescka C, Moraes T, Rosa A, et al. *In vivo* neuroprotective effect of L-carnitine against oxidative stress in maple syrup urine disease. *Metabolic Brain Disease* 2011; 26:21-8.

[53] Scaini G, Teodorak BP, Jeremias IC, et al. Antioxidant administration prevents memory impairment in an animal model of maple syrup urine disease. *Behavioral Brain Research* 2012;231:92-6.

[54] Scaini G, Jeremias GC, Furlanetto CB, et al. Behavioral Responses in Rats Submitted to Chronic Administration of Branched-Chain Amino Acids. *JIMD Reports* 2013.

[55] Scaini G, de Rochi N, Jeremias IC, et al. Evaluation of acetylcholinesterase in an animal model of maple syrup urine disease. *Molecular Neurobiology* 2012;45:279-86.

[56] Scaini G, Jeremias IC, Morais MO, et al. DNA damage in an animal model of maple syrup urine disease. *Molecular Genetics and Metabolism* 2012;106:169-74.

[57] de Franceschi ID, Rieger E, Vargas AP, et al. Effect of leucine administration to female rats during pregnancy and lactation on oxidative stress and enzymes activities of phosphoryltransfer network in cerebral cortex and hippocampus of the offspring. *Neurochemical Research* 2013;38:632-43.

[58] Barschak AG, Sitta A, Deon M, et al. Oxidative stress in plasma from maple syrup urine disease patients during treatment. *Metabolic Brain Disease* 2008;23:71-80.

[59] Lombeck I, Kasperek K, Harbisch HD, et al. The selenium state of children. II. Selenium content of serum, whole blood, hair and the activity of erythrocyte glutathione peroxidase in dietetically treated patients with phenylketonuria and maple-syrup-urine disease. *European Journal of Pediatrics* 1978;128:213-23.

[60] Borglund M, Sjoblad S, Akesson B. Effect of selenium supplementation on the distribution of selenium among plasma proteins of a patient with maple syrup urine disease. *European Journal of Pediatrics* 1989;148:767-9.

[61] Barschak AG, Sitta A, Deon M, et al. Erythrocyte glutathione peroxidase activity and plasma selenium concentration are reduced in maple syrup urine disease patients during treatment. *International Journal of Developmental Neuroscience* 2007;25:335-8.

[62] Mescka CP, Wayhs CA, Vanzin CS, et al. Protein and lipid damage in maple syrup urine disease patients: l-carnitine effect. *International Journal of Developmental Neuroscience* 2013;31:21-4.

[63] Chace DH, DiPerna JC, Kalas TA, Johnson RW, Naylor EW. Rapid diagnosis of methylmalonic and propionic acidemias: quantitative tandem mass spectrometric analysis of propionylcarnitine in filter-paper blood specimens obtained from newborns. *Clinical Chemistry* 2001;47:2040-4.

[64] Deodato F, Boenzi S, Santorelli FM, Dionisi-Vici C. Methylmalonic and propionic aciduria. *American Journal of Medical Genetics Part C, Seminars in Medical Genetics* 2006;142C:104-12.

[65] Fenton WA, Gravel RA, Rosenblatt DS. Disorders of Propionate and Methylmalonate Metabolism. In: Scriver CR, Beaudet AL, Sly WS, Valle D, eds. *The Metabolic & Molecular Bases of Inherited Disease*: McGraw-Hill Professional; 2001.

[66] Chandler RJ, Venditti CP. Genetic and genomic systems to study methylmalonic acidemia. *Molecular Genetics and Metabolism* 2005;86:34-43.

[67] Shevell MI, Matiaszuk N, Ledley FD, Rosenblatt DS. Varying neurological phenotypes among muto and mut- patients with methylmalonylCoA mutase deficiency. *Am. J. Med. Genet.* 1993;45:619-24.

[68] Baumgarter ER, Viardot C. Long-term follow-up of 77 patients with isolated methylmalonic acidaemia. *Journal of Inherited Metabolic Disease* 1995;18:138-42.

[69] Radmanesh A, Zaman T, Ghanaati H, Molaei S, Robertson RL, Zamani AA. Methylmalonic acidemia: brain imaging findings in 52 children and a review of the literature. *Pediatric Radiology* 2008;38:1054-61.

[70] Brismar J, Ozand PT. CT and MR of the brain in disorders of the propionate and methylmalonate metabolism. *AJNR American Journal of Neuroradiology* 1994; 15: 1459-73.

[71] Morath MA, Okun JG, Muller IB, et al. Neurodegeneration and chronic renal failure in methylmalonic aciduria--a pathophysiological approach. *Journal of Inherited Metabolic Disease* 2008;31:35-43.

[72] Sauer SW, Opp S, Mahringer A, et al. Glutaric aciduria type I and methylmalonic aciduria: simulation of cerebral import and export of accumulating neurotoxic dicarboxylic acids in *in vitro* models of the blood-brain barrier and the choroid plexus. *Biochimica et Biophysica Acta* 2010;1802:552-60.

[73] Wajner M, Latini A, Wyse AT, Dutra-Filho CS. The role of oxidative damage in the neuropathology of organic acidurias: insights from animal studies. *Journal of Inherited Metabolic Disease* 2004;27:427-48.

[74] Wajner M, Goodman SI. Disruption of mitochondrial homeostasis in organic acidurias: insights from human and animal studies. *Journal of Bioenergetics and Biomembranes* 2011; 43:31-8.

[75] Maciel EN, Kowaltowski AJ, Schwalm FD, et al. Mitochondrial permeability transition in neuronal damage promoted by Ca^{2+} and respiratory chain complex II inhibition. *Journal of neurochemistry* 2004;90:1025-35.

[76] Wajner M, Coelho JC. Neurological dysfunction in methylmalonic acidaemia is probably related to the inhibitory effect of methylmalonate on brain energy production. *Journal of Inherited Metabolic Disease* 1997;20:761-8.

[77] Fontella FU, Pulrolnik V, Gassen E, et al. Propionic and L-methylmalonic acids induce oxidative stress in brain of young rats. *Neuroreport* 2000;11:541-4.

[78] Pettenuzzo LF, Schuck PF, Wyse AT, et al. Ascorbic acid prevents water maze behavioral deficits caused by early postnatal methylmalonic acid administration in the rat. *Brain Research* 2003;976:234-42.

[79] Fernandes CG, Borges CG, Seminotti B, et al. Experimental evidence that methylmalonic acid provokes oxidative damage and compromises antioxidant defenses in nerve terminal and striatum of young rats. *Cellular and Molecular Neurobiology* 2011;31:775-85.

[80] Schuck PF, Rosa RB, Pettenuzzo LF, et al. Inhibition of mitochondrial creatine kinase activity from rat cerebral cortex by methylmalonic acid. *Neurochemistry International* 2004;45:661-7.

[81] Wyse AT, Streck EL, Barros SV, Brusque AM, Zugno AI, Wajner M. Methylmalonate administration decreases Na+,K+-ATPase activity in cerebral cortex of rats. *Neuroreport* 2000;11:2331-4.

[82] Ribeiro LR, Della-Pace ID, de Oliveira Ferreira AP, et al. Chronic administration of methylmalonate on young rats alters neuroinflammatory markers and spatial memory. *Immunobiology* 2013;218:1175-83.

[83] Ribeiro MC, de Avila DS, Schneider CY, et al. alpha-Tocopherol protects against pentylenetetrazol- and methylmalonate-induced convulsions. *Epilepsy Research* 2005; 66:185-94.

[84] Viegas CM, Zanatta A, Grings M, et al. Disruption of redox homeostasis and brain damage caused in vivo by methylmalonic acid and ammonia in cerebral cortex and striatum of developing rats. *Free Radical Research* 2014;48:659-69.

[85] Fighera MR, Queiroz CM, Stracke MP, et al. Ascorbic acid and alpha-tocopherol attenuate methylmalonic acid-induced convulsions. *Neuroreport* 1999;10:2039-43.

[86] Furian AF, Fighera MR, Oliveira MS, et al. Methylene blue prevents methylmalonate-induced seizures and oxidative damage in rat striatum. *Neurochemistry International* 2007; 50:164-71.

[87] Royes LF, Fighera MR, Furian AF, et al. Effectiveness of creatine monohydrate on seizures and oxidative damage induced by methylmalonate. *Pharmacology Biochemistry and Behavior* 2006;83:136-44.

[88] Royes LF, Fighera MR, Furian AF, et al. Involvement of NO in the convulsive behavior and oxidative damage induced by the intrastriatal injection of methylmalonate. *Neuroscience Letters* 2005;376:116-20.

[89] Ribeiro LR, Fighera MR, Oliveira MS, et al. Methylmalonate-induced seizures are attenuated in inducible nitric oxide synthase knockout mice. *International Journal of Developmental Neuroscience* 2009;27:157-63.

[90] Schuck PF, Januario SB, Simon KR, et al. Acute renal failure potentiates brain energy dysfunction elicited by methylmalonic acid. *International Journal of Developmental Neuroscience* 2013;31:245-9.

[91] Andrade VM, Dal Pont HS, Leffa DD, et al. Methylmalonic acid administration induces DNA damage in rat brain and kidney. *Molecular and Cellular Biochemistry* 2014; 391:137-45.

[92] Richard E, Monteoliva L, Juarez S, et al. Quantitative analysis of mitochondrial protein expression in methylmalonic acidemia by two-dimensional difference gel electrophoresis. *Journal of Proteome Research* 2006;5:1602-10.

[93] Richard E, Alvarez-Barrientos A, Perez B, Desviat LR, Ugarte M. Methylmalonic acidaemia leads to increased production of reactive oxygen species and induction of apoptosis through the mitochondrial/caspase pathway. *The Journal of Pathology* 2007; 213:453-61.

[94] Richard E, Jorge-Finnigan A, Garcia-Villoria J, et al. Genetic and cellular studies of oxidative stress in methylmalonic aciduria (MMA) cobalamin deficiency type C (cblC) with homocystinuria (MMACHC). *Human Mutation* 2009;30:1558-66.

[95] Treacy E, Arbour L, Chessex P, et al. Glutathione deficiency as a complication of methylmalonic acidemia: response to high doses of ascorbate. *The Journal of Pediatrics* 1996; 129:445-8.

[96] Ribas GS, Manfredini V, de Marco MG, et al. Prevention by L-carnitine of DNA damage induced by propionic and L-methylmalonic acids in human peripheral leukocytes *in vitro*. *Mutation Research* 2010;702:123-8.

[97] Seshadri S, Beiser A, Selhub J, et al. Plasma homocysteine as a risk factor for dementia and Alzheimer's disease. *The New England Journal of Medicine* 2002;346:476-83.

[98] Welch GN, Loscalzo J. Homocysteine and atherothrombosis. *The New England Journal of Medicine* 1998;338:1042-50.

[99] Kolluru GK, Shen X, Bir SC, Kevil CG. Hydrogen sulfide chemical biology: pathophysiological roles and detection. *Nitric oxide: Biology and Chemistry* 2013;35:5-20.

[100] Mansoor MA, Ueland PM, Svardal AM. Redox status and protein binding of plasma homocysteine and other aminothiols in patients with hyperhomocysteinemia due to cobalamin deficiency. *The Journal of Clinical Nutrition* 1994;59:631-5.

[101] Mudd SH. Hypermethioninemias of genetic and non-genetic origin: A review. *American Journal of Medical Genetics Part C, Seminars in Medical Genetics* 2011; 157C:3-32.

[102] Petras M, Tatarkova Z, Kovalska M, et al. Hyperhomocysteinemia as a risk factor for the neuronal system disorders. *Journal of Physiology and Pharmacology* 2014; 65:15-23.

[103] Herrmann W, Obeid R. Homocysteine: a biomarker in neurodegenerative diseases. *Clinical Chemistry and Laboratory Medicine* 2011;49:435-41.

[104] Obeid R, Herrmann W. Mechanisms of homocysteine neurotoxicity in neurodegenerative diseases with special reference to dementia. *FEBS Letters* 2006; 580:2994-3005.

[105] Piazza F, Galimberti G, Conti E, et al. Increased tissue factor pathway inhibitor and homocysteine in Alzheimer's disease. *Neurobiology of Aging* 2012;33:226-33.

[106] Zhuo JM, Wang H, Pratico D. Is hyperhomocysteinemia an Alzheimer's disease (AD) risk factor, an AD marker, or neither? *Trends in Pharmacological Sciences* 2011; 32:562-71.

[107] Li L, Cao D, Desmond R, et al. Cognitive performance and plasma levels of homocysteine, vitamin B12, folate and lipids in patients with Alzheimer disease. *Dementia and Geriatric Cognitive Disorders* 2008;26:384-90.

[108] Surtees R, Bowron A, Leonard J. Cerebrospinal fluid and plasma total homocysteine and related metabolites in children with cystathionine beta-synthase deficiency: the effect of treatment. *Pediatric Research* 1997;42:577-82.

[109] Loscalzo J. The oxidant stress of hyperhomocyst(e)inemia. *The Journal of Clinical Investigation* 1996;98:5-7.

[110] Upchurch GR, Jr., Welch GN, Fabian AJ, Pigazzi A, Keaney JF, Jr., Loscalzo J. Stimulation of endothelial nitric oxide production by homocyst(e)ine. *Atherosclerosis* 1997; 132:177-85.

[111] Upchurch GR, Jr., Welch GN, Fabian AJ, et al. Homocyst(e)ine decreases bioavailable nitric oxide by a mechanism involving glutathione peroxidase. *The Journal of Biological Chemistry* 1997;272:17012-7.

[112] Yan SK, Chang T, Wang H, Wu L, Wang R, Meng QH. Effects of hydrogen sulfide on homocysteine-induced oxidative stress in vascular smooth muscle cells. *Biochemical and Biophysical Research Communications* 2006;351:485-91.

[113] Ho PI, Ashline D, Dhitavat S, et al. Folate deprivation induces neurodegeneration: roles of oxidative stress and increased homocysteine. *Neurobiology of Disease* 2003;14:32-42.

[114] Tjiattas L, Ortiz DO, Dhivant S, Mitton K, Rogers E, Shea TB. Folate deficiency and homocysteine induce toxicity in cultured dorsal root ganglion neurons via cytosolic calcium accumulation. *Aging Cell* 2004;3:71-6.

[115] Racek J, Rusnakova H, Trefil L, Siala KK. The influence of folate and antioxidants on homocysteine levels and oxidative stress in patients with hyperlipidemia and hyperhomocysteinemia. *Physiological Research* 2005;54:87-95.

[116] White AR, Huang X, Jobling MF, et al. Homocysteine potentiates copper- and amyloid beta peptide-mediated toxicity in primary neuronal cultures: possible risk factors in the Alzheimer's-type neurodegenerative pathways. *Journal of Neurochemistry* 2001; 76: 1509-20.

[117] Kruman, II, Culmsee C, Chan SL, et al. Homocysteine elicits a DNA damage response in neurons that promotes apoptosis and hypersensitivity to excitotoxicity. *The Journal of Neuroscience* 2000;20:6920-6.

[118] Lafon-Cazal M, Pietri S, Culcasi M, Bockaert J. NMDA-dependent superoxide production and neurotoxicity. *Nature* 1993;364:535-7.

[119] Lipton SA, Kim WK, Choi YB, et al. Neurotoxicity associated with dual actions of homocysteine at the N-methyl-D-aspartate receptor. *Proceedings of the National Academy of Sciences of the United States of America* 1997; 94:5923-8.

[120] Jara-Prado A, Ortega-Vazquez A, Martinez-Ruano L, Rios C, Santamaria A. Homocysteine-induced brain lipid peroxidation: effects of NMDA receptor blockade, antioxidant treatment, and nitric oxide synthase inhibition. *Neurotoxicity Research* 2003; 5:237-43.

[121] Streck EL, Vieira PS, Wannmacher CM, Dutra-Filho CS, Wajner M, Wyse AT. *In vitro* effect of homocysteine on some parameters of oxidative stress in rat hippocampus. *Metabolic Brain Disease* 2003;18:147-54.

[122] Matte C, Monteiro SC, Calcagnotto T, Bavaresco CS, Netto CA, Wyse AT. *In vivo* and *in vitro* effects of homocysteine on Na+, K+-ATPase activity in parietal, prefrontal and cingulate cortex of young rats. *International Journal of Developmental Neuroscience* 2004;22:185-90.

[123] Loureiro SO, Romao L, Alves T, et al. Homocysteine induces cytoskeletal remodeling and production of reactive oxygen species in cultured cortical astrocytes. *Brain Research* 2010; 1355:151-64.

[124] da Cunha AA, Scherer E, da Cunha MJ, et al. Acute hyperhomocysteinemia alters the coagulation system and oxidative status in the blood of rats. *Molecular and Cellular Biochemistry* 2012; 360:205-14.

[125] Wyse AT, Zugno AI, Streck EL, et al. Inhibition of Na(+),K(+)-ATPase activity in hippocampus of rats subjected to acute administration of homocysteine is prevented by vitamins E and C treatment. *Neurochemical Research* 2002;27:1685-9.

[126] Matte C, Scherer EB, Stefanello FM, et al. Concurrent folate treatment prevents Na+,K+-ATPase activity inhibition and memory impairments caused by chronic hyperhomocysteinemia during rat development. *International Journal of Developmental Neuroscience* 2007;25:545-52.

[127] Kamat PK, Kalani A, Givvimani S, Sathnur PB, Tyagi SC, Tyagi N. Hydrogen sulfide attenuates neurodegeneration and neurovascular dysfunction induced by intracerebral-administered homocysteine in mice. *Neuroscience* 2013;252:302-19.

[128] Baydas G, Ozer M, Yasar A, Tuzcu M, Koz ST. Melatonin improves learning and memory performances impaired by hyperhomocysteinemia in rats. *Brain Research* 2005; 1046:187-94.

[129] Baydas G, Ozveren F, Akdemir I, Tuzcu M, Yasar A. Learning and memory deficits in rats induced by chronic thinner exposure are reversed by melatonin. *Journal of Pineal Research* 2005;39:50-6.

[130] Baydas G, Reiter RJ, Akbulut M, Tuzcu M, Tamer S. Melatonin inhibits neural apoptosis induced by homocysteine in hippocampus of rats via inhibition of cytochrome c translocation and caspase-3 activation and by regulating pro- and anti-apoptotic protein levels. *Neuroscience* 2005;135:879-86.

[131] da Cunha AA, Ferreira AG, Loureiro SO, et al. Chronic hyperhomocysteinemia increases inflammatory markers in hippocampus and serum of rats. *Neurochemical Research* 2012;37:1660-9.

[132] Au-Yeung KK, Woo CW, Sung FL, Yip JC, Siow YL, O K. Hyperhomocysteinemia activates nuclear factor-kappaB in endothelial cells via oxidative stress. *Circulation Research* 2004;94:28-36.

[133] Shea TB, Rogers E. Folate quenches oxidative damage in brains of apolipoprotein E-deficient mice: augmentation by vitamin E. *Brain Research Molecular Brain Research* 2002;108:1-6.

[134] da Cunha AA, Ferreira AG, da Cunha MJ, et al. Chronic hyperhomocysteinemia induces oxidative damage in the rat lung. *Molecular and Cellular Biochemistry* 2011; 358:153-60.

[135] Kanani PM, Sinkey CA, Browning RL, Allaman M, Knapp HR, Haynes WG. Role of oxidant stress in endothelial dysfunction produced by experimental hyperhomocyst(e)inemia in humans. *Circulation* 1999;100:1161-8.

[136] Garcia SC, Wyse AT, Valentini J, et al. Butyrylcholinesterase activity is reduced in haemodialysis patients: is there association with hyperhomocysteinemia and/or oxidative stress? *Clinical Biochemistry* 2008;41:474-9.

[137] Vanzin CS, Biancini GB, Sitta A, et al. Experimental evidence of oxidative stress in plasma of homocystinuric patients: a possible role for homocysteine. Molecular *Genetics and Metabolism* 2011;104:112-7.

[138] Vanzin CS, Manfredini V, Marinho AE, et al. Homocysteine contribution to DNA damage in cystathionine beta-synthase-deficient patients. *Gene* 2014;539:270-4.

In: Reactive Oxygen Species, Lipid Peroxidation …
Editor: Angel Catalá

ISBN: 978-1-63321-886-4
© 2015 Nova Science Publishers, Inc.

Chapter 11

LIPID PEROXIDATION OF PHOSPHOLIPIDS IN RETINAL MEMBRANES AND IN LIPOSOMES MADE OF RETINAL LIPIDS: SIMILARITIES AND DIFFERENCES

Angel Catalá[*]

Instituto de Investigaciones Fisicoquímicas Teóricas y Aplicadas,
(INIFTA-CCT La Plata-CONICET), Facultad de Ciencias Exactas,
Universidad Nacional de La Plata, Argentina

ABSTRACT

The *retina* is the *neurosensorial tissue* of the *eye*. It is very rich in membranes and, therefore, in polyunsaturated fatty acids. Oxygen radicals participate in a variety of eye pathological processes because reactive oxygen species production induces the lipid peroxyl radical formation. This specie initiates chain reaction of lipid peroxidation what can injure the retina, especially the membranes that play important roles in visual function. Furthermore, bio-molecules such as proteins or amino lipids can be covalently modified by lipid decomposition products. In retinal membranes, peroxidation of lipids is also usually accompanied by oxidation of membrane proteins. In consequence, lipid peroxidation may alter the arrangement of proteins in bilayers and by that interfere with their physiological role on the membrane function. In this chapter, I review a series of studies on the lipid peroxidation of phospholipids in retinal membranes and in liposomes made of retinal lipids. Particular emphasis is placed on the molecular changes of very long chain polyunsaturated fatty acids associated with protein modifications during peroxidation of photoreceptor membranes. Furthermore we suggest the use of liposomes as a tool to analyze peroxidation of retinal lipids. Conjugated dienes formed from the double-bond rearrangement of oxidized PUFAs, and TBARS products derived from the breakdown of these fatty acids located in phospholipids can be analyzed during progress of lipid peroxidation of sonicated and non-sonicated liposomes made of retinal lipids in different aqueous media using Fe^{2+} and Fe^{3+} as initiators.

[*] Tel.: 54-221-425-7430 54-221-425-7291 (Ext. 105), Fax 54-221-425- 4642, E-mail: catala@inifta.unlp.edu.ar.
The author is Member of National Council of Scientific and Technical Research (CONICET) Argentina.

ABBREVIATIONS

4-HHE	4-hydroxy-2-hexenal
4-HNE	4-hydroxy-2-nonenal
AMD	Age- Related Macular Degeneration
C18:2 n-6	linoleic acid
C20:4 n-6	arachidonic acid
DHA; 22:6n3	docosahexaenoic acid
NSL	non-sonicated liposomes
PC	phosphatidylcholine
PE	phosphatidylethanolamine
Pls	phospholipids
PS	phosphatidylserine
PUFAs	polyunsaturated fatty acids
ROS	reactive oxygen species
ROSg	rod outer segment
SL	sonicated liposomes
TBARS	Thiobarbituric acid reactive substances

INTRODUCTION

Peroxidation of polyunsaturated fatty acids (PUFAs) in lipid bilayer membranes causes loss of fluidity, a fall in membrane potential, increased permeability to protons and calcium ions, and eventually, breakdown of cell membranes because of cellular deformities. The structural and functional integrity of the cell membranes is necessary for signal transduction, molecular recognition and transport, cellular metabolism, etc. The damage inflicted upon biological systems by reactive oxygen species have been implicated in numerous disease processes including inflammation, degenerative diseases tumor formation and involved in physiological phenomena such as aging. Initiation is the most important phase of lipid peroxidation especially in a cellular context; preventive therapy of lipid peroxidation-associated disease would target the initiation process. Indeed, many ocular disorders including glaucoma, cataracts, diabetic retinopathy and retinal degeneration have been attributed to lipid peroxidation processes. Because of intense exposure to light and oxygen and their high PUFA content which is prone to lipid peroxidation, the retina is highly susceptible to oxidative stress.

1. PHOSPHOLIPID SPECIES IN THE RETINA

Lipids represent approximately 20% of dry weight of bovine retina, of which about two-thirds are phospholipids. Although existing data are sparse, nonpolar lipids (i.e., acyl glycerides, sterols, and free fatty acids) account for about one-fourth of total retinal lipids. In general, ratio (wt/wt) of nonpolar lipid to phospholipids is in the range 0.3-0.5. Phosphatidylcholine (PC) (40-50 %) and phosphatidylethanolamine (PE) (30-35 %) account for the majority of phospholipids, with lesser amounts of phosphatidylserine (PS) (5-10 %), phosphatidylinositol (3-6 %) and sphingomyelin (2-8 %). Phosphatidic acid and cardiolipin are very minor phospholipid constituents [1].

2. VERY LONG CHAIN POLYUNSATURATED FATTY ACIDS IN THE RETINA

The major fatty acids (wt %) of bovine retinas are 16:0 ($\approx$25 %), 18:0 ($\approx$17 %), 18:1 ($\approx$17 %), and a 22-carbon polyunsaturated acid ($\approx$23 %) which was later identified as all-cis docosahexaenoic acid (22:6 n3) by Hands and Bartley [2]. Over 50 % of total bovine retina fatty acids are unsaturated, of which polyunsaturated acids account for at least 60 %.

Lipids containing the very long chain polyunsaturated fatty acid docosahexaenoic (DHA 22:6n3) are found at high concentrations in brain synaptosomes and the retina. They are essential for the development of the human brain [3].

The retina contains very high levels of 22:6n-3 representing the highest concentration of PUFAs of any vertebrate tissue [4]. In fact, 50% of all acyl chains in the outer segments of photoreceptors phospholipids (both sn-1 and sn-2) are 22:6n-3 (in PC, PE, and PS). Minor phospholipids, like phosphatidylinositol and phosphatidic acid, contain predominantly 20:4n-6 [5].

Thus, rod outer segments represent an excellent model to define the role of 22:6n-3 in membrane structure and function.

It had been suggested that polyunsaturation alters membrane properties that are critical for activity of integral receptor proteins [6]. Therefore, exploring the structure of polyunsaturated bilayers is a prerequisite for understanding how neural membranes function. It has been demonstrated that distribution of saturated and polyunsaturated hydrocarbon chains differs significantly, supporting the hypothesis that DHA-containing membranes are under considerable elastic stress that may influence the function of integral membrane proteins [7].

The rod outer segment (ROSg) membranes are essentially lipoprotein complexes. Rhodopsin, the major integral protein of ROSg, is surrounded by phospholipids highly enriched in docosahexaenoic acid (C22:6 n3), Figure 1.

Thus, ROSg membranes are highly susceptible to oxidative damage. The most careful studies on the effects of DHA-enriched diets have been performed on the visual system because DHA is a major constituent of photoreceptor membranes [7, 8]. In retina, a slight reduction in DHA content in membrane phospholipids has a critical effect on the renewal of new photoreceptor discs [9].

To produce gross DHA deficiency, it is necessary to deprive rats of n-3 fatty acids during development and throughout life for more than two generations. Supplementation of rats with an n-3 fatty acid enriched diet results in normalization of retinal and occipital cortex DHA contents. These changes are reflected in alterations in the electroretinogram and visual acuity tests in human and nonhuman primates [10].

Thus DHA induced changes in neural membrane fatty acid composition may lead to restoration of many membrane properties such as membrane fluidity, receptor affinities, ion fluxes, and activities of membrane-bound enzymes.

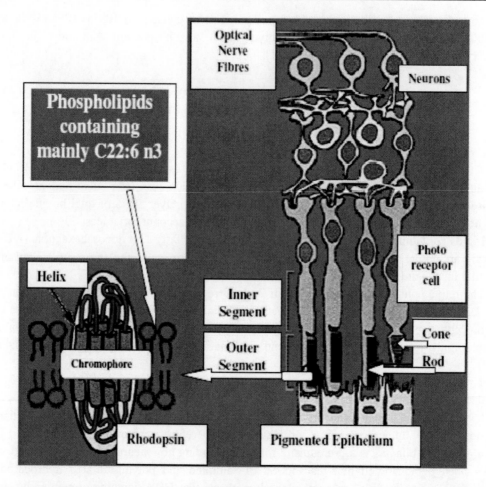

Figure 1. Schematic diagram of rhodopsin in the membrane of the photoreceptor cell.

3. ROD OUTER SEGMENTS OF RETINA ARE SUSCEPTIBLE TO LIPID PEROXIDATION BECAUSE OF THEIR HIGH CONTENT OF DOCOSAHEXAENOIC ACID

Oxidative stress has been proposed as a possible cause of the progression of AMD. [11–18]. The retina is particularly susceptible to oxidative stress because of its high metabolic activity, oxygen tension, and concentration of easily oxidized polyunsaturated fatty acids (PUFAs), as well as the presence of retinal pigments that generate reactive oxygen species when illuminated by light [19].

Rod outer segments (ROSg) of retina are susceptible to lipid peroxidation because of their high content of PUFAs, mainly docosahexaenoic acid (C22:6 n3) [20]. It has been suggested that lipid peroxidation participates in the oxidative damage leading to retinal degeneration. The lipid peroxidation process proceeds via radical chain reaction resulting in the formation of lipid hydroperoxides (LOOH). Lipid peroxidation is a complex system where the generation of the initiator molecule is followed by chain initiation, propagation, branching and termination reactions, Figure 2.

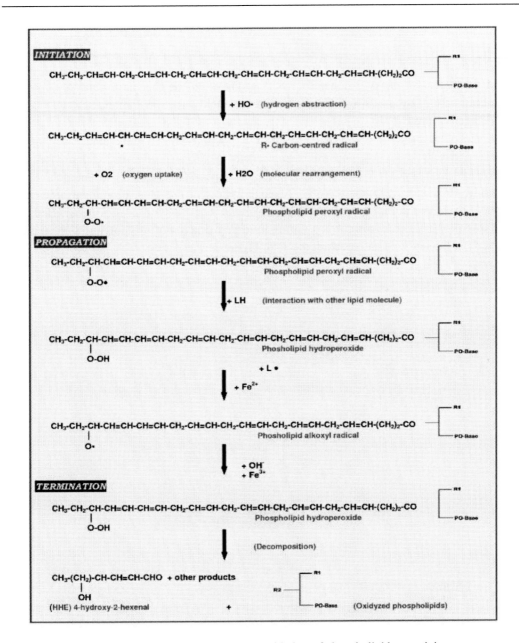

Figure 2. Chemical diagram of the steps in lipid peroxidation of phospholipids containing docosahexaenoic acid (22:6 n-3), R1 = fatty acid, R2 = fragmentation products of fatty acid oxidation.

4. PEROXIDATION OF LIPIDS IN RETINA IS ACCOMPANIED BY OXIDATION OF MEMBRANE PROTEINS

Lipids containing polyunsaturated fatty acids are susceptible to free radical–initiated oxidation and can contribute in chain reactions that amplify damage to bio-molecules as described above. Lipid peroxidation often occurs in response to oxidative stress, and a great diversity of aldehydes is formed when lipid hydroperoxides break down in biological systems. Some of these aldehydes are highly reactive and may be considered as second toxic messengers, which disseminate and augment initial free radical events. The aldehydes most intensively studied up to now are 4-hydroxy-2-nonenal, 4-hydroxy-2-hexenal, and malondialdehyde. 4-hydroxy-2-nonenal (HNE) is known to be the main aldehyde formed during lipid peroxidation of n-6 polyunsaturated fatty acids, such as linoleic acid C18:2 n-6 and arachidonic acid C20:4 n-6, [21].

On the other hand, lipid peroxidation of n-3 polyunsaturated fatty acids such as α-linolenic acid C18:3 n-3 and docosahexaenoic acid C22:6 n-3 generates a closely related compound, 4-hydroxy-2-hexenal (HHE), which is a potential mediator of mitochondrial permeability transition [22]. 4-hydroxy-2-alkenals represent the most prominent aldehydes substances generated during lipid peroxidation. Among them, 4-hydroxy-2-nonenal (HNE) is known to be the main aldehyde formed during lipid peroxidation of n-6 polyunsaturated fatty acids, such as linoleic acid and arachidonic acid, Figure 3.

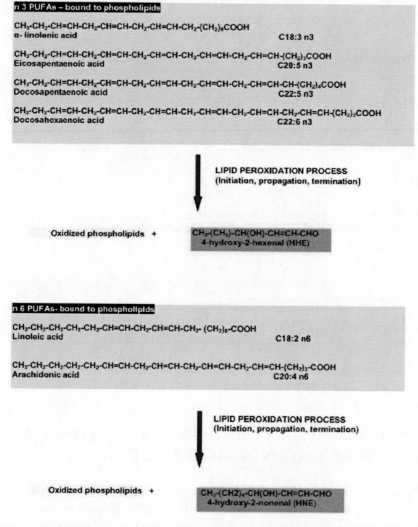

Figure 3. Schematic diagram of reactive hydroxy-alkenals generated during lipid peroxidation of n-3 and n-6 polyunsaturated fatty acids.

4-hydroxynonenal (HNE) was identified three decades ago as a cytotoxic aldehyde formed during the NADPH-Fe^{++} induced peroxidation of liver microsomal lipids [23]. Since then, a vast number of reports have been available, which sustain a function for this compound in a diversity of disease processes. HNE is considered as an indicator of oxidative stress and a probable contributing agent of several diseases.

5. THE RETINA AS A MODEL TO STUDY LIPID PEROXIDATION

The membranes of the rod outer segments (ROSg) are essentially lipoprotein complexes. Rhodopsin, the major integral protein of ROSg, is surrounded by phospholipids highly enriched in docosahexaenoic acid (C22:6n-3). This fluid environment plays an important role for conformational changes after photoactivation. Thus, ROSg membranes are highly susceptible to oxidative damage. We have studied the changes in the fatty acid composition of ROSg membranes isolated from bovine retina submitted to non-enzymatic lipid peroxidation during different time intervals (0–180 min). Oxidative stress was monitored by increase in the chemiluminescence and loss of PUFAs. Protein carbonyl and protein thiol groups were utilized as biomarkers of protein oxidation. Simultaneously the alterations of membrane proteins of the retinal ROSg under oxidative stress were studied using SDS-PAGE. Lipid peroxidation reduces the 22:6n-3 content from 35.50 ± 2.90% to 23.79 ± 3.79%, 15.93 ± 2.98% and 12.65 ± 1.86% during 60, 120 and 180 min of incubation, respectively. An increase in protein carbonyls, a decrease in protein thiols and in the content of all the proteins (mainly rhodopsin) in the peroxidized membranes with respect to native ones, that was time-peroxidation dependent, showed the oxidative damage of proteins. These results suggest that lipid peroxidation products in ROSg membranes mediate protein degradation [24].

Lipid peroxidation of n-3 and n-6 PUFAs bound to phospholipids generates hydroxyl-alkenals that produce covalent modifications of proteins and amino phospholipids. These aldehydes exhibit great reactivity with bio-molecules, such as proteins, DNA, and phospholipids, generating a variety of intra and intermolecular covalent adducts. These aldehydes can also act as bioactive molecules in physiological and/or pathological conditions. They can affect and regulate, at very low and nontoxic concentration, several cell functions, including signal transduction, gene expression, cell proliferation, and, more generally, the response of the target cell(s) [25]. Membranes modified by lipid peroxidation products are repaired by PLA2s which generates selective cleavage of the peroxidized fatty acids residues and their subsequent replacement by native fatty acids Figure 4.

6. LIPOSOMES AS A TOOL TO ANALYZE PEROXIDATION OF RETINAL LIPIDS

Biological membranes in retina are complex systems. In view of this complexity and in order to avoid collateral effects that may arise during the lipid peroxidation of whole retinal membranes, we have attempted to gain understanding of the mechanisms responsible for oxidation in simple model systems, made by dispersing retinal lipids in the form of liposomes.

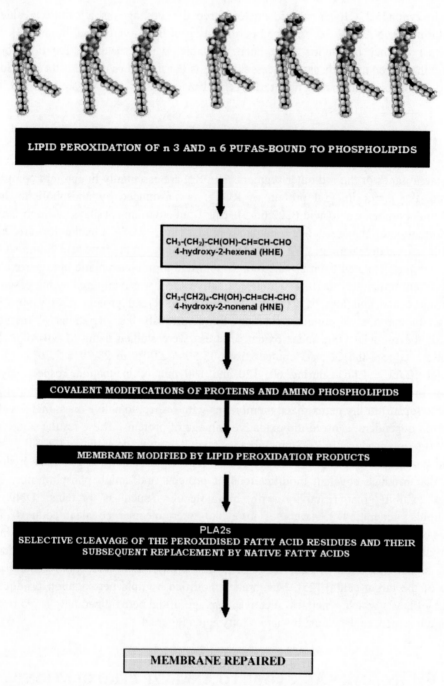

Figure 4. Scheme of the formation and modifications at the level of membranes by the lipid peroxidation products HNE and HHE. The scheme shows one of the mechanisms by which damaged membranes are repaired.

In such systems it is possible to monitor peroxidation under varying conditions while changing the factors that govern the reaction in a controllable fashion, one at a time.

Relatively simple liposomal model membranes are still quite complex, but unlike biological membranes, they enable evaluation of effects of different prooxidants, varying lipid composition and/or arrangement of membranes on consequences of lipid peroxidation. Liposomes, in which phospholipid composition, structure and dynamics can be fully controlled, are usually accepted to be a fitting model for in vitro studies of membrane structures and properties. They are surrounded by a lipid bilayer, structurally comparable to cell membrane lipidic matrix [26, 27].

Phospholipid vesicles are frequently used as model systems to study the physical principles behind the activities of biological membranes. Conjugated dienes are formed from the double-bond rearrangement of oxidized PUFAs, and TBARS are products derived from the breakdown of these fatty acids located in phospholipids. We have analyzed the behavior of these compounds during progress of lipid peroxidation of sonicated and non-sonicated liposomes made of retinal lipids in different aqueous media using Fe^{2+} and Fe^{3+} as initiators [28].

As initiator of lipid peroxidation, we used Fe^{2+} or Fe^{3+}, which generated free radical species in the presence of LOOHs. LOOH-dependent initiation has been proposed to occur by two pathways: LOOH breakdown by Fe^{3+} and subsequent hydrogen abstraction by LOO• (reactions 1 and 2).

$$Fe^{3+} + LOOH \rightarrow Fe^{2+} + LOO• + H^+ \tag{1}$$

$$LOO• + LH \rightarrow L• + LOOH \tag{2}$$

or LOOH breakdown by Fe^{2+} to free radicals (reactions 3 and 4)

$$Fe^{2+} + LOOH \rightarrow Fe^{3+} + LO• + OH^- \tag{3}$$

$$LO• + LH \rightarrow L• + LOH \tag{4}$$

In compartmentalized systems such as liposomes, it is practical to suppose that free radical inducers, such as Fe^{2+} and Fe^{3+} used in our study, located in the external medium must first achieve access to the unsaturated fatty acyl chains buried inside the membrane bilayer to start the chain reaction of lipid peroxidation. If this is the case, both the transition metal ions and oxygen should enter into the membrane bilayer and higher water permeability of the latter would certainly assist this process. Several physical studies on the acyl chain structure of phospholipid bilayer vesicles propose that acyl chain packing depends in part on the radius of curvature of the vesicles [29, 30].

Many model membranes can be used to learn more about issues that cannot be studied in biological membranes. We have used sonicated liposomes (SL) and non-sonicated liposomes (NSL) prepared with lipids isolated from bovine retina and characterized by dynamic light-scattering, to study lipid peroxidation, under air atmosphere at 22°C, with Fe^{2+} or Fe^{3+} as initiator, in different aqueous media [28]. Conjugated dienes and trienes, determined by absorption at 234 and 270 nm respectively, and thiobarbituric acid-reactive substances were measured as a function of time. Peroxidation of SL or NSL initiated with 25 μM FeSO4 in 20 mM Tris–HCl pH 7.4 resulted in an increase in TBARS production after a lag phase of 60 min. Incubation of both types of liposomes in water resulted in shortening of the lag phase at 30 min. When lipid peroxidation was performed in 0.15 M NaCl, lag phase completely disappeared. On the other hand, FeCl3 (25 μM) induced a limited production of TBARS only just after 30 min of incubation. When Fe^{2+} or Fe^{3+} lipid peroxidation of both types of liposomes was carried out in water or 0.15 M NaCl, formation of conjugated dienes and conjugated trienes were higher than in reactions carried out in 20 mM Tris–HCl pH 7.4.

Our results established that both liposome types were susceptible to Fe^{2+} and Fe^{3+} initiated lipid peroxidation. However, Fe^{2+} showed a clearly enhanced effect on peroxidation rate and steady state concentration of oxidation products. In this study, we have performed studies using a simple liposomal model that facilitate evaluation of the kinetics of the lipid peroxidation process without the interference produced by retinal proteins. Liposomes, in which phospholipid composition, structure and dynamics can be controlled, are frequently accepted to be an appropriate model for in vitro studies of membrane structures and properties. They are composed by lipid bilayers, structurally similar to cell membrane lipidic environment [27]. Conjugated dienes formed from oxidized PUFAs, and TBARS products derived from the breakdown of these fatty acids located in phospholipids could be analyzed during peroxidation of liposomes made of retinal lipids using Fe^{2+} as initiator. We verified that peroxidation of liposomes made of retinal lipids is affected not only by type of initiator but also by aqueous media. This model constitutes a useful system to study formation of lipid peroxidation intermediaries and products in an aqueous environment.

CONCLUSION

It is clear that the adaptability of biological membranes is dependent on their structures and biophysical properties, which are determined by the types of lipids and proteins that make up the membranes. Lipid peroxidation of membrane lipids is accompanied by addition of numerous polar moieties on polyunsaturated fatty acyl chains present in the ''non-raft'' matrix phase. Thus, phospholipid oxidation products are very likely to alter the properties of biological membranes, because their polarity and shape may differ significantly from the structures of their parent molecules. Thus, they may modify lipid–lipid and lipid–protein interactions and, as a consequence, also membrane protein functions.

Thus, as cell membranes undergo oxidation, if not remodelled through the actions of phospholipases, they may "grow whiskers" comprised of a variety of projecting oxidized sn-2 fatty acids of diverse structures. It will be especially interesting to determine functions and mechanisms regulating the recently identified and how the lipid peroxidation process affects it's remodelling and provide insights into their organization.

In view of the complexity of biological membranes, a large amount of work was devoted to the latter issues in basic model systems, frequently lipid vesicles (liposomes). Although peroxidation in model membranes may be very different from peroxidation in biological membranes, the results obtained in model membranes may be used to advance our understanding of issues that cannot be analyzed in biological membranes.

ACKNOWLEDGMENT

Studies in the author laboratory were supported by PIP-0157 National Council of Scientific and Technical Research (CONICET) Argentina.

REFERENCES

[1]   S. J. Fliesler and R. E.: Anderson R. E. Chemistry and metabolism of lipids in the vertebrate retina. *Prog. Lipid Res.*, 22, 79-131 (1983).

[2]   A. R. Hands and W. Bartley: All-cis-Docosa-4,7,10,13,16,19-hexaenoic acid in ox retina. *Biochem. J.*, 87, 263-265 (1963).

[3]   N. Jr. Salem, B. Litman, H. Y. Kim and K. Gawrisch: Mechanisms of action of docosahexaenoic acid in the nervous system. *Lipids,* 36, 945-959 (2001).

[4]   A. M. Stinson, R. D. Wiegand and R. E. Anderson: Fatty acid and molecular species compositions of phospholipids and diacylglycerols from rat retinal membrane. *Exp. Eye Res.,* 52, 213-218 (1991).

[5]   F. J. M. Daemen: Vertebrate rod outer segment membranes. *Biochim. Biophys. Acta.,* 300, 255-288 (1973).

[6]   R. S. Cantor: Lipid composition and the lateral pressure profile in bilayers. *Biophys. J.,* 76, 2625-2639 (1999).

[7]   M. Mihailescu and K. Gawrisch: The structure of polyunsaturated lipid bilayers important for rhodopsin functions: a neutron diffraction study. *Biophys. J.,* 90, L04–L06 (2006).

[8]   M. Neuringer, G. J. Anderson and W. E. Connor: The essentiality of n-3 fatty acids for the development and function of the retina and brain. *Annu. Rev. Nutr.,* 8, 517-541 (1988).

[9]   M. Neuringer and W. E. Connor: n-3 fatty acids in the brain and retina: evidence for their essentiality. *Nutr. Rev.,* 44, 285–294 (1986).

[10] R. E. Anderson, D. J. Landis and P. A. Dudley: Essential fatty acid deficiency and renewal of rod outer segments in the albino rat. *Invest. Ophthalmol.,* 15, 232–236 (1976).

[11] W. E. Connor, M. Neuringer and D. S. Lin: Dietary effects on brain fatty acid composition: the reversibility of n-3 fatty acid deficiency and turnover of docosahexaenoic acid in the brain, erythrocytes, and plasma of rhesus monkeys. *J. Lipid Res.,* 31, 237-247 (1980).

[12] J. R. Vingerling A. Hofman, D. E. Grobbee and P. T. de Jong: Age-related macular degeneration and smoking. The Rotterdam Study. *Arch. Ophthalmol.,* 114, 1193–1196 (1996).

[13] K. J. Cruickshanks, R. Klein and B. E. Klein: Sunlight and age-related macular degeneration. The Beaver Dam Eye Study. *Arch. Ophthalmol.,* 111, 514–518 (1993).

[14] A. randomized, placebo-controlled, clinical trial of high-dose supplementation with vitamins C and E, beta carotene, and zinc for age-related macular degeneration and vision loss: AREDS report no. 8. *Arch. Ophthalmol.,* 119, 1417–1436 (2001).

[15] P. Hahn, A. H. Milam and J. L. Dunaief: Maculas affected by age-related macular degeneration contain increased chelatable iron in the retinal pigment epithelium and Bruch's membrane. *Arch. Ophthalmol.,* 121, 1099–1105 (2003).

[16] S. Warburton, K. Southwick, R. M. Hardman, A. M. Secrest, R. K. Grow, H. Xin, A. T. Woolley, G. F. Burton and C. D. Thulin: Examining the proteins of functional retinal lipofuscin using proteomic analysis as a guide for understanding its origin. *Mol. Vis.,* 11, 1122–1134 (2005).

[17] F. Schutt, M. Bergmann, F. G. Holz and J. Kopitz: Proteins modified by malondialdehyde, 4-hydroxynonenal, or advanced glycation end products in lipofuscin of human retinal pigment epithelium. *Invest. Ophthalmol. Vis. Sci.,* 44, 3663–3668 (2003).

[18] J. W. Crabb, M. Miyagi, X. Gu, K. Shadrach, K. A. West, H. Sakaguchi, M. Kamei, A. Hasan, L. Yan, M. E. Rayborn, R. G. Salomon, J. G. Hollyfield: Drusen proteome analysis: an approach to the etiology of age-related macular degeneration. *Proc. Natl. Acad. Sci. USA,* 99, 14682–14687 (2002).

[19] Y. Imamura, S. Noda, K. Hashizume, K. Shinoda, M. Yamaguchi, S. Uchiyama, T. Shimizu, Y. Mizushima, T. Shirasawa and K. Tsubota: Drusen, choroidal neovascularization, and retinal pigment epithelium dysfunction in SOD1-deficient mice: a model of age-related macular degeneration. *Proc. Natl. Acad. Sci.,* 103,11282–11287 (2006).

[20] S. Beatty, H. Koh, M. Phil, D. Henson and M. Boulton: The role of oxidative stress in the pathogenesis of age-related macular degeneration *Surv. Ophthalmol.,* 45, 115–134 (2000).

[21] A. Catalá: Lipid peroxidation of membrane phospholipids generates hydroxy-alkenals and oxidized phospholipids active in physiological and/or pathological conditions. *Chem. Phys. Lipids,* 157, 1-11 (2009).

[22] B. S. Kristal, B. K. Park, B. P. Yu: 4-Hydroxyhexenal is a potent inducer of the mitochondrial permeability transition *J. Biol. Chem.,* 271, 6033–6038 (1996).

[23] A. Benedetti, M. Comporti and H. Esterbauer: Identification of 4- hydroxynonenal as a cytotoxic product originating from the peroxidation of liver microsomal lipids. *Biochim. Biophys. Acta.,* 620, 281–296 (1980).

[24] M. H. Guajardo M. H., A. M. Terrasa, A. C atalá: Lipid-protein modifications during ascorbate-Fe2+ peroxidation of photoreceptor membranes: protective effect of melatonin. *J. Pineal Res.,* 41, 201-210 (2006).

[25] K. Uchida. 4-Hydroxy-2-nonenal: a product and mediator of oxidative stress. *Prog. Lipid Res.,* 42, 318–343 (2003).

[26] A. M. Samuni, A. Lipman, Y. Barenholz: Damage to liposomal lipids: protection by antioxidants and cholesterol-mediated dehydration. *Chem. Phys. Lipids*, 105, 121–134 (2000).

[27] F. Castelli, D. Trombetta, A. Tomaino, F. Bonina, G. Romeo, N. Uccella, A. Saija: Dipalmitoylphosphatidylcholine/linoleic acid mixed unilamellar vesicles as model membranes for studies on novel free-radical scavengers. *J. Pharmacol. Toxicol. Methods*, 37, 135–141 (1997).

[28] N. Fagali, A. Catala: Fe^{2+} and Fe^{3+} initiated peroxidation of sonicated and non-sonicated liposomes made of retinal lipids in different aqueous media. *Chem. Phys. Lipids*, 159, 88-94 2009.

[29] W. A. Talbot, L. X. Zheng and B. R. Lentz: Acyl chain unsaturation and vesicle curvature alter outer leaflet packing and promote poly (ethylene glycol)-mediated membrane fusion. *Biochemistry,* 36, 5827-5836 (1997).

[30] L. J. Korstanje, E. E. van Taassen, Y. K. Levine: Reorientational dynamics in lipid vesicles and liposomes studied with ESR: effects of hydration, curvature and unsaturation. *Biochim. Biophys. Acta.,* 982, 196-204 (1989).

EDITOR CONTACT INFORMATION

Dr. Angel Catalá, Prof. Director
Instituto de Investigaciones Fisicoquímicas Teóricas y Aplicadas
(INIFTA-CCT La Plata-CONICET)
Facultad de Ciencias Exactas
Universidad Nacional de La Plata, Argentina
Tel: 54-221-425-7430 54-221-425-7291 (Ext. 105)
Fax: 54-221-425- 4642
E-mail: catala@inifta.unlp.edu.ar

INDEX

C

F

G

M

N

W

Z